INTRODUCTORY
NUCLEAR THEORY

FIG. 6.7. AMPLITUDE OF WAVE FOR 18 MeV α-PARTICLES
SCATTERED BY Ca⁴⁰

The dark zone indicates the 90-10 per cent density zone of nuclear matter.
The α-particle wave enters from the top left and is attenuated throughout the
nucleus, except that it is re-focused on the far side.

[By kind permission of N. Austern and R. M. Drisko]

(T.811)   (*frontispiece*)

Introductory

NUCLEAR THEORY

by

L. R. B. ELTON, D.Sc., F.Inst.P.

Professor of Physics
Battersea College of Technology

Second Edition

1966

W. B. SAUNDERS COMPANY

PHILADELPHIA

First published 1959
Reprinted 1960
Reprinted 1962
Reprinted 1963
Second edition 1966

PUBLISHERS:

SIR ISAAC PITMAN AND SONS LTD
Pitman House, Parker Street, Kingsway, London wc2

SOLE DISTRIBUTORS FOR THE WESTERN HEMISPHERE

W. B. SAUNDERS COMPANY—PHILADELPHIA

Library of Congress Catalog Card Number *66—18339*

PRINTED IN GREAT BRITAIN AT
THE UNIVERSITY PRESS
ABERDEEN
F6—(T. 811)

Preface to the Second Edition

IN the last six years the main interest in nuclear physics has shifted from the investigation of nuclear forces to that of nuclear structure. In consequence the major changes and additions in this edition have been made in the chapters on nuclear models and nuclear reactions. However, the book has been revised as a whole, and substantial additions have also been made in other parts. Thus I have included a treatment of the scattering of polarized beams in Chapter 4, and a much more thorough treatment of parity violation and the coupling constants in β-decay in Chapter 9. Contrary to a maxim that I thought to establish in the previous preface, I have found it necessary to put some mathematical material, that is wanted in several chapters, into an appendix. I plead with users of this book to prove me wrong by reading it. In response to some demand, I have extended considerably the list of references, but I have retained one feature which had led to criticism. It is that the book gets harder as it goes along. This seems to me to be a virtue in a book designed to be read in conjunction with a lengthy course of lectures, which presumably in most instances runs parallel to other courses in related subjects. By the end of the course a student's powers of comprehension *should* be greater than they were at the beginning.

It is impossible for me to name all those who helped me to improve this edition by pointing out errors and omissions in the previous one, but I am grateful to them all. My special thanks go to J. S. Blair, R. J. Blin-Stoyle, L. Castillejo, Daphne F. Jackson and R. J. N. Phillips, whose advice on individual parts of this edition of the book has been quite invaluable. I am also grateful to Mr. J. Law for his help in proof-reading and the very careful preparation of the index. Finally, and most sincerely, I wish to thank my wife for her patience and understanding.

LONDON, 1964   L. R. B. E.

From the Preface to the First Edition

THE trouble with nuclear physics is that it is not a subject that develops logically, but a collection of topics. It is thus not possible to start axiomatically and proceed from there. This makes it a difficult subject both to teach and learn.

This book has grown out of a lecture course which for eight years I gave to final honours physics students at King's College, London. I have tried to overcome some of the difficulties of presentation that I encountered and in particular I have tried to use as little as possible the maddening phrase "it can be shown." I have not been able to avoid it altogether, but I have generally been able to give an easily accessible reference. At one stage I thought of putting some of the lengthier pieces of mathematics into an appendix, but I have not done this, for few people read appendices and it is my experience that he who does not work through the mathematics does not understand the physics.

My thanks are due to my colleagues both in London and Cambridge, Mass., who read various parts of the manuscript and especially to Mr. L. Castillejo without whose encouragement the book would probably never have been completed and to Dr. M. E. Fisher who not only read the whole book in proof, but made most valuable suggestions for its improvement.

LONDON, 1958   L. R. B. E.

Contents

Fundamental Constants

THE five fundamental constants of modern physics, which will be denoted by the same symbols throughout the book, are (Cohen, 1957):

The electron mass, m_e $= 9{\cdot}109 \times 10^{-28}$ g

The proton charge, e $= 4{\cdot}803 \times 10^{-10}$ esu

The velocity of light, $c = 2{\cdot}998 \times 10^{10}$ cm/sec

Planck's constant divided by 2π, $\hbar = 1{\cdot}054 \times 10^{-27}$ erg-sec
$= 0{\cdot}659 \times 10^{-15}$ eV-sec

Avogadro's number (physical scale) $N_0 = 6{\cdot}023 \times 10^{23}$ per mole

A full list of the latest values of the physical constants is given in *Physics To-day* (Feb., 1964), p. 48.

Introduction

NUCLEAR physics differs in two very important aspects from the physics of the outer atom, of which it might be considered to be a logical extension. The first difference lies in the enormous disparity between the distances and energies involved in the two sets of phenomena. The distances of nuclear physics are of the order of a million times smaller and the energies a million times larger than those of atomic physics. Now quantum mechanics has shown that even in atomic physics the concepts and models derived from classical physics, which were so successful in describing macroscopic, i.e. large-scale, phenomena, are frequently useless or even misleading. In the realm of nuclear physics our imagination and physical intuition, both of which depend ultimately on associating a new set of phenomena with one that is already well understood, are likely to be even poorer guides. One of the great difficulties of modern physics is the fact that when we first meet the subject, our minds have been for perhaps twenty years conditioned by the ideas of classical physics, and that not only in the classroom and laboratory, but also in everyday life. From the moment that we are first conscious of our surroundings and put our macroscopic toes into our macroscopic mouths we are in direct physical contact with most of the building stones from which classical physics is constructed. The world of atoms and nuclei on the other hand is not directly accessible to our senses, and the physical facts which we deduce from our observations are in general several logical steps further removed from these observations than is the rule in classical physics. It is not surprising therefore that the physics of the twentieth century—and if this is true of atomic physics, how much more will it be true of nuclear physics—is based on mathematical ideas, which by their very nature are not the direct outcome of experience, while the physics of the nineteenth century was largely based on the concepts of engineering.

The second aspect in which nuclear physics differs from atomic physics is due to the physicists rather than the physics, and it may therefore be hoped that the difficulties which arise from it may one day disappear. Before a consistent scheme describing a set of physical phenomena can be built up, the laws governing these phenomena must be known. The three stages by which such a scheme is built up are beautifully illustrated by the discovery of

1

the law of universal gravitation. Tycho Brahe collected a vast number of individual observations about the motion of the planets and Kepler brought order into these by deducing from them his three laws, but not until Newton had proposed his law of universal gravitation, which was not deduced from experiment like Kepler's laws, but was really an inspired guess, could a consistent scheme be built up.

Now in the physics of the outer atom all the fundamentals are known. The force between particles is the ordinary electrostatic Coulomb force, the laws are those of quantum mechanics. In the realm of nuclear physics the state of affairs is quite different. Here we do not know the laws of force, and we can only assume, though probably correctly, that the laws of quantum mechanics hold. In fact, we have hardly got further than the Tycho Brahe stage. The second stage, that of attempting to unify a set of experimental data by means of empirical laws and to deduce theories from them —known nowadays as the phenomenological approach—is being actively pursued with a good deal of success. The third stage, that of discovering the laws of nuclear forces by an inspired guess, has led to meson theory. This theory is of such complexity that quantitative predictions are difficult to obtain, although qualitative agreement with experimental results is often good. The validity of the theory cannot therefore at present be established.

The approach in this book is almost entirely phenomenological, so that we shall have to refer again and again to experimental results, and it is only in the last chapter that a purely theoretical approach will be outlined. Our theoretical edifice could in fact not stand up at all, were it not strengthened in many places by experimental struts and supports. Had we adopted the purely theoretical approach, we might have succeeded in producing a building capable of standing on its own. But if we had stepped back to admire it, we should not have seen much. It would have been enveloped in the mists of nuclear physics, which will probably take a very long time to disperse.

The first chapter will be concerned with a brief survey of the field which will be covered more thoroughly in the later chapters. Because of the phenomenological approach it is necessary for the understanding of any one part of nuclear physics to have some knowledge of all parts, and it is hoped that this method has made it possible to avoid a large number of forward references to later parts of the book.

CHAPTER 1

Qualitative Facts about Nuclei

1.1 Elementary Particles

WE shall consider particles to be elementary if we do not need to concern ourselves with their internal structure, but can treat them as geometrical points with certain constant physical properties, such as mass and charge. On this definition, the elementary particles of classical mechanics are the molecules and those of classical chemistry the atoms.

The elementary particles of nuclear physics can be divided into four groups, according to their masses, although this division may not be as fundamental as it would appear at first sight.

(a) The *photon*, which is the quantum of electromagnetic energy. This has neither mass nor charge.

(b) Light particles, called *leptons*. Here we have the *positon* and the *negaton*,† each of mass m_e, and of charge $+ e$ and $- e$ respectively, and the *neutrinos*, of which there are now two kinds and which are neutral particles of very small mass.

(c) Heavy particles, called *baryons*. Of these the lightest, and the only ones that are going to concern us, are the *proton* and the *neutron*. Their masses are not quite the same, that of the neutron being a little larger, but they are both of the order of 1840 m_e. The proton charge is $+ e$, and the neutron is neutral. The other baryons with which we shall not be concerned are highly unstable and decay rapidly into protons or neutrons.

(d) Intermediate in mass are the *mesons*. There are several of these, but we shall restrict ourselves to the two best known and most studied ones, the *muon* or μ-meson and the *pion* or π-meson. These can exist with charge $+ e$ or $- e$, and there is also a neutral pion. The existence of a neutral muon has not been established, and it probably does not exist. It should be pointed out that, apart from its mass, the muon is much closer in its properties to the electron than to the pion. For that reason it is actually classified as a lepton.

In addition to mass and charge, elementary particles have two other very important properties: spin angular momentum and magnetic moment. We must be careful not to jump to the conclusion

† The names positon and negaton are more symmetrical than the older positron and electron. We shall use the word " electron " to mean either a positon or a negaton.

3

that because an elementary particle has a spin, we must think of it as turning about an axis in itself, and that therefore it must have a finite radius, since a point turning about itself is a meaningless idea. Such a conclusion would be an unwarrantable extrapolation of our macroscopic ideas. Instead, we must simply accept the fact that certain experiments can be explained only on the assumption of elementary particles having spin and magnetic moment.

These facts follow for the negaton from certain observations on spectral lines, in particular from the existence of doublets, such as the sodium D-lines, and from the anomalous Zeeman effect. These show that the negaton has a spin angular momentum of magnitude $\frac{1}{2}\hbar$ units of angular momentum and a magnetic moment, $\mu_{e^-} = - e\hbar/2m_e c$. The quantity $e\hbar/2m_e c$ is called one Bohr magneton. The negative sign indicates that the spin and magnetic moment vectors are in opposite directions. These facts are also necessary consequences of Dirac's relativistic equation for the electron.

Similar experiments lead to the conclusion that protons and neutrons also have intrinsic spins $\frac{1}{2}\hbar$, but their measured magnetic moments are not, as might be expected $\mu_p = e\hbar/2M_p c$ and $\mu_n = 0$. The experimental values are (Cohen, 1957; Cohen, 1956)

$$\mu_p = + 2 \cdot 7927 \text{ nuclear magnetons,}$$

$$\mu_n = - 1 \cdot 9131 \text{ nuclear magnetons,}$$

where a nuclear magneton is $e\hbar/2M_p c$. So while the spin gives an indication that nucleons may obey a Dirac equation, the magnetic moments show they cannot be such simple particles as negatons.

The question of the spin and magnetic moment of the other elementary particles cannot be gone into here, but the spins are listed for completeness sake together with other properties of the elementary particles in Table 1.1 (Cohen, 1957).

TABLE 1.1 ELEMENTARY PARTICLES

Name	Symbol	Mass (in units of m_e)	Charge (in units of e)	Spin (in units of $\hbar$)
Photon	γ	0	0	1
Neutrino	ν	< 0·001	0	$\frac{1}{2}$
Electron	e±	1	+ 1 or − 1	$\frac{1}{2}$
Muon-neutrino	$\nu\mu$	< 9	0	$\frac{1}{2}$
Muon	μ±	206·9	+ 1 or − 1	$\frac{1}{2}$
Pion	π±	273·3	+ 1 or − 1	0
Neutral pion	π^0	264·3	0	0
Proton	p	1836·1	1	$\frac{1}{2}$
Neutron	n	1838·7	0	$\frac{1}{2}$

1.2 Size, Mass and Charge of the Nucleus

The existence of a heavy, positively charged nucleus of very small dimensions at the centre of the atom was first demonstrated by Rutherford (1911). He bombarded thin foils with α-particles, which he had previously shown to be doubly ionized helium atoms, and observed the angles of deflexion which they suffered through the scattering in the foil. He found that the effective deflecting force was the Coulomb repulsion $2Ze^2/r^2$, where Z is the number assigned to the element responsible for the scattering in the periodic table of the elements. Furthermore, some of the scattering angles indicated that the α-particle had passed within a distance of about 10^{-12} cm from the centre of an atom. This showed that they had passed right through the atom, the radius of which is about 10^{-8} cm. On the other hand, for almost head-on collisions, for which the distance of closest approach was even less than 10^{-12} cm, deviations from the Coulomb law were observed. Hence the nucleus had a finite size. Also, the nucleus had to contain almost the whole mass of the atom, since otherwise the α-particles would have been deflected by the outer regions of the atom. Lastly, the whole atom was neutral, and since the nucleus had a charge $+ Ze$, it had to be surrounded by Z negatons which surrounded the nucleus at distances of the order of 10^{-8} cm. The emptiness of the atom is almost unimaginable. The atom is often compared to the planetary system. But if the nucleus were enlarged to the size and mass of the sun, then the mass of a negaton would be that of the earth and its distance from the nucleus ten times greater than that of the furthest planet from the sun. The variations in density and distance are thus vastly greater in the atom than in the solar system.

Next, J. J. Thomson (1913) discovered that the mass of the nucleus was not uniquely determined by its charge. Although the mass in general increased as the charge increased, there were often several masses corresponding to the same charge. Such nuclei had of course the same number of negatons surrounding them. Now nuclei do not enter into the interactions between atoms, since the negatons surrounding them prevent them from coming close to each other, and thus the chemical behaviour of an atom is determined solely by the number of its negatons, i.e. by the charge number Z. Thomson discovered, therefore, that the atoms which made up a chemically pure substance of an element did not all have the same mass. Such atoms are known as *isotopes*. And just as atoms of the same type are said to belong to the same element so nuclei of the same type are said to belong to the same *nuclide*.

The mass of any isotope is very close to a whole multiple of the mass of the proton, which is the nucleus of the hydrogen atom. (Actually the atomic unit of mass is not taken to be the proton mass, but $\frac{1}{12}$ of the mass of that carbon isotope which has approximately 12 times the proton mass. In this way the whole multiple rule is more nearly true. The reason for the different choice of mass unit will be made clear in section 2.1.) Thus a nuclide is specified by its *mass number A*, which is the nearest integer to the mass when measured in atomic units, and its *charge number Z*. It was thought originally that a nucleus consisted of A protons, to give the correct mass, and $A - Z$ negatons, to give the correct charge. We now know, however, that negatons cannot exist in the nucleus, and that a nucleus consists of Z protons and $N = A - Z$ neutrons. A nuclide of the chemical element X, of mass number A and charge number Z is described by the symbol $_Z^N X^A$, e.g. the nuclide tritium (very heavy hydrogen : $A = 3$, $Z = 1$) is $_1^2 H^3$. Often the numbers on the left are omitted, since in fact the nuclide is completely determined by the symbol X^A. Protons and neutrons are referred to as *nucleons*, when we do not wish to distinguish between them.

In a light nucleus, A is approximately equal to twice Z, so that the number of protons and neutrons are nearly equal, but as Z increases the ratio A/Z increases too, so that in heavy nuclei it is over 2·5. This indicates an excess of neutrons over protons which we shall see is accounted for by the fact that protons, which are electrically charged, tend to repel each other while neutrons, which are neutral, do not and are thus more firmly bound than the protons by the nuclear forces that hold the nucleus together. What these nuclear forces are will be one of the main studies of this book.

We have already mentioned the existence of isotopes which are nuclides with equal Z, but different N. Nuclides with equal N, but different Z are known as *isotones*. (Equal *protons*—isoto*pes*, equal *neutrons*—iso*tones* !) Nuclides with equal A, but different N and Z, are *isobars*. From the point of view of nuclear physics these are very similar to each other, since they are made up of the same number of nucleons, while from the point of view of chemistry isotopes are similar to each other. Lastly, we can have nuclei which have the same A, N and Z, but differ in their internal energies. They are similar to excited atoms, in which one or more negatons have an excess of energy, which they give up as light quanta (observable as spectral lines) in returning to their unexcited state. In the same way excited nuclei are unstable and change to the stable state by emission of a light quantum, known in this connexion as a γ-ray. However, while atoms cannot exist in an excited state for any appreciable time, some excited nuclides have life-times of several hours. A nucleus X in an excited state is denoted by X*, and in a long-lived excited state is known as an *isomer*.

1.3 Binding Energy

The particles that constitute a stable nucleus are held together by strong attractive forces, and therefore work must be done in separating them from each other until they are a very large distance apart. In other words, energy must be supplied to the nucleus to separate it into its individual constituents, so that the total energy of the constituents when a very large distance apart is greater than when they form the nucleus. The question arises as to what form this energy takes.

The clue to the answer lies in the mass-energy relation of the special theory of relativity,

$$E = Mc^2 \qquad (1.1)$$

where E and M are the energy and mass of a particle and c is the velocity of light *in vacuo*. This means that mass is a form of energy, and we should therefore expect the total mass of a nucleus to be less than the sum of the masses of the constituent parts. This is indeed the case, and experiments on nuclei have verified (1.1) with a high degree of accuracy.

The difference between the mass of a nucleus M and that of its separate constituent parts is called the *mass defect* or, if translated into energy terms by means of (1.1), the *binding energy* of the nucleus, i.e.

$$B = (NM_n + ZM_p - M)c^2 \qquad (1.2)$$

where M_p is the mass of the proton and M_n that of the neutron. Since the state of infinite separation of the nucleons in a nucleus is taken to be the zero level of energy, the total energy of a nucleus is just $- B$.

Binding energies and mass defects are not of course peculiar to nuclei. Negatons in atoms, atoms in molecules, molecules in crystal lattices all have binding energies, but these are so small that their mass equivalents cannot be detected experimentally.

We must now turn to the question of units of mass and energy. The atomic mass unit u is defined as $\frac{1}{12}$ of the mass of the neutral isotope C^{12} of carbon. This differs slightly from the chemical definition which is based on naturally occurring oxygen which has a small admixture of O^{17} and O^{18}. In consequence the chemical atomic mass unit is 1·000046 times the physical atomic mass unit, and C^{12} has in fact been chosen as a standard, because it makes the two units very nearly the same. It is important to realize that the standard of mass is not the nucleus C^{12}, but the neutral atom C^{12}, i.e. the nucleus with its surrounding six negatons. The reason for this is of course that a determination of the mass of a stripped carbon nucleus would be difficult. Because of the conservation of charge the number of negatons on each of the two sides of an equation describing a nuclear reaction is the same, so that their masses cancel out and no complication is introduced by the use of neutral C^{12} as a standard. Thus in (1.2) M will be taken to be the mass of the neutral atom and M_p that of neutral hydrogen. The one exception to this is any equation that involves positons, since the addition of a positon and a negaton to one side of a nuclear equation changes the mass without changing the charge (see section 9.2). We have ignored here the difference in the binding energies of the negatons in the different atoms, but when translated into mass defects these are so small as to be in general outside any experimental accuracy attainable.

The atomic unit of energy is the *electron-volt* (eV), which is the energy acquired by a particle of charge e in being accelerated through a potential difference of one volt. Multiples of this unit are

$$1 \text{ keV ("kilovolt")} = 10^3 \text{ eV}$$
$$1 \text{ MeV ("million volt")} = 10^6 \text{ eV}$$
$$1 \text{ GeV ("giga volt")} = 10^9 \text{ eV}.$$

It will be noticed that the word electron is generally omitted in referring to the unit. In America, where a billion is 10^9, the GeV is referred to as the BeV.

Relations between atomic units and the c.g.s. system can be calculated from a knowledge of Avogadro's number, $N_0 = 6 \cdot 025 \times 10^{23}$ per mole, the elementary electric charge, $e = 4 \cdot 803 \times 10^{-10}$ esu, and the velocity of light, $c = 2 \cdot 998 \times 10^{10}$ cm/sec. The atomic mass unit is the reciprocal of Avogadro's number in grams,

$$1 \text{ u} = 1 \cdot 660 \times 10^{-24} \text{ g}$$

and since 1 volt $= 1/300$ esu,

$$1 \text{ eV} = 1 \cdot 601 \times 10^{-12} \text{ erg}.$$

(1.1) then gives as the energy equivalent of 1 u

$$1 \text{ u} = 1 \cdot 49 \times 10^{-3} \text{ ergs} = 931 \cdot 44 \text{ MeV}.$$

In these units the mass of an electron is $0 \cdot 000549$ u which is equivalent to $0 \cdot 511$ MeV.

We can now describe a reaction which verifies (1.1). If lithium is bombarded with slow protons, it disintegrates into two α-particles

of kinetic energy 8·6 MeV each, according to the following reaction—
$$Li^7 + H^1 \rightarrow He^4 + He^4.$$
The atomic masses of these nuclei in u are
$$Li^7 = 7\cdot01601, \quad H^1 = 1\cdot00783, \quad He^4 = 4\cdot00260.$$
Hence the decrease in mass is 0·01864 u which is equivalent to 17·3 MeV and is thus exactly equivalent to the total kinetic energy gained. The kinetic energy of the lithium target and of the slow proton are negligibly small.

1.4 Stability

The binding energy is also a measure of the stability of a nucleus, since a nucleus is clearly stable against breaking up into two fragments if its mass is less than the combined mass of the two fragments. An example will illustrate this. $_3^3Li^6$ can be imagined to split up in the following ways—

$$_3^3Li^6 \rightarrow {}_0^1n^1 + {}_3^2Li^5 \tag{i}$$
$$_1^0H^1 + {}_2^3He^5 \tag{ii}$$
$$_0^2n^2 + {}_3^1Li^4 \tag{iii}$$
$$_1^1H^2 + {}_2^2He^4 \tag{iv}$$
$$_2^0He^2 + {}_1^3H^4 \tag{v}$$
$$_1^2H^3 + {}_2^1He^3. \tag{vi}$$

We first deal with (iv) and (vi), since here the masses involved can all be measured directly. They are: $Li^6 - 6\cdot0151$, $H^2 - 2\cdot0141$, $H^3 - 3\cdot0160$, $He^3 - 3\cdot0160$, $He^4 - 4\cdot0026$. Hence the relative mass defect of Li^6 against reaction (iv) is 0·0016, and against reaction (vi) 0·0169. In (i) and (ii), $H^1 - 1\cdot0078$ can be measured directly, but n^1, He^5 and Li^5 are unstable against the following reactions—

$$_0^1n^1 \rightarrow {}_1^0H^1 + e^-$$
$$_2^3He^5 \rightarrow {}_2^2He^4 + {}_0^1n^1$$
$$_3^2Li^5 \rightarrow {}_2^2He^4 + {}_1^0H^1.$$

The mass of He^5 can be obtained from the reaction

$$_3^4Li^7 + {}_1^1H^2 \rightarrow {}_2^2He^4 + {}_2^3He^5.$$

The masses of Li^7, H^2 and He^4 are known and their kinetic energies in the reaction can be measured. It is then found that the mass of He^5 is 5·0123. The mass of Li^5 is obtained from the theory of mirror nuclei (see section 2.2) and is estimated to be 5·0125. The mass of n^1 is obtained from a knowledge of the energy needed to split up a deuteron, H^2, into a proton and a neutron, rather than from the decay process of the neutron mentioned above, and is found to be

1·0087. Thus the mass defects against these reactions are 0·0061 and 0·0050 respectively. Reactions (iii) and (v) produce fragments all of which are unstable. They must be replaced by

$$_3^3\text{Li}^6 \to \,_0^1\text{n}^1 + \,_0^1\text{n}^1 + \,_1^0\text{H}^1 + \,_2^1\text{He}^3 \tag{iii'}$$
$$\to \,_1^0\text{H}^1 + \,_1^0\text{H}^1 + \,_0^1\text{n}^1 + \,_1^2\text{H}^3 \tag{v'}$$

and the mass defects here are 0·0261 and 0·0252 respectively. Hence Li⁶ is stable. In general it is of course not necessary to investigate all possible decays, since reactions which result in two unstable fragments can always be ignored.

When the list of stable nuclides is grouped according to whether A and Z are even or odd, it is seen that nuclides of even Z are much more numerous than those of odd Z, and those of even A much more numerous than those of odd A. Further nearly all nuclides with even A have even Z. The only exceptions are the four lightest even A, odd Z nuclides $_1^1\text{H}^2$, $_3^3\text{Li}^6$, $_5^5\text{B}^{10}$, $_7^7\text{N}^{14}$, and possibly a few very rare isotopes of heavier elements. These facts are summarized in Table 1.2. On investigating the matter further, it is

TABLE 1.2 NUMBER OF STABLE NUCLIDES WITH EVEN AND ODD A AND Z

A	Z	N	Number of stable isotopes
even	even	even	149
odd	even	odd	51
odd	odd	even	47
even	odd	odd	4

found that there are far more isotopes with even Z than with odd Z, and far more isotones with even N than with odd N. For an even Z there are often six or more isotopes, most of which have even N, the isotopes with odd N between being unstable, and similarly for isotones. This can be studied in Fig. 1.1. It seems to indicate an underlying regularity in the structure of nuclei which will be investigated more fully in section 5.6.

1.5 Nuclear Reactions

Towards the end of section 1.3 we considered a reaction in which lithium nuclei were bombarded by protons and the result was two α-particles. This is an example of a nuclear reaction. In such a reaction we should expect to have to conserve energy and charge. This is indeed so and in addition we shall have to conserve angular momentum. A general nuclear reaction can be written as

$$X + x \to Y + y + Q \tag{1.3}$$

of kinetic energy 8·6 MeV each, according to the following reaction—

$$Li^7 + H^1 \rightarrow He^4 + He^4.$$

The atomic masses of these nuclei in u are

$$Li^7 = 7{\cdot}01601, \quad H^1 = 1{\cdot}00783, \quad He^4 = 4{\cdot}00260.$$

Hence the decrease in mass is 0·01864 u which is equivalent to 17·3 MeV and is thus exactly equivalent to the total kinetic energy gained. The kinetic energy of the lithium target and of the slow proton are negligibly small.

1.4 Stability

The binding energy is also a measure of the stability of a nucleus, since a nucleus is clearly stable against breaking up into two fragments if its mass is less than the combined mass of the two fragments. An example will illustrate this. $_3^3Li^6$ can be imagined to split up in the following ways—

$$_3^3Li^6 \rightarrow {_0^1}n^1 + {_3^2}Li^5 \tag{i}$$
$$_1^0H^1 + {_2^3}He^5 \tag{ii}$$
$$_0^2n^2 + {_3^1}Li^4 \tag{iii}$$
$$_1^1H^2 + {_2^2}He^4 \tag{iv}$$
$$_2^0He^2 + {_1^3}H^4 \tag{v}$$
$$_1^2H^3 + {_2^1}He^3. \tag{vi}$$

We first deal with (iv) and (vi), since here the masses involved can all be measured directly. They are: $Li^6 - 6{\cdot}0151$, $H^2 - 2{\cdot}0141$, $H^3 - 3{\cdot}0160$, $He^3 - 3{\cdot}0160$, $He^4 - 4{\cdot}0026$. Hence the relative mass defect of Li^6 against reaction (iv) is 0·0016, and against reaction (vi) 0·0169. In (i) and (ii), $H^1 - 1{\cdot}0078$ can be measured directly, but n^1, He^5 and Li^5 are unstable against the following reactions—

$$_0^1n^1 \rightarrow {_1^0}H^1 + e^-$$
$$_2^3He^5 \rightarrow {_2^2}He^4 + {_0^1}n^1$$
$$_3^2Li^5 \rightarrow {_2^2}He^4 + {_1^0}H^1.$$

The mass of He^5 can be obtained from the reaction

$$_3^4Li^7 + {_1^1}H^2 \rightarrow {_2^2}He^4 + {_2^3}He^5.$$

The masses of Li^7, H^2 and He^4 are known and their kinetic energies in the reaction can be measured. It is then found that the mass of He^5 is 5·0123. The mass of Li^5 is obtained from the theory of mirror nuclei (see section 2.2) and is estimated to be 5·0125. The mass of n^1 is obtained from a knowledge of the energy needed to split up a deuteron, H^2, into a proton and a neutron, rather than from the decay process of the neutron mentioned above, and is found to be

1·0087. Thus the mass defects against these reactions are 0·0061 and 0·0050 respectively. Reactions (iii) and (v) produce fragments all of which are unstable. They must be replaced by

$$_3\mathrm{Li}^6 \rightarrow {}_0\mathrm{n}^1 + {}_0\mathrm{n}^1 + {}_1\mathrm{H}^1 + {}_2\mathrm{He}^3 \qquad (\mathrm{iii}')$$

$$\rightarrow {}_1\mathrm{H}^1 + {}_1\mathrm{H}^1 + {}_0\mathrm{n}^1 + {}_1\mathrm{H}^3 \qquad (\mathrm{v}')$$

and the mass defects here are 0·0261 and 0·0252 respectively. Hence Li^6 is stable. In general it is of course not necessary to investigate all possible decays, since reactions which result in two unstable fragments can always be ignored.

When the list of stable nuclides is grouped according to whether A and Z are even or odd, it is seen that nuclides of even Z are much more numerous than those of odd Z, and those of even A much more numerous than those of odd A. Further nearly all nuclides with even A have even Z. The only exceptions are the four lightest even A, odd Z nuclides ${}_1\mathrm{H}^2$, ${}_3\mathrm{Li}^6$, ${}_5\mathrm{B}^{10}$, ${}_7\mathrm{N}^{14}$, and possibly a few very rare isotopes of heavier elements. These facts are summarized in Table 1.2. On investigating the matter further, it is

TABLE 1.2 NUMBER OF STABLE NUCLIDES WITH EVEN AND ODD A AND Z

A	Z	N	Number of stable isotopes
even	even	even	149
odd	even	odd	51
odd	odd	even	47
even	odd	odd	4

found that there are far more isotopes with even Z than with odd Z, and far more isotones with even N than with odd N. For an even Z there are often six or more isotopes, most of which have even N, the isotopes with odd N between being unstable, and similarly for isotones. This can be studied in Fig. 1.1. It seems to indicate an underlying regularity in the structure of nuclei which will be investigated more fully in section 5.6.

1.5 Nuclear Reactions

Towards the end of section 1.3 we considered a reaction in which lithium nuclei were bombarded by protons and the result was two α-particles. This is an example of a nuclear reaction. In such a reaction we should expect to have to conserve energy and charge. This is indeed so and in addition we shall have to conserve angular momentum. A general nuclear reaction can be written as

$$X + x \rightarrow Y + y + Q \qquad (1.3)$$

where the bombarding particle x strikes the target nucleus X and produces the nucleus Y and the outgoing particle y. The energy released in the reaction is Q, so that Q is positive for an exothermic

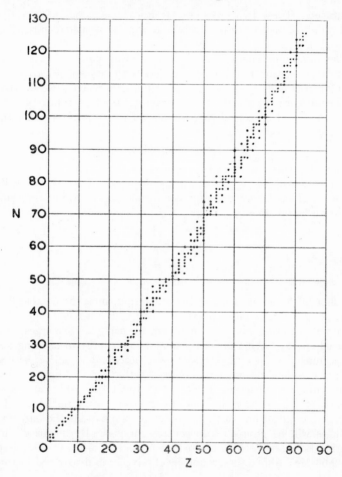

Fig. 1.1. Stable Nuclides

reaction and negative for an endothermic reaction. The whole reaction is written more briefly

$$X(x, y)Y. \qquad (1.4)$$

The bombarding particle is generally a neutron n, proton p, deuteron d, triton t, or α-particle α. In this connexion it is usual to use the single-letter abbreviations rather than n^1, H^1, H^2, H^3 and He^4 which they represent. A special case arises when x or y is a photon γ and we shall treat the cases

$$X(\gamma, y)Y \text{ and } X(x, \gamma)Y \qquad (1.5)$$

separately. These two processes are known as *photo-disintegration* and *radiative capture* respectively and will be discussed in sections 8.5 and 8.6.

The minimum energy of the bombarding particle which will make the reaction take place is called the *threshold*. Clearly it is zero when Q is positive and greater than zero when Q is negative. In the nuclear reactions (i)-(vi) of section 1.4 the threshold is positive in all cases and by considering the mass balance it is seen that the reaction

$$Li^6 \rightarrow H^2 + He^4$$

requires the smallest threshold energy.

A reaction of the type (1.3) is by no means determined by its left-hand side. Under different conditions the following reactions might all be possible :

$$\begin{aligned} X + x &\rightarrow X + x \\ &\quad\ X^* + x \\ &\quad\ B + b \\ &\quad\ C + c, \text{ etc.} \end{aligned}$$

The first of these represents elastic scattering, since the bombarding particle re-emerges without loss of energy, the second represents inelastic scattering, since the bombarding particle re-emerges with reduced energy having given up some of its energy in exciting the target nucleus. In addition to these there may then be several nuclear reactions proper, represented by the last two lines. Thus, for example, the reactions $Li^6(d, \alpha)He^4$ and $Li^6(d, p)Li^7$ have both been observed. Further, in each of these the product nuclei may be in their ground or one of their excited states, so that the outgoing particles will be grouped into several energies. By means of the reaction $Be^9(\alpha, n)C^{12}$ three excited energy levels of C^{12} at 4·43, 7·66 and 9·63 MeV above the ground level have been discovered in this way.

1.6 Unstable Nuclei

An unstable nucleus does not decay at once, as soon as it is formed, but instead there is a finite probability that it will decay in any given time interval. This fact, which was inexplicable by means of classical mechanics, can be explained, as will be seen, using quantum mechanics.

If the probability per unit time of a nucleus disintegrating is λ, and if there are N nuclei, of which dN decay in time dt, then

$$dN = - N\lambda dt.$$

Hence

$$N = N_0 \exp(-\lambda t) \qquad (1.6)$$

where N_0 is the number of nuclei at the beginning. The *lifetime* of the decay is defined as the reciprocal of the decay probability per unit time, i.e.

$$\tau = 1/\lambda \quad \text{and} \quad N = N_0 \exp(-t/\tau). \qquad (1.7)$$

The lifetime is therefore the time in which the number of nuclei is reduced to the fraction e^{-1} of the value it had at the beginning of the time interval. In general, a nuclear lifetime is observable if it lies between about 10^{-6} sec and 10^{14} years. Lifetimes outside these limits can, however, be sometimes estimated rather more indirectly. A quantity closely related to the lifetime is the *half-life* T, which is the time in which half of a given number of nuclei have decayed. Thus

$$\tfrac{1}{2}N_0 = N_0 \exp(-T/\tau).$$

Therefore

$$T = \tau \ln 2 = 0.693\,\tau. \qquad (1.8)$$

In a nuclear decay we must distinguish between the emission of (*a*) heavy particles, (*b*) electrons, and (*c*) photons. These decays will be discussed in turn.

1.6.1 EMISSION OF HEAVY PARTICLES. The heavy particles that a nucleus is most likely to emit are those that are particularly stable, i.e. neutrons, protons and α-particles. Other particles are never emitted spontaneously. This will be discussed below.

To understand the mechanism of decay it is necessary to see how a particle is held in the nucleus. The attractions due to the other nucleons result on the average in a central attraction, so that to a first approximation each constituent particle of a nucleus moves in a central potential and has, as long as it is bound in the nucleus, a negative total energy. If the particles are charged, then the electrostatic repulsion between them and the rest of the nucleus, which leads to a positive potential, has to be superimposed on to the nuclear attraction. Potentials for uncharged and charged particles in the field of a nucleus are given schematically in Fig. 1.2.

It is clear from Fig. 1.2 (*a*) that if the binding energy of a neutron in a nucleus is positive, then it will be bound, but that if the binding energy is negative, it will be free, so that the lifetime for neutron emission will be of the same order as the time it takes a neutron to travel across a nucleus (10^{-12} to 10^{-21} sec). Nuclei unstable to neutron emission are in fact never observable, but their momentary existence can be inferred from a knowledge of their decay products. An example of such a nucleus, mentioned in the previous section, is He[5].

The situation is quite different for protons and α-particles, since these can be bound in the potential well, even though their binding energies are negative, as long as they are below the maximum of the potential energy curve in Fig. 1.2 (b). Classically, such a particle would be firmly bound, but we shall see in section 7.3 that according to quantum mechanics there is a small but finite probability for the

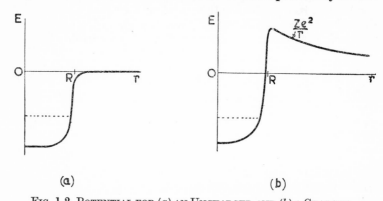

(a)   (b)

FIG. 1.2. POTENTIAL FOR (a) AN UNCHARGED AND (b) A CHARGED
PARTICLE IN THE FIELD OF A NUCLEUS

($r = R$ is the radius of the nucleus, and . . . indicates the energy of a bound particle.)

particle to leak through the barrier and to appear as a free particle on the far side of it. This is known as the tunnel effect. Depending on the energy of the particle inside the well, the lifetime of such a decay can vary from the unobservably short to the unobservably long, and lifetimes increase rapidly with the mass and charge of the particle emitted. Thus the only proton decay known is that of Li[5] and that is really unobservably short. α-decays are generally observable, although some of them are probably unobservably long. The theoretically calculated lifetimes for the emission of C[12] and O[16] nuclei are of the order of 10^{100} years, and such emissions have never been observed. Emissions of other nuclei are even less likely.

Lastly, there is the possibility of spontaneous fission, which is the breaking up of a heavy nucleus into two fragments of approximately equal size. The mechanism for this process must be quite different from that for, say, α-decay, since the central potential approximation is clearly inapplicable here. A better analogy is an oscillating liquid drop which can form a neck and then break up. The spontaneous fission of U^{238} with a lifetime in the region of 10^{24} sec has been observed (Petrzhak and Flerov, 1940).

1.6.2 EMISSION OF ELECTRONS. A totally different type of disintegration is that of β-decay in which a nucleus emits an electron. In such a decay the mass number of the nucleus remains the same and the charge number increases or decreases by one. This looks as if the only change between the initial and final nucleus is that a neutron has been changed into a proton or conversely, and it seems possible, therefore, that a β-decay of a nucleus really consists of a β-decay of a nucleon ; thus,

$$_0n^1 \rightarrow {_1}H^1 + e^- \tag{1.9}$$

$$_1^0H^1 \rightarrow {_0}n^1 + e^+. \tag{1.10}$$

A process which occurs simultaneously with the second of these is that in which a nucleus captures one of its orbital negatons. Such a capture takes place in general from the K-shell, since this is the shell nearest to the nucleus, and the process is therefore known as K-capture. It is given by

$$_1^0H^1 + e_K^- \rightarrow {_0}n^1. \tag{1.11}$$

Processes (1.10) and (1.11) can only happen inside nuclei, since a free proton is stable.

The main difficulty that arises in any theory of β-decay is that, as has already been mentioned, electrons do not exist in the nucleus. It must therefore be assumed that they are created in the process of emission, rather like photons are created in the outer atom, when a negaton in a higher energy level drops to a lower energy level, with the emission of light. This analogy will form the basis of the β-decay theory developed in section 9.3.

It is found experimentally that electrons in β-decay have all energies between zero and a certain maximum energy, depending on the decay. Now if a stationary neutron decays into a proton and a negaton, as in (1.9), then, since the total energy available for the process is fixed, energy and momentum can be conserved for one and only one negaton energy. (The muzzle velocities of identical shells fired from a gun are all equal, and so are the recoil velocities of the gun.) If, however, two particles are emitted, the energy and momentum available can be distributed in an infinite number of ways, since we can vary the angles between the proton and the two emitted particles. Thus to account for the variable energy of the emitted negaton, we postulate that another particle is emitted simultaneously which takes up the remaining energy and momentum.

This particle must be neutral, and since in all β-decays the maximum electron energy observed is practically equal to the total energy available, its mass must be very small, certainly much less than that of the electron. It has been given the name *neutrino* and is denoted by ν. Since protons, neutrons and electrons each have spin $\frac{1}{2}\hbar$, it is necessary that the neutrino also have spin $\frac{1}{2}\hbar$, so that angular momentum may be conserved. This may indicate that it also satisfies a Dirac equation.

The neutrino is a most elusive particle, and it has been calculated that on the average it will penetrate 50 light years of lead before being stopped. The reason for this extraordinarily long mean free path does not lie in its small mass and zero charge, but in its almost total lack of interaction with other particles. Photons, which also have zero mass and charge, are observed easily because of their strong interaction with charged particles. Cowan and Reines (1956) have used the huge neutrino flux from an atomic pile, together with a liquid scintillation counter the size of a large bath, to observe the capture of a neutrino, which leads to the inverse β-decay

$$\nu + {}_1\mathrm{H}^1 \rightarrow \mathrm{e}^+ + {}_0\mathrm{n}^1. \tag{1.12}$$

Some neutrinos interacted with nuclei in the counter and the emitted positons were observed as scintillations. In this way we may say that the neutrino has now actually been " seen."

1.6.3 EMISSION OF PHOTONS. As mentioned in section 1.2 a nucleus can change from one energy state to another with the emission of a light quantum or photon, known as a γ-ray. The energy of such a γ-ray is considerably higher than that of a quantum emitted when a negaton in the outer atom changes from one state to another, because energies in the nucleus are generally higher than in the outer atom, and its wavelength cannot be measured by the usual diffraction grating method. However, in its passage through the outer atom the γ-ray is frequently absorbed by one of the orbital negatons, which is then ejected from the atom, and its energy can be measured much more easily than that of the γ-ray. The phenomenon is of course a special case of the photoelectric effect and is known as *internal conversion*.

The lifetime of an excited state is in general extremely short (10^{-17} to 10^{-12} sec). However, as we shall see in section 2.3, nuclei have angular momenta in the same way as atoms, and if the angular momenta of a ground state and an excited state are very different, then the lifetime of the excited state can be comparatively long. The same applies, incidentally, to atoms and if atoms in excited states with very different angular momenta from their ground states could be prevented from losing energy non-radiatively by collisions with other atoms, then atomic isomers might exist. Nuclei are of course shielded by their negatons from coming into direct collision with each other and so can lose energy only by emitting radiation.

1.7 Nuclear Forces

So far we have dealt with the properties of nuclei without enquiring into the mechanism by which the nuclei are held together, except that in section 1.6, we postulated an average attractive field in which the nucleons move. To obtain a better insight into the forces between nucleons, we must study first the simplest nuclear system, the deuteron, and the related problem of the scattering of one nucleon by another. We shall do this in Chapter 3, but even without going into any detail, we can find out something about nuclear forces.

It is immediately obvious that the forces cannot be of an electrical or a gravitational nature, and these are the only two kinds of forces known to us so far. They cannot be electrical, because the neutron carries no charge, and they cannot be gravitational, because gravitational forces give far too small binding energies. Thus if the attraction between the proton and the neutron in a deuteron were purely gravitational, the binding energy would be given by the gravitational potential $- GM_pM_n/r$, where G is the gravitational constant and r the average distance between the nucleons which is 2 to 4 fm.† This gives a value for the binding energy of about 3×10^{-37} MeV, as against the experimental value of 2·2 MeV.

In the region of the nucleus the nuclear forces are thus enormously larger than any forces encountered in macroscopic physics, On the other hand, Rutherford's scattering experiments show that at distances as small as about 10 fm from the centre of a nucleus the nuclear forces are so weak that they are completely negligible compared with the electrostatic forces due to the same nucleus. It is for that reason that we say that nuclear forces have a finite and very short range, which turns out to be about 2 to 3 fm, beyond which they are negligible. Forces that obey the inverse square law can in principle be detected at all distances, and such forces are called long-range forces. The difference between the natures of the two kinds of force accounts of course for the principal differences between the physics of the nucleus and of the outer atom, which were mentioned in the introduction.

† The unit of length in nuclear physics is the femtometre, previously called the fermi, after the famous physicist. 1 fm = 10^{-15}m. (Femten is Danish for fifteen.)

A closer estimate of the range of nuclear forces can be obtained from a consideration of the binding energies of the lightest stable nuclei, $_1H^2$, $_2He^3$ and $_2He^4$ (Wigner, 1933). The number of possible nuclear bonds in these nuclei is 1, 3 and 6 respectively, and so we would expect their binding energies to be in the ratio of these numbers. The experimentally found binding energies, however, are

$$B(_1H^2) = 2\cdot22 \text{ MeV}, \ B(_2He^3) = 7\cdot72 \text{ MeV}, \ B(_2He^4) = 28\cdot3 \text{ MeV},$$

and these are in the ratio 1 : 3·5 : 12·7. This discrepancy can be explained on the assumption of a very short range of nuclear forces of the order 2 to 3 fm. With such a short range the nucleons in the deuteron will spend about half their time outside the range of each other's forces. (This feature of the deuteron is similar to the tunnel effect, mentioned in the last section, and will be discussed more fully in section 3.4.) In the $_2He^4$ nucleus the increased number of bonds per nucleon brings the nucleons sufficiently close together for them to be inside the range of their mutual attraction for nearly all the time. Hence $B(_2He^4)$ is much more than six times as large as $B(_1H^2)$.

1.8 Mesons

One of the most important results of the quantum theory is that the energy of the electromagnetic field exists in discrete units, known as quanta or photons. Now the forces which hold nucleons together are, as we have seen, not of an electromagnetic nature, but it is nevertheless tempting to postulate that it should be possible to describe them by a field, which would be closely analogous to the electromagnetic field. The properties of the quanta of energy of such a field would, however, differ considerably from those of photons, due to the different natures of the two kinds of forces described by their respective fields. Photons have neither mass nor charge and it can be shown that this follows from the fact that electrostatic forces are long-range and act only between charged particles. We shall see in section 10.1 that forces, such as the nuclear forces, which are short-range and act between uncharged as well as charged bodies, can be represented by a field, the quanta of which possess both mass and charge. From the known range of nuclear forces the mass of such a quantum can in fact be calculated and it is found to be somewhere between those of a proton and an electron. These quanta are the mesons mentioned in section 1.1 and their field is called the mesonic field.

It was by an argument of this nature that Yukawa (1935) predicted the existence of charged particles of mass about 200 electron masses, and in the following year such particles were detected by Anderson and Neddermeyer (1937) in cosmic radiation, which is a radiation that enters the earth's atmosphere from outside. In the interest of historical accuracy it should be mentioned that the meson which most closely resembles that predicted by Yukawa is the pion, but that the meson discovered by Anderson and Neddermeyer was the muon. The pion was not discovered until ten years later (Lattes, Occhialini and Powell, 1947).

1.9 Particles and Anti-particles

Dirac's theory of the negaton requires that a negaton can exist in states of negative energy as well as those of positive energy. From the relativistic energy equation

$$E^2 = p^2c^2 + m_e{}^2c^4 \qquad (1.13)$$

where E, p and m_e are the energy, momentum and mass of a negaton, it follows that for a given momentum p there are two values of the energy, and as p can have any value between zero and infinity, there are clearly two ranges of energy :

$$m_ec^2 < E < \infty \quad \text{and} \quad -m_ec^2 > E > -\infty.$$

According to classical mechanics energy varies continuously and so a positive energy negaton could never reach a negative energy state, since this necessitates an energy jump of $2m_ec^2$. In quantum mechanics such a jump is possible, and as negatons in negative energy states are not observed, Dirac postulated that all negative energy states are filled, but that negatons in these states are not physically observable. The Pauli exclusion principle then prevents a positive energy negaton from jumping into a negative energy state.

However, electromagnetic fields with quanta of energies greater than $2m_ec^2$ (approximately 1 MeV) can raise a negaton from this sea of negative energy negatons into state of positive energy. It is then observed as an ordinary positive energy negaton and the hole left behind, which is the absence of a negative energy negaton, is observable as the presence of a positive energy particle of opposite charge, the positon. For that reason the positon is known as the anti-particle of the negaton. Conversely, it should be possible for a negaton to unite with a positon, i.e. for a negaton to drop into a hole, and for the two particles to disappear with the creation of a γ-ray. Actually, at least two γ-rays would have to be produced, to conserve energy and momentum. [A γ-ray of definite energy also has a definite momentum, but a pair of particles of definite energy may in any given direction have any momentum between zero and a maximum fixed by (1.13).] These two processes are known as *pair-production* and *pair-annihilation*, and they have both been observed experimentally.

As has been mentioned in sections 1.1 and 1.6, nucleons and also neutrinos should obey a Dirac equation and so have anti-particles. After a hunt lasting many years, the anti-proton and anti-neutron have been observed (Chamberlain, 1955, and Cork, 1956) through the large amount of energy released when they annihilate with ordinary nucleons, and they seem to have much the expected properties. This was indeed a cause of much relief and rejoicing amongst nuclear physicists.

A process by which the anti-neutrino can be distinguished from the neutrino is that of double β-decay, which is observed for some nuclides. Basically the reaction is

$$2n \rightarrow 2p + 2e^- \qquad (1.14)$$

where we omit for the moment the neutrinos. The reaction can be imagined to take place in two stages, the first of which is

$$2n \rightarrow n + p + e^- + \nu. \qquad (1.15)$$

Now if the neutrino and the anti-neutrino are different particles, then the second stage must be

$$n + p + e^- + \nu \rightarrow 2p + 2e^- + 2\nu \qquad (1.16)$$

but if they are in fact one and the same particle, then the second β-decay can take place through the absorption of the neutrino emitted in the first β-decay, since the emission of a neutrino is equivalent to the absorption of an anti-neutrino. In that case we can have

$$n + p + e^- + \nu \rightarrow 2p + 2e^- + \text{no neutrinos} \qquad (1.17)$$

and this process would have a much shorter lifetime. Unfortunately double β-decay is an extremely unlikely process, and even the shorter life-time is very long indeed ($\sim 10^{15}$ years). However, recent experiments by Awshalom (1956) seem in favour of the longer lifetime ($\sim 10^{19}$ years), so that it would appear that the anti-neutrino is really different from the neutrino.

So far it is a matter of convention whether we call the neutral particle in (1.12) a neutrino or an anti-neutrino. In section 9.2 we shall refer briefly to the possibility that there is a conservation law which states that leptons can be neither created nor destroyed (i.e. that the difference between the number of leptons and that of anti-leptons remains constant in a nuclear interaction). If we call the positon an anti-lepton, then it follows that what we called a neutrino in (1.12), (1.15), (1.16) and (1.17) is in fact an anti-neutrino.

1.10. EXAMPLES

1.10.1. A spring of length l and modulus of elasticity $\lambda = W$ is stretched to a length nl. Find the mass equivalent M of the energy stored in the spring and show that if $W = 1$ kg, $l = 20$ cm, and $n = 2$, then $M \simeq 10^{-14}$ g.

1.10.2. A cosmic ray particle of energy 100 GeV strikes a weight of 1 mg from below and gives up all its energy to it. Show that the weight will rise through 1·6 mm. (Such an event cannot really happen, since a particle of such energy would go straight through the weight, but it illustrates the fact that single elementary particles can have energies on a macroscopic scale.)

1.10.3. Investigate the stability of Be^8 against decay into (a) $Li^7 + H^1$, (b) $Li^6 + H^2$, (c) $He^4 + He^4$.

1.10.4. Verify that a proton is stable against both positon decay and negaton capture.

1.10.5. Be^9 is bombarded with α-particles of energy 6 MeV. Using the figures given at the end of section 1.5, show that the neutrons coming off in the forward direction have energies 11·60, 6·90, 3·57 and 0·69 MeV.

[Hint : The recoil energy of the carbon nucleus is not negligible.]

CHAPTER 2

General Properties of Nuclei

2.1 Binding Energy

THE binding energy of a nucleus was defined in the last chapter and it was stated there that it gave a measure of the stability of the nucleus against splitting up into fragments. If, however, we want to investigate the absolute stability of a nucleus, i.e. the stability against splitting up into all its A nucleons, then the binding energy is not a suitable measure. We would expect the absolute value of the binding energy to increase with A, irrespective of the degree of stability of the nucleus, merely to bind the increasing number of nucleons. That is indeed the case and to measure the degree of stability we employ the *binding fraction f* which is the binding energy per nucleon and is defined by

$$f = \frac{B}{A} = \frac{c^2}{A} (ZM_p + NM_n - M).\qquad(2.1)$$

This quantity is related to, but not identical with, the *packing fraction* $(M - A)/A$, which is used in some books instead of f. The packing fraction depends on the choice of atomic mass unit and is therefore not a really fundamental quantity like the binding fraction. It will not be used in this book.

The binding fraction is plotted against the mass number in Fig. 2.1. It can be seen from the figure that it is almost constant at ~ 8.7 MeV per nucleon between $A = 30$ and $A = 100$ and decreases for small and large A. Even for as light a nucleus as C^{12} it is still 7.7 MeV per nucleon, although for a proton it is of course zero. It is for this reason that nuclear masses are near to whole integers when measured in units based on $\frac{1}{12}$ of the mass of C^{12}, but not when measured in units of the proton mass.

The constancy of the binding fraction is an indication of the short range of the nuclear forces, for it implies that a nucleon in a large nucleus is not bound to any more nucleons than in a small one. This can only be so if the range of nuclear forces is substantially smaller than the diameter of even quite light nuclei. The decrease for large A is due to the long-range Coulomb repulsion between the protons, the importance of which increases as the nuclei grow larger, until it eventually becomes dominating and limits the size of nuclei.

At the other end, in light nuclei, the individual nucleons are attracted by only a few other nucleons and hence their distances of separation are larger, which again reduces the stability. The same reasoning also leads us to conclude that the density of nuclear matter at first increases with A, but becomes constant as the binding fraction becomes constant.

The nuclei of $_2\text{He}^4$, $_6\text{C}^{12}$ and $_8\text{O}^{16}$ lie above the general binding fraction curve. They are the first three members of a series of nuclei which can be thought of as being made up entirely of α-particles

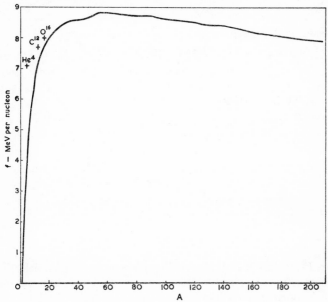

FIG. 2.1. BINDING FRACTIONS OF STABLE NUCLIDES
The continuous curve is an average, but the binding fractions of all stable nuclides except He^4, C^{12} and O^{16} lie very close to it.

and which are particularly stable. A disconcerting exception is $_4\text{Be}^8$ which is unstable and decays into two α-particles. It has been suggested on the basis of this series, as well as on other evidence, that the α-particle is actually a constituent of nuclei. This will be discussed further in section 5.5.

Closely allied to the binding energy is the separation energy $S_a(X)$, which is the energy needed to remove to infinity a constituent a from a nucleus X, leaving a residual nucleus Y. Both X and Y must be in their ground states. Clearly

$$S_a(X) = (M_a + M_Y - M_X)c^2 \qquad (2.2)$$

and using the binding energy equation (1.2) this can be written

$$S_a(X) = B_X - B_Y - B_a. \tag{2.3}$$

In general $S_n(X)$ and $S_p(X)$, i.e. the energies needed to remove a single nucleon from a nucleus, are approximately equal to 8 MeV, so that the energy needed to remove one nucleon is approximately equal to the average binding energy per nucleon. There are, however, exceptions. Thus $S_p = 14.2$ MeV for Ne^{21} and $S_p = 1.95$ MeV for N^{13}, $S_n = 16.8$ MeV for Si^{28} and $S_n = 1.85$ MeV for N^{16}.

The separation energy for neutrons can be written

$$S_n = B(Z, N) - B(Z, N - 1) \tag{2.4}$$

and this can be rewritten as

$$S_n = (A - 1)[f(Z, N) - f(Z, N - 1)] + f(Z, N). \tag{2.5}$$

If $f(Z, N)$ is a function of A only, which is approximately true for medium and heavy nuclei, and if $f(Z, N)$ varies sufficiently smoothly with A for its derivative with respect to A to exist, then (2.5) reduces to

$$S_n(A) \simeq (A - 1)\frac{df}{dA} + f(A). \tag{2.6}$$

Hence $S_n(A) \simeq f$ for medium nuclei, for which df/dA is very small, but $S_n(A) < f$ for heavy nuclei, for which the binding fraction decreases with increasing A. To this approximation $S_n(A) = S_p(A)$.

For $S_\alpha(A)$ we obtain similarly

$$S_\alpha(A) = - B(\alpha) + 4f(A) + 4(A - 4)\frac{df}{dA} \tag{2.7}$$

where $B(\alpha) = 28$ MeV is the binding energy of the α-particle. Now for heavy nuclei, $f \simeq 7.5$ MeV and so $4f(A) - B(\alpha) \simeq 2$ MeV which is much smaller than the corresponding term f in (2.6). Also, for large A, $df/dA < 0$. Therefore,

$$S_n - S_\alpha = - 3f(A) + B(\alpha) - (3A - 15)\frac{df}{dA} \gg 0. \tag{2.8}$$

This is of course borne out by experiment, since many heavy nuclei are α-radioactive, but stable against emission of protons or neutrons. For these S_α is actually negative, while S_n and S_p are positive.

Now that an average value of the total energy of a nucleon in a nucleus has been found, $E \simeq - 8$ MeV, it is possible to give an estimate of the depth of the averaged potential inside a nucleus (see Fig. 1.2) and of the average kinetic energy of the nucleons. Because of the short-range interaction with neighbouring nucleons, any nucleon will occupy a volume, the radius of which is roughly half the range of the nuclear forces, $b \simeq 2\text{--}3$ fm. This is of the order of the reduced de Broglie wavelength of a nucleon inside a nucleus. The corresponding kinetic energy of the nucleon is

$$T = \frac{1}{2M}\left(\frac{\hbar}{\frac{1}{2}b}\right)^2 \simeq 10\text{--}20 \text{ MeV}. \tag{2.9}$$

Thus the depth of the potential well is of the order of 20–30 MeV and the binding energy of a nucleon is actually due to the partial cancellation of the numerically much larger kinetic and potential energies.

2.2 Nuclear Radii

After all that has been said about the inapplicability of macroscopic ideas to nuclei, it may seem surprising that so essentially macroscopic an idea as the radius of a particle should be discussed at all. A particle can be said to have a radius if a surface can be drawn, inside which the density of matter is high and outside which it is negligibly small. This certainly cannot be done for atoms, since the electron density in an atom decreases gradually with increasing distance from the centre and there is no abrupt change

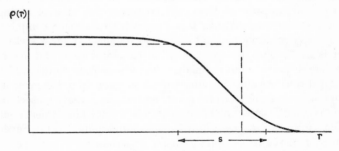

FIG. 2.2. APPROXIMATE VARIATION OF NUCLEAR DENSITY WITH DISTANCE FROM THE CENTRE OF THE NUCLEUS

The equivalent uniform density is indicated by broken lines, and the thickness s of the transition region from 90 per cent to 10 per cent of maximum density is also shown.

from high to low density. A heavy nucleus, however, is somewhat more like the proverbial billiard ball, the image of which always arises when we think of " particles." All experiments confirm that for heavy nuclei the nuclear density is approximately constant up to a certain distance from the centre and that it decreases to zero in a further distance which is small compared with the former. For such nuclei we can speak, at least approximately, of a nuclear radius.

In fact many experimental methods cannot measure the detailed variation of the nuclear density, but merely give a value for an average radius R_u, which is the radius of a nucleus of uniform density containing the same total mass as the actual nucleus and having the same second moment about the centre.† (See Fig. 2.2.)

The methods of measurement of the nuclear radius can be divided into two classes, according as to whether nuclear or electric probes are used. As we shall see, these actually tend to measure different radii. In particular, electric methods are sensitive only to the protons, which may be distributed differently from the neutrons.

We have found from binding fraction data that the density of nuclear matter varies little from nucleus to nucleus, so that an average nuclear radius is given approximately by

$$R_u \simeq r_0 A^{1/3} \qquad (2.10)$$

where, however, the constant r_0 may well be different for different measuring methods.

2.2.1 NUCLEAR METHODS. The most direct of these depends on the scattering of fast neutrons of several MeV energy by thin foils. Those neutrons that hit a nucleus are deflected and from the attenuation of the transmitted beam the cross-sectional area of a single nucleus can be worked out. If a nucleus is treated as a completely opaque sphere, then we shall show that its effective cross-sectional area is $2\pi R^2$. Fast neutrons must be employed since the neutron wavelength must be much smaller than the nuclear radius, and for such neutrons the effective cross-section is made up of the geometrical cross-sectional area, which is πR^2, and an additional cross-sectional area due to diffraction at the edges (this is a wave mechanical effect) which turns out to be πR^2 too. [See equation (6.17).] Several corrections have to be applied to the experimental result. On the one hand, the theoretical result is true only for neutrons of infinite energy and for finite energies the cross-section is larger. On the other hand, nuclei become partially transparent for neutrons of very high energies, which makes the cross-section smaller than it would be for an opaque sphere. The method will be discussed more fully in sections 6.7 and 6.8.

The same type of experiment can of course be performed with protons. The results are more difficult to interpret, because of the interference of nuclear and Coulomb scattering, but the measure-

† This means that the two distributions give identical results for each of the two volume integrals

$$\int \rho(r)\mathrm{d}\tau \quad \text{and} \quad \int r^2\rho(r)\mathrm{d}\tau.$$

ments are more accurate. The two methods are in substantial agreement, and give $r_0 \simeq 1\cdot3 - 1\cdot4$ fm. The proton experiments also give an estimate for the thickness s of the transition region, in which the nuclear density drops from 90 to 10 per cent of its maximum value (see Fig. 2.2), $s \simeq 2\cdot5$ fm. This is independent of A.

Lastly, a value of the radius of α-radioactive nuclei ($A > 208$) can be derived from the energies and lifetimes of α-particles emerging from radioactive decays (see section 7.4). The radial parameter introduced there is certainly not the same physical quantity as the nuclear radius obtained from scattering experiments, and it is apparent from the theory, that it should be somewhat larger. It is therefore satisfactory that this method yields radii of the order $1\cdot4 \, A^{1/3}$ fm.

2.2.2 ELECTRIC METHODS. By far the most important of these is the scattering of very fast negatons by nuclei. To investigate the details of the charge distribution of the protons, the negatons must have a wavelength small compared with nuclear dimensions, which means that they must have energies of 200 to 500 MeV. Experiments performed at such energies give very similar results for s to those from proton scattering experiments, but a substantially smaller value for r_0, ranging from $1\cdot20$ fm for heavy nuclei to $1\cdot30$ fm for the lighter ones.

The smaller value of r_0 is confirmed by two other electric methods. The first of these depends on the isotope shift of spectral lines. Although two isotopes have the same number of protons, they have different numbers of neutrons, and so the proton distributions in the nuclei of two isotopes are not the same. The atomic negatons therefore find themselves in slightly different electrostatic fields, i.e. their energy levels differ. The resultant splitting of spectral lines can be used to estimate the difference in the nuclear radii of isotopes, and hence to estimate r_0.

The second method makes use of the fact that muons are very similar to negatons, except for their much larger mass. When captured by atoms, they perform orbits, just like negatons, only, because of their greater mass, the radii of these orbits are some 200 times smaller. This brings them very close to the surface of the nucleus, so that the energy of a muon in an orbit depends very sensitively on the nuclear radius. The effect is much greater than that of the isotope shift, but the accuracy of measurement much less, since muons are so short lived. The results based on the X-ray emitted when the muon makes a 2P − 1S transition bear out those obtained for r_0 from negaton scattering.

There is one more piece of experimental evidence, and this at one time was considered to give the most reliable value of r_0. Although it is now somewhat discredited, it must be mentioned here, since it held the field for so long. Among the light nuclei there are pairs of the type $_Z^{Z+1}X^{2Z+1}$ and $_{Z+1}^{Z}Y^{2Z+1}$. They are identical except that one has one neutron replaced by a proton compared with the other. For that reason they are known as mirror nuclei. They can exist only for values of A for which $N = Z - 1$ or $Z + 1$ and, as can be seen from Fig. 1.1, this implies $A < 40$. Examples of such pairs of nuclei are $_6^5B^{11}$ and $_5^6C^{11}$, $_{11}^{12}Na^{23}$ and $_{12}^{11}Mg^{23}$, $_{17}^{18}Cl^{35}$ and $_{18}^{17}A^{35}$.

Of a pair of such nuclei one decays into the other with emission of a positon—

$$_{Z+1}^{Z}X^{2Z+1} \rightarrow _{Z+1}^{Z}Y^{2Z+1} + e^+. \qquad (2.11)$$

Now the positon decay of a nucleus is really due to the positon decay of one of its protons (see section 1.6) and apart from the nucleon which decays, the two nuclei are quite identical. Therefore, if we assume that the forces between nucleons are the same, irrespective of whether the nucleons are protons or neutrons, then the difference in binding energy between the two nuclei will be due to the Coulomb repulsion of the last proton in the field of all the other protons. This repulsion disappears after the decay, since the proton is replaced by a neutron. The difference must be equal to the energy released in the process (2.11), which in view of (1.1) is equal to

$$E_e^+ + (M_n' + m_e - M_p')c^2 \qquad (2.12)$$

where E_e^+ is the kinetic energy of the positon, and M_n' and M_p' are nuclear masses and not atomic masses. In atomic masses (2.12) becomes

$$E_e^+ + (M_n + 2m_e - M_p)c^2. \qquad (2.13)$$

It may not be clear why in the above considerations we have restricted ourselves to mirror nuclei. After all, in any β-decay the total number of nucleons is unchanged and if the forces do not depend on the nature of the nucleons, it would not seem to matter whether there are equal numbers of protons and neutrons or not. This is not so because the nuclear binding of the last nucleon to the rest of the nucleus is the same for a proton or a neutron only if the nucleon is in the same quantum state in the two cases. And because of the exclusion principle this can only be if the rest of the nucleus contains equal numbers of neutrons and protons. This will be gone into more fully when we discuss the shell model in section 5.6.

The Coulomb repulsion energy can be calculated on the assumption that the protons are uniformly distributed over a sphere of radius R_u, and that the last proton is also smeared out over the whole sphere. The potential in which the last proton moves is that due to a uniformly charged sphere which is

$$V = \frac{Ze}{2R_u} \left(3 - \frac{r^2}{R_u^2} \right) \tag{2.14}$$

and the repulsion energy of the last proton is

$$E = \int_0^{R_u} \frac{3e}{4\pi R_u^3} \cdot \frac{Ze}{2R_u} \left(3 - \frac{r^2}{R_u^2} \right) . 4\pi r^2 \mathrm{d}r = \frac{6}{5} \frac{Ze^2}{R_u}. \tag{2.15}$$

The measurement of E can be made with great accuracy, and leads to $r_0 = 1 \cdot 45$ fm. This result, which is of course much too large compared with the other electric determinations of r_0, is due to a gross oversimplification in the interpretation of the experimental results. The assumption that the last proton is smeared out uniformly over the nucleus is quite certainly wrong. Just because this is the proton that decays, it is the least firmly bound of all the protons, while the uniform smearing out of it implies that it is just as firmly bound as all the others. A further reduction in energy is due to the exclusion principle. This prevents identical particles from coming as close to each other as they could if they were classical particles, so that identical particles effectively suffer a repulsion that keeps them apart. This exclusion principle effect, therefore, leads to a reduction in the total binding energy when compared with that of the corresponding classical system. If account is taken of these two effects, the nuclear radius must be reduced if we are to obtain the same total energy. Calculations along these lines have shown that a value $r_0 = 1 \cdot 2$ fm is perfectly compatible with the mirror nuclei evidence.

We thus have a fairly satisfactory state of affairs. All electric methods give

$$R_u \simeq 1 \cdot 2 A^{1/3} \text{ fm} \tag{2.16}$$

while all nuclear methods give values somewhat larger. (An interesting exception to this will be discussed in section 6.10.) One obvious explanation of this discrepancy is that nuclear methods do not measure the nuclear density distribution, but the potential resulting from this distribution. This is likely to extend somewhat further than the distribution itself. Another, but less likely, explanation is that the neutrons in a nucleus spread out somewhat further than the protons and that this will of course not be observed by electric methods. There may be such an effect, but recent work on nuclear structure has indicated that it can probably account for at most a small part of the discrepancy. We shall therefore take it that neutrons and protons have the same mass distributions, and that it is given most accurately by the negaton scattering experiments. For most purposes we shall take the value of R_u given by (2.16). However, the very accurate negaton scattering results confirm the hypothesis that the nucleus consists really of a sphere of almost constant density surrounded by a comparatively thin shell in which the density drops to zero. It can be described by a radius c to the point where the density has dropped to half its maximum value and by the thickness s of the transition region. These are given in fm by

$$c = 1 \cdot 12 A^{1/3} - 0 \cdot 94 A^{-1/3} \tag{2.17}$$

and
$$s = 2 \cdot 5 \pm 0 \cdot 3. \tag{2.18}$$

(See also example 2.9.2.)

The radius of the equivalent uniform distribution is then

$$R_u = 1 \cdot 12 A^{1/3} + 2 \cdot 35 A^{-1/3} - 2 \cdot 07 A^{-1}. \tag{2.19}$$

The radii c and R_u are both accurate to about 2 per cent.

It is worth noting here that the agreement between the value of the nuclear radius based on mirror nuclei evidence and on the other methods shows that the forces between like nucleons are approximately independent of whether the nucleons are charged or not. This is known as the hypothesis of the *charge symmetry* of nuclear forces. From it also follows that, apart from the Coulomb repulsion effect on the protons, the numbers of neutrons and protons in a nucleus are roughly equal. For if the n — n forces were much greater than the p — p forces, the nucleus would consist purely of neutrons and conversely. As Z increases, the p — p interaction does become smaller because of the Coulomb repulsion and this accounts for the neutron excess in medium and heavy nuclei. The above argument cannot of course give any indication of the strength of the n — p interaction.

The nuclear methods, which will be discussed in sections 6.7 and 6.8, show that the distributions of neutrons and protons in a nucleus are very similar indeed. If we then assume that they are identical, we can deduce a nuclear density by simply multiplying the proton density by A/Z. When this is done, it is found that the maximum nuclear density is remarkably constant at $\rho_{max} = 0 \cdot 17$ fm^{-3} over the whole range of A beyond Li[6], which is in good accord with our ideas of the saturation properties of nuclear forces. A few typical examples of nuclear densities are shown in Fig. 2.3, where the dip in the densities of the lighter nuclei is due to the use of rather more correct nuclear wave functions than is possible for heavier nuclei.

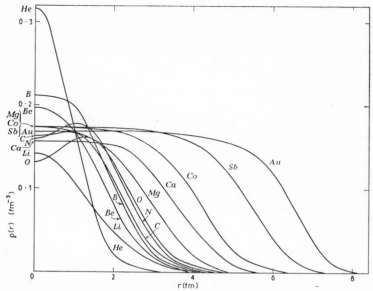

FIG. 2.3. DENSITY DISTRIBUTIONS OF NUCLEI FROM
ELECTRON SCATTERING
[After Elton, L. R. B., *Nuclear Sizes* (Oxford, 1961)]

2.3 Angular Momentum and Magnetic Moment

The angular momentum of nuclei is often referred to as their
spin. This is most unfortunate since the word spin should refer only
to the intrinsic angular momentum of elementary particles, and this
will be its meaning throughout this book. The total angular momentum of nuclei is then made up of the spins of the nucleons and of
their orbital angular momenta. Associated with the angular
momentum of any charged particle there is always a magnetic
moment. Thus a nucleus has a magnetic moment, which is, however,
much smaller than that of the orbital negatons in the outer atom.
Their ratio is of the order m_e/M_p, as will be clear from section 1.1.

The nuclear angular momentum $\mathbf{I}$ (in future angular momentum
will be measured in units of $\hbar$, unless otherwise stated) is subject to
the same rules of quantization as the angular momentum $\mathbf{J}$ of the
negatons in the outer atom.† Thus the total angular momentum
of an atom, $\mathbf{F}$, is given by

$$\mathbf{F} = \mathbf{I} + \mathbf{J} \tag{2.20}$$

† Before reading further the student should make sure that he is familiar
with these rules.

and the same rules apply as in the outer atom, i.e. the possible values of F are—

$$F = J + I, J + I - 1, \ldots, J - I \quad \text{if } J \geqslant I \ (2I + 1 \text{ values})$$
$$F = I + J, I + J - 1, \ldots, I - J \quad \text{if } J \leqslant I \ (2J + 1 \text{ values}).$$
$$(2.21)$$

Because of the coupling of the nucleus and the negatons due to the magnetic interaction the energies of the states (2.21) are not the same. Since the nuclear magnetic moment is so very much smaller than the electronic one the coupling is small, and this in turn leads to only small differences between the energy levels of the states (2.21). The structure of a level J split into $2I + 1$ or $2J + 1$ closely spaced levels according as $J \geqslant I$ or $J \leqslant I$, is known as the hyperfine structure of the level. This is to distinguish it from the fine structure of a level, which is due to the coupling of the orbital and spin angular momentum of a negaton. Each fine structure level can have hyperfine structure.

The energy of interaction due to the magnetic coupling is proportional to the scalar product of the angular momenta,

$$W = A\,\mathbf{I}.\mathbf{J} = AIJ \cos \theta \tag{2.22}$$

where θ is the angle between $\mathbf{I}$ and $\mathbf{J}$. But from (2.20),

$$2\mathbf{I}.\mathbf{J} = \mathbf{F}^2 - \mathbf{I}^2 - \mathbf{J}^2 = F(F + 1) - I(I + 1) - J(J + 1) \tag{2.23}$$

because in quantum mechanics any square of an angular momentum $\mathbf{L}^2$ must be replaced by the product $L(L + 1)$. If we substitute for F from (2.21), we see that W has the series of values

$$A[IJ], \ A[IJ - I - J], \ A[IJ + 1 - 2(I + J)],$$
$$A[IJ + 3 - 3(I + J)], \ \ldots, \tag{2.24}$$

so that the energy differences between successive states are

$$A(I + J), \ A(I + J - 1), \ A(I + J - 2), \ \ldots A\,|\,I - J\,|. \tag{2.25}$$

The energy differences are thus proportional to the values (2.21) of F. This is known as the *interval rule*.

If $I \leqslant J$, it is immediately possible to find I, by merely counting the levels into which a given J-level is split. Spectral lines correspond of course to the energy difference between levels. Thus if a transition takes place between two levels each of which has hyperfine structure, then the corresponding splitting of the spectral line will be much more complicated than the splitting of either of the two levels. It is therefore necessary to select two levels, one of which has a much more widely spaced hyperfine structure than the other. In that case the splitting of the spectral line will be due essentially only to the splitting of that level. If $I > J$, then J can be determined in the above way and F is found from the relative separations of the levels, by the use of the interval rule. Hence I can be determined.

The above method of determining I depends on the existence of a nuclear magnetic moment, but is quite independent of its magnitude. The magnitude can be found from the absolute separation of the levels, but this method is not very accurate. A better method is the molecular beam method originally developed by Rabi (1934). It is based on the so-called *Larmor precession* of a magnetic dipole in a magnetic field. To explain this we must first consider the connexion between the angular momentum and magnetic moment of a single particle.

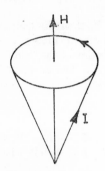

FIG. 2.4. LARMOR
PRECESSION

Consider a particle of mass M and charge e. Its orbital angular momentum is $\{l(l+1)\}^{\frac{1}{2}}\hbar$, where l is its orbital quantum number. (In this paragraph it is convenient not to work in units of $\hbar$.) In a magnetic field the component of the angular momentum in the direction of the field is also quantized and equal to $m\hbar$, where m is the magnetic quantum number, $-l \leqslant m \leqslant l$. As the particle has a charge e, it is equivalent to an electric current of strength $i = e\omega/2\pi$, where ω is the frequency of revolution. Now the magnetic field of a circular current is equivalent to that of a magnetic dipole of moment $\pi r^2 i/c$ in Gaussian units, where r is the radius of the orbit, and the angular momentum component is $m\hbar = Mr^2\omega$. The maximum magnetic moment is given by $m = l$, so that

$$\mu_{\text{max.}} = \frac{e\hbar l}{2Mc}. \tag{2.26}$$

This is defined as the magnetic moment of the particle in the given orbit. If the angular momentum is due to an intrinsic spin $\frac{1}{2}\hbar$, then it can be shown that the corresponding magnetic moment is

$$\mu = \frac{e\hbar}{2Mc} \tag{2.27}$$

which is twice the expected value. This is the result quoted in section 1.1.

Owing to the fact that the total angular momentum of a nucleus is made up partly of orbital and partly of spin angular momentum, it is not possible to calculate the magnetic moment of a nucleus from a knowledge merely of its angular momentum I. It is convenient then to write the magnetic moment as

$$\mathbf{\mu} = \frac{e\hbar}{2M_p c} g\mathbf{I} \tag{2.28}$$

where g is a constant, known as the *gyromagnetic ratio*. M_p is of course the mass of the proton. We have written here $\mathbf{\mu}$ instead of μ, since the measured magnetic moment is a vector in the direction of $\mathbf{I}$.

If a nucleus is now put into a magnetic field $\mathbf{H}$, then the couple with which the field acts on the magnetic moment makes the angular momentum vector precess about the direction of the field in a way that is familiar from the motion of a top. The energy of this motion, which is known as the Larmor precession, is

$$E = \mathbf{\mu} \cdot \mathbf{H} = \frac{e\hbar}{2M_p c} gmH \tag{2.29}$$

where m is the magnetic quantum number $(\mathbf{I} \cdot \mathbf{H} = mH)$. In a magnetic field a given energy level is thus split into levels with separation

$$h\nu_L = 2\pi\hbar\nu_L = \frac{e\hbar}{2M_p c} gH. \tag{2.30}$$

This defines the Larmor frequency

$$\nu_L = \frac{e}{4\pi M_p c} gH. \tag{2.31}$$

Rabi's method consists of passing a stream of neutral molecules having no negaton magnetic moment through three successive magnetic fields (see Fig. 2.5). The first is a long inhomogeneous field with a gradient perpendicular to the beam. Because the field is inhomogeneous it exerts a resultant force on the molecules through their nuclear magnetic moments which is different for different spatial orientations of the magnetic moment and hence causes the beam to spread out. The third field is similar but inhomogeneous in the opposite direction, and refocuses the beam. The second field is homogeneous and has no effect on the beam beyond giving each nucleus a constant Larmor precession. Into this field is now inserted a small loop of wire carrying an oscillating current. This current will transmit energy to the nuclei only if its frequency is in resonance with the Larmor frequency of the nuclei. When it is in resonance, many of the nuclei obtain sufficient energy to change their magnetic quantum number. This changes the direction of their magnetic moments and hence they are not refocused by the third field. Therefore if the current in the loop of wire oscillates with the Larmor frequency, the intensity of the final beam will be reduced. This method determines only the gyromagnetic ratio and it must therefore be combined with a method that determines the angular momentum in order that the magnetic moment may be determined.

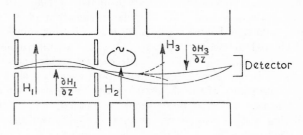

FIG. 2.5. SCHEMATIC DESCRIPTION OF RABI'S MOLECULAR BEAM APPARATUS

There is another method for determining nuclear angular momenta, depending on the intensity of alternate lines in the band spectra of molecules. This will be discussed in section 2.5.

From these experiments the following facts emerge—

(a) all stable nuclei with even A and even Z have angular momentum zero,

(b) all stable nuclei with even A and odd Z have integral non-zero angular momentum between 1 and at most 7, and

(c) all stable nuclei with odd A have half integral angular momentum varying between $\frac{1}{2}$ and $\frac{9}{2}$.

These facts strongly support the hypothesis that nuclei consist of protons and neutrons, each of spin $\frac{1}{2}$. If they consisted of protons and negatons, exactly the opposite results would be expected. For instance an even A odd Z nucleus would consist of A protons and $A—Z$ negatons, giving an odd number of particles and thus a half-integral angular momentum. The fact that the angular momentum of $_7N^{14}$ is 1, was the first indication that nuclei could not consist of protons and negatons.

It may be noticed that it does not necessarily follow from these results that the spin of the neutron is $\frac{1}{2}$. The angular momenta of the proton and the deuteron can be measured directly and they are $\frac{1}{2}$ and 1 respectively. If we assume that in the ground state of the deuteron neither the proton nor the neutron have an orbital angular momentum, and this is likely to be correct, then the spin of the neutron, which cannot be measured directly, can still be $\frac{1}{2}$ or $\frac{3}{2}$, but we shall see below that it must be $\frac{1}{2}$.

The fact that nuclear angular momenta are very much smaller than $\frac{1}{2}A$ indicates that nuclear spins do not combine at random. Rather, like nucleons seem to combine in pairs giving a resultant zero angular momentum. The angular momentum of an odd A nucleus would then be due to the last nucleon having spin $\frac{1}{2}$ and an orbital angular momentum 0, 1, 2, . . . ; the angular momentum of even A, odd Z nuclei would be due to the last proton and neutron. This theory is due originally to Landé and is, as we shall see, a natural consequence of the shell model of nuclei (see section 5.6).

There is now an even more accurate method than Rabi's for determining nuclear magnetic moments. This is based on the use of polarized beams, in which the nuclear angular momenta are not randomly oriented. By this method even the sign of the neutron magnetic moment can be determined, which is not possible by Rabi's method. The results (Ramsey, 1953) for the proton, neutron and deuteron are, in units of the nuclear magneton,

$$\mu_p = 2\cdot7927, \qquad \mu_n = -1\cdot9131, \qquad \mu_d = 0\cdot8574.$$

As has already been mentioned in section 1.1, the results show that the proton and the neutron are not as simple particles as the electron. Further, $\mu_p + \mu_n = 0\cdot8796$, which is nearly equal to μ_d, but the difference is well outside experimental error. We can expect μ_d to be the sum of μ_p and μ_n only if there is no orbital contribution to the magnetic moment. The small discrepancy indicates that in the ground state of the deuteron the proton and the neutron must for a small part of the time be in a state of non-zero orbital angular momentum. We shall return to this fact in section 4.2. However, since the discrepancy is so small, the magnetic moment of the deuteron must be essentially due to the addition of the proton and neutron magnetic moments, and hence the total angular momentum of the deuteron, $I = 1$, is due to the addition and not the subtraction of the proton and neutron spins. It then follows that the neutron spin is $\frac{1}{2}$.

2.4 Electric Quadrupole Moment

So far we have assumed that nuclei are spherically symmetrical. There is really no reason to suppose this, although rotating nuclei must on the average have cylindrical symmetry, if the average is taken over times that are long compared with the period of rotation of the nuclei. In practice this is always the case. Now the potential due to a charge distribution with cylindrical symmetry can be developed in inverse powers of r, the distance from the origin,

$$\phi(r,\,\theta) = \frac{e}{r}\left\{ Z + \frac{D}{r}\,P_1\,(\cos\theta) + \frac{Q}{r^2}\,P_2\,(\cos\theta) + \ldots \right\} \quad (2.32)$$

where θ is the angle between the radius vector and the axis of rotation, and $P_1\,(\cos\theta)$, $P_2\,(\cos\theta)$, . . . are the Legendre polynomials, i.e.

$$P_1\,(\cos\theta) = \cos\theta,\ P_2\,(\cos\theta) = \tfrac{1}{2}\,(3\cos^2\theta - 1),\ \ldots \quad (2.33)$$

Z is of course the nuclear charge and D and Q are constants known as the *electric dipole moment* and the *electric quadrupole moment*. It will be shown in section 2.6 that nuclei cannot have electric dipole moments ; hence the spherical asymmetry of nuclei is measured by Q. Nuclei with $I = 0$ clearly must have $Q = 0$, since when $I = 0$, the nucleus has no prefered axis and so the charge distribution appears spherical on a time average. Surprisingly, nuclei with $I = \tfrac{1}{2}$ also have no quadrupole moment. This is a quantum mechanical effect and a proof of it is beyond the scope of this book.

The electric dipole and quadrupole moments due to a classical charge distribution $\rho(\mathbf{r})$ can be evaluated as follows. The potential due to a charge element $\rho(\mathbf{r}')\,dV'$ in a volume element dV' is

$$d\phi(\mathbf{r}) = \frac{\rho(\mathbf{r}')dV'}{|\mathbf{r} - \mathbf{r}'|}. \quad (2.34)$$

Now since $|\mathbf{r} - \mathbf{r}'| = (r^2 + r'^2 - 2rr'\cos\alpha)^{\frac{1}{2}}$, where α is the angle between $\mathbf{r}$ and $\mathbf{r}'$, we have for large r

$$\frac{1}{|\mathbf{r} - \mathbf{r}'|} = \frac{1}{r}\left\{ 1 + \frac{r'}{r}\cos\alpha + \frac{r'^2}{2r^2}(3\cos^2\alpha - 1) + \ldots \right\}. \quad (2.35)$$

Hence

$$\phi(\mathbf{r}) = \int \frac{\rho(\mathbf{r}')}{r}\left\{ 1 + \frac{r'}{r}\cos\alpha + \frac{r'^2}{2r^2}(3\cos^2\alpha - 1) + \ldots \right\}dV'. \quad (2.36)$$

This expression must be identical with (2.32) for all values of r and θ, and we can therefore obtain D and Q by equating coefficients of like powers of r for any θ. This is done most easily for $\theta = 0$, when r is along the z-axis, so that $r'\cos\alpha = z'$. Hence

$$D = \frac{1}{e}\int \rho(\mathbf{r}')z'\,dV' \quad (2.37)$$

$$Q = \frac{1}{e}\int \rho(\mathbf{r}')(3z'^2 - r'^2)dV'. \quad (2.38)$$

Clearly D has the dimensions of a length and Q those of an area. Q is generally measured in units of 1 barn $= 10^{-24}$ cm^2. This is the unit in which areas are usually measured in nuclear physics.

In quantum mechanics the charge element $\rho(\mathbf{r}')\,dV'$ in a nucleus is found by multiplying the proton charge e by the chance $P_i(\mathbf{r}')\,dV'$ of finding the ith proton in a volume element dV' at $\mathbf{r}'$ and summing over all the Z protons in the nucleus, i.e.

$$\rho(\mathbf{r}')dV' = \sum_{i=1}^{Z} eP_i(\mathbf{r}')dV'. \qquad (2.39)$$

$P_i(\mathbf{r})$ is obtained from the nucleus wave function $\psi(\mathbf{r}_1, \mathbf{r}_2, \ldots, \mathbf{r}_A)$ which is a function of the position of all the nucleons, and not only of the protons, by integrating $|\psi|^2$ over all possible positions of the other $A-1$ nucleons. Therefore

$$P_i(\mathbf{r}') = \int |\psi(\mathbf{r}_1, \ldots, \mathbf{r}_{i-1}, \mathbf{r}', \mathbf{r}_{i+1}, \ldots, \mathbf{r}_A)|^2\, dV_1 \ldots$$
$$dV_{i-1}\, dV_{i+1} \ldots dV_A. \quad (2.40)$$

If we now write $r' = r_i$, we see that each proton contributes to the dipole moment a term

$$\int z_i\, |\psi(r_1, \ldots, r_A)|^2 dV_1 \ldots dV_A$$

and the integration is over the co-ordinates of all the A nucleons. Therefore if we write $d\tau$ for the volume element $dV_1 \ldots dV_A$,

we have $\qquad D = \sum_{i=1}^{Z} \int z_i\, |\psi(\mathbf{r}_1, \ldots, \mathbf{r}_A)|^2 d\tau \qquad (2.41)$

$$Q = \sum_{i=1}^{Z} \int (3z_i^2 - \mathbf{r}_i^2)\, |\psi(\mathbf{r}_1 \ldots, \mathbf{r}_A)|^2 d\tau \qquad (2.42)$$

where the integrations are over the $3A$ co-ordinates (x_i, y_i, z_i).

If the charge distribution in nuclei is assumed uniform and forms an ellipsoid of rotation of semi-axis a along the axis of symmetry and semi-axis b perpendicular to it, then from (2.38),

$$Q = \frac{2}{5} Z(a^2 - b^2). \qquad (2.43)$$

Hence positive Q corresponds to prolate spheroids $(a > b)$ and negative Q to oblate spheroids $(a < b)$.

Nuclear quadrupole moments can be determined experimentally by observing deviations from the interval rule in energy levels. The interval rule is based on the fact that the energy of interaction between negatons and nuclei which depends on the angle θ between I and J, is proportional to $\cos\theta$, due to the magnetic coupling

(2.22). If, however, in addition to the magnetic coupling there is an electric coupling of the type (2.32), then there will also be a term in the interaction energy proportional to $\cos^2 \theta$. Thus the deviations of the observed intervals from the calculated ones should obey a $\cos^2 \theta$ law. This was found. Quadrupole moments vary from + 8 barns for Lu^{176} to — 8 barns for Sn^{119}. A particularly interesting case is that of the deuteron which has been shown by Kellogg and his co-workers (1939) to have a quadrupole moment, the most recent value of which is + 0·00282 barns (Auffray, 1961). This fact is, as we shall see, fundamental to any theory of nuclear forces.

2.5 Identical Particles

The properties of particles and nuclei that we have discussed so far all have classical analogues. We now come to two properties which are essentially quantum mechanical and they will be discussed in this section and the one following. The first of these concerns the indistinguishability of identical particles. In classical physics it is assumed that we can attach labels to identical particles, so that the situation in which particle 1 is at A and particle 2 at B is different from the situation in which particle 2 is at A and particle 1 at B. These situations are clearly indistinguishable from each other and in quantum mechanics we therefore say that there is only one situation, with one particle at A and the other at B. To give another example, in a collision process, in which we can observe only the initial and final momenta of the colliding particles, the two classical situations depicted in Fig. 2.6 are indistinguishable quantum mechanically, if the two particles are identical.

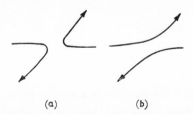

(a)   (b)

FIG. 2.6. TWO DIFFERENT CLASSICAL COLLISIONS (a) AND (b) OF IDENTICAL PARTICLES WHICH ARE INDISTINGUISHABLE QUANTUM MECHANICALLY

There must therefore be an essential difference between the treatment of two non-identical particles and that of two identical particles and this difference must appear in the mathematical formalism. The theory is of course true for any number of particles, but we shall confine ourselves to two.

The Schrödinger equation for two identical particles can be written

$$H(1, 2)\psi(1, 2) = E\psi(1, 2) \qquad (2.44)$$

where 1 and 2 refer each to all the co-ordinates of one particle. Since the particles are identical, we can exchange them without affecting the mathematical descriptions of the system. Hence the Hamiltonian $H(1, 2)$ of the system must be symmetric in the co-ordinates of the particles, i.e.

$$H(1, 2) = H(2, 1). \qquad (2.45)$$

From this it follows on interchanging 1 and 2 in (2.44) that

$$H(1, 2)\psi(2, 1) = E\psi(2, 1) \qquad (2.46)$$

so that $\psi(2, 1)$ is also a solution of this equation. In other words both $\psi(1, 2)$ and $\psi(2, 1)$ are eigenfunctions of the operator $H(1, 2)$ belonging to the same eigenvalue E. Hence the system is degenerate and any linear combination

$$\Psi(1, 2) = A\psi(1, 2) + B\psi(2, 1) \qquad (2.47)$$

is also an eigenfunction belonging to E. Now since the particles are indistinguishable, all physically measurable quantities must be independent of the interchange of 1 and 2, in particular we must have

$$| \Psi(1, 2) |^2 = | \Psi(2, 1) |^2 \qquad (2.48)$$

since the square of a wave function—although not a wave function itself—is physically measurable. It is easily seen (see ex. 2.9.10) that this is only possible if $A = \pm B$, so that there are two possible wave functions,

$$\Psi_{sym}(1, 2) = \psi(1, 2) + \psi(2, 1) = \Psi_{sym}(2, 1) \qquad (2.49)$$

and

$$\Psi_{anti}(1, 2) = \psi(1, 2) - \psi(2, 1) = - \Psi_{anti}(2, 1) \qquad (2.50)$$

which are respectively symmetric and anti-symmetric in 1 and 2. It will be clear from the above that if any solution, say $\psi(1, 2)$, of the wave equation (2.44) has been obtained, then it is always possible to construct a symmetric and an anti-symmetric solution. It can further be shown (see ex. 2.9.11) that the symmetry character of the wave function does not change in time, so that a pair of identical particles will be described by a wave function of definite symmetry. We therefore speak of symmetric and anti-symmetric particles. Only experiment can decide in any particular case which sign is correct.

The above considerations apply not only to elementary particles, but also to tightly bound aggregates such as α-particles or even atoms and molecules, provided their internal motions can be neglected in their interactions with other particles. It is found quite generally that systems with half-integral angular momentum are anti-symmetric and systems with integral angular momentum are symmetric. In particular, protons, neutrons, positons and negatons all are anti-symmetric.

It is easily seen that a system of A anti-symmetric particles will be symmetric if A is even and anti-symmetric if A is odd and that hence the symmetry properties of a system can be deduced from the symmetry properties of its constituents. The fact that the neutron is anti-symmetric is actually a deduction from the experimental fact that the proton is anti-symmetric and the deuteron symmetric.

When particles are treated in large numbers by the methods of statistical mechanics, it is found that symmetric and anti-symmetric particles must be treated differently. The former are said to obey *Bose-Einstein statistics* and the latter *Fermi-Dirac statistics*. These are both different from classical Boltzmann statistics.

We shall now see that the above considerations immediately lead to the exclusion principle which states that in a system of identical particles obeying Fermi-Dirac statistics (e.g. the negatons of an atom) no two particles can be in the same state. This again we shall prove for a system of two identical particles only.

An important special case arises when the two particles do not interact with each other. In that case the Hamiltonian can be written

$$H(1, 2) = H(1) + H(2). \tag{2.51}$$

If now the wave equation for one of the particles is

$$H\phi_k = E_k\phi_k \tag{2.52}$$

then the solution of the equation for two particles (2.51) which corresponds to the energy $E_m + E_n$ is

$$\Psi_{mn}(1, 2) = 2^{-\frac{1}{2}} [\phi_m(1)\phi_n(2) \pm \phi_n(1)\phi_m(2)] \tag{2.53}$$

where the factor $2^{-\frac{1}{2}}$ ensures correct normalization. For $m = n$ this vanishes when Ψ_{mn} is anti-symmetric, but does not vanish when Ψ_{mn} is symmetric. Hence the probability of two anti-symmetric identical particles occupying identical states is zero. This is a particular statement of the exclusion principle, which strictly speaking applies only to non-interacting particles, but applies approximately also to weakly interacting particles.

To determine the statistics of nuclei, we must find how an exchange of identical nuclei in a diatomic molecule affects the sign of the wave function of the molecule. As we shall see, this will show up in the band spectrum of the molecule.

The wave function of such a molecule depends on

(*a*) the motion of the atomic negatons,

(*b*) the vibrational motion of the nuclei along the line joining them,

(*c*) the rotational motion of the nuclei about their common centre of mass,

(*d*) the intrinsic angular momentum of the nuclei, **I**.

It can therefore be written

$$\Psi = \psi_{at}\,\psi_{vib}\,\psi_{rot}\,\psi_{I}. \tag{2.54}$$

We now denote the operation of exchanging two nuclei by R. Then

$$R\psi_{at} = \pm\,\psi_{at} \tag{2.55}$$

and the sign can be determined from molecular spectra. It is usually $+$, and we assume it to be so in the rest of the proof. Next,

$$R\psi_{vib} = +\,\psi_{vib} \tag{2.56}$$

for ψ_{vib} only depends on the distance between the nuclei and this is unchanged by the exchange. The behaviour of ψ_{rot} is more complicated. It is a spherical harmonic, i.e.

$$\psi_{rot} = P_l^m(\cos\theta)e^{lm\phi} \tag{2.57}$$

where θ and ϕ are the spherical polar angle co-ordinates of one of the nuclei relative to the centre of mass. On exchanging the nuclei, θ goes to $\pi - \theta$ and ϕ to $\pi + \phi$ (see Fig. 2.7). It might be thought that θ goes to $\pi + \theta$, but this is not so, since θ is the angle of longitude and this is always less than π. Since

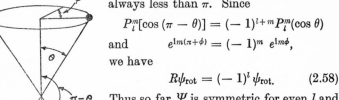

$$P_l^m[\cos(\pi - \theta)] = (-1)^{l+m}P_l^m(\cos\theta)$$

and

$$e^{lm(\pi+\phi)} = (-1)^m\,e^{lm\phi},$$

we have

$$R\psi_{rot} = (-1)^l\,\psi_{rot}. \tag{2.58}$$

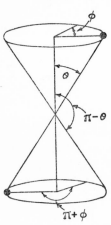

FIG. 2.7.

Thus so far Ψ is symmetric for even l and anti-symmetric for odd l, where l is the orbital angular momentum quantum number of the nuclei.

Lastly we consider the part ψ_I of the wave function. The total angular momentum **I** of a nucleus can have a component m in a prescribed direction, where $m = I$, $I - 1, \ldots, -I$. Thus there are $2I + 1$ states for each nucleus and for two nuclei we can construct $(2\,I+1)^2$ wave functions of the type $\psi_{m_1}\,(1)\,\psi_{m_2}\,(2)$. If $m_1 = m_2$ these are symmetric and there are $2I + 1$ of them. If $m_1 \neq m_2$, they are not symmetrized and every pair, $\psi_{m_1}\,(1)\,\psi_{m_2}\,(2)$ and $\psi_{m_2}\,(1)\,\psi_{m_1}\,(2)$, must be replaced by one symmetric wave function, $\psi_{m_1}\,(1)\,\psi_{m_2}\,(2) + \psi_{m_2}\,(1)\,\psi_{m_1}\,(2)$, and one anti-symmetric one, $\psi_{m_1}\,(1)\,\psi_{m_2}\,(2) - \psi_{m_2}\,(1)\,\psi_{m_1}\,(2)$. Thus there will be altogether $I(2I + 1)$ anti-symmetric wave functions and $I(2I + 1) + (2I + 1)$ symmetric ones. The ratio of the number of symmetric to anti-symmetric wave functions is therefore $(I + 1)/I$.

Now the complete wave function must certainly be either symmetric or anti-symmetric. If it is symmetric then the symmetric $\psi_\mathbf{I}$ must combine with the ψ_{rot} for even l and the anti-symmetric $\psi_\mathbf{I}$ with the ψ_{rot} for odd l. Now all the states given by the different wave functions are equally likely and thus the intensity of a line of even l in the band spectrum to that of the next line of odd l is $(I + 1)/I$. The converse is true if $\varPsi$ is antisymmetric. Thus both the statistics and the spins of nuclei can be obtained by this method. The method is particularly useful for nuclei of zero angular momentum, for which every second line will be missing, since the methods described in section 2.3 cannot distinguish between zero angular momentum and zero magnetic moment. The band spectrum method cannot of course give any information about the nuclear magnetic moment.

2.6 Parity

We next investigate what happens to a wave function when we reflect the co-ordinate system which describes it in the origin, i.e. when we replace (x, y, z) by $(- x, - y, - z)$ throughout. This is called the *parity operation* P, and it is equivalent to changing from a right-handed to a left-handed system of co-ordinate axes.

For an n-particle system we have

$$P\psi(\mathbf{r}_1, \mathbf{r}_2, \ldots, \mathbf{r}_n) = \psi(-\mathbf{r}_1, -\mathbf{r}_2, \ldots, -\mathbf{r}_n). \qquad (2.59)$$

On repeating the operation, we obtain

$$P^2\psi(\mathbf{r}_1, \mathbf{r}_2, \ldots, \mathbf{r}_n) = \psi(\mathbf{r}_1, \mathbf{r}_2, \ldots, \mathbf{r}_n). \qquad (2.60)$$

so that P^2 has the eigenvalue 1. Hence the only possible eigenvalues of P are $+ 1$ and $- 1$. We shall now show that under certain conditions parity is a constant of motion.

If the energy operator H of an n-particle system is unchanged under co-ordinate reflexion, then the wave equation

$$H\psi(\mathbf{r}_1, \ldots, \mathbf{r}_n) = E\psi(\mathbf{r}_1, \ldots, \mathbf{r}_n) \qquad (2.61)$$

becomes under co-ordinate reflexion

$$H\psi(-\mathbf{r}_1, \ldots, -\mathbf{r}_n) = E\psi(-\mathbf{r}_1, \ldots, -\mathbf{r}_n). \tag{2.62}$$

Therefore $\psi(\mathbf{r}_1, \ldots, \mathbf{r}_n)$ and $\psi(-\mathbf{r}_1, \ldots, -\mathbf{r}_n)$ are wave functions belonging to the same energy level E. If this energy level is non-degenerate, then the two wave functions must be proportional to each other, i.e.

$$\psi(-\mathbf{r}_1, \ldots, -\mathbf{r}_n) = K\psi(\mathbf{r}_1, \ldots, \mathbf{r}_n). \tag{2.63}$$

If we replace $\mathbf{r}$ by $-\mathbf{r}$ throughout in this equation, we have

$$\psi(\mathbf{r}_1, \ldots, \mathbf{r}_n) = K\psi(-\mathbf{r}_1, \ldots, -\mathbf{r}_n) = K^2\psi(\mathbf{r}_1, \ldots, \mathbf{r}_n)$$

by (2.63), so that

$$K = \pm 1 \tag{2.64}$$

in agreement with (2.60). But (2.63) can be written in terms of the parity operator as

$$P\psi(\mathbf{r}_1, \ldots, \mathbf{r}_n) = K\psi(\mathbf{r}_1, \ldots, \mathbf{r}_n). \tag{2.65}$$

This is an eigenvalue equation for the parity operator P. Hence parity is a constant of motion, and its value is either $+1$ or -1.

The necessary condition for the wave function of a system to have a definite parity is that the energy operator H of the system is unchanged under co-ordinate reflexion. This means that H contains only scalar, but not pseudo-scalar terms.† If, for instance, the nuclear force law was such that the Hamiltonian of a nuclear system contained a small pseudo-scalar term, then the wave function of the system would contain a corresponding small admixture, amplitude, F, of the opposite parity to that of the leading term. This in turn would allow certain nuclear reactions to occur, which would be forbidden if parity was strictly conserved. Such reactions have been looked for (Wilkinson, 1958), but have not been found. In this way an upper limit.

$$F^2 \leqslant 10^{-7}$$

has been established. Thus, within experimental error, nuclear forces conserve parity, and this is equally true of electromagnetic forces. It is known, however, (Wu, 1957) that it is not true of β-decay (see section 9.4), which is due to a different kind of force again.

If we accept that parity is strictly conserved in nuclear reactions, then we can show that a nucleus cannot have an electric dipole

---

† An example of a pseudo-scalar quantity is the scalar product of an angular and a linear momentum $\mathbf{L} \cdot \mathbf{p}$. On reflexion, the polar vector $\mathbf{p}$ changes sign, the axial vector $\mathbf{L}$ does not, so that $\mathbf{L} \cdot \mathbf{p}$ changes sign. Another example is the scalar triple product of three linear momenta $\mathbf{p}_1 \cdot \mathbf{p}_2 \times \mathbf{p}_3$.

moment (2.41). Since a nucleus has definite parity, we have for its wave function

$$| \psi(\mathbf{r}_1, \ldots, \mathbf{r}_A) |^2 = |\psi (- \mathbf{r}_1, \ldots, - \mathbf{r}_A) |^2 \qquad (2.66)$$

so that $| \psi |^2$ is an even function of the co-ordinates. On the other hand z_i is clearly an odd function, and each one of the integrands in (2.41) is therefore an odd function. But the integral of an odd function over all space vanishes. Hence each term in the sum of (2.41) vanishes separately, which proves that $D = 0$.

It is clear that our discussion of parity will break down in a non-isotropic space, and that if a nucleus were located in such a space, it might show an electric dipole moment. In an isotropic space the dipole of a nucleus is equally likely to point in any direction, and so averages to zero. It would show up in an electric field strong enough to disturb the motion of the nucleus. It should be noted that such a field is not required to polarize the nucleus, i.e. give it an induced dipole moment, but merely to orient it. Such strong fields are not obtainable in practice for nuclei, in contrast with molecules, where the required fields are very much weaker and intrinsic dipoles are easily measurable.

2.7 Spin Operators

So far all our functions have been functions of only the position co-ordinates of the particles which they described. But since an elementary particle can have spin $\frac{1}{2}$, which may be in either of two directions (referred to as " up " and " down "), such a particle is only completely described by its three space co-ordinates (x, y, z) which fix its position and by a spin co-ordinate s_z which determines the direction of spin. The space co-ordinates x, y, z can of course take any value from $- \infty$ to $+ \infty$; the spin co-ordinate s_z has only two values, $\pm \frac{1}{2}$, where we are as usual measuring angular momentum in units of $\hbar$. The suffix z denotes the fact that we conventionally take the z-direction along the measured direction of spin. The wave function of an elementary particle is then

$$\psi(x, y, z, s_z).$$

At low velocities forces acting on the spin and on the position do not interfere (this is no longer true at relativistic velocities, but we shall rarely be concerned with these) and it is then possible to write the wave function as a product

$$\psi(x, y, z, s_z) = \phi(x, y, z) \, \chi(s_z). \qquad (2.67)$$

Since spin is a physical observable it must correspond in quantum mechanics to an operator which operates on $\chi(s_z)$, and since spin

3

is a vector quantity it must correspond to a vector operator. Let this be $\mathbf{s}(s_x, s_y, s_z)$. Then $\mathbf{s}^2$ is a constant of motion of magnitude $\frac{1}{2}(\frac{1}{2} + 1) = \frac{3}{4}$ and s_z can have two values, $+\frac{1}{2}$ "up" and $-\frac{1}{2}$ "down." Thus s_z has two eigenfunctions only, which we shall call α and β, so that

$$\chi(+\tfrac{1}{2}) = \alpha, \quad \chi(-\tfrac{1}{2}) = \beta \tag{2.68}$$

and

$$s_z\alpha = \tfrac{1}{2}\alpha, \ s_z\beta = -\tfrac{1}{2}\beta, \ s^2\alpha = \tfrac{3}{4}\alpha, \ s^2\beta = \tfrac{3}{4}\beta. \tag{2.69}$$

The wave function of a particle of arbitrary spin direction must thus be of the form

$$\psi(x, y, z, s_z) = \phi(x, y, z)(a\alpha + b\beta), \tag{2.70}$$

where a and b are constants. The physical interpretation of the wave function in terms of probability yields

$$\sum_{\text{spin space}} \int \ |\ \phi(x, y, z)\ \chi(s_z)\ |^2\ \mathrm{d}\tau = 1. \tag{2.71}$$

Substituting (2.70), we then have

$$|\ a\ |^2\ |\ \alpha\ |^2 + |\ b\ |^2\ |\ \beta\ |^2 + a^*b\alpha^*\beta + b^*a\beta^*\alpha = 1, \tag{2.72}$$

since

$$\int |\ \phi(x, y, z)\ |^2\ \mathrm{d}\tau = 1. \tag{2.73}$$

It follows from very general quantum mechanical principles, relating to the reality of eigenvalues (see also ex. 2.9.7) that

$$\alpha^*\beta = \beta^*\alpha = 0 \tag{2.74}$$

and it is usual to normalize the spin wavefunctions to

$$|\ \alpha\ |^2 = |\ \beta\ |^2 = 1. \tag{2.75}$$

It then follows that

$$|\ a\ |^2 + |\ b\ |^2 = 1. \tag{2.76}$$

The physical interpretation of this is that the particle described by (2.70) has spin up with probability $|\ a\ |^2$ and spin down with probability $|\ b\ |^2$.

It is convenient to define a new operator through

$$\mathbf{s} = \tfrac{1}{2}\boldsymbol{\sigma}. \tag{2.77}$$

Then (2.69) can be written

$$\sigma_z\alpha = \alpha, \quad \sigma_z\beta = -\beta, \quad \sigma^2\alpha = 3\alpha, \quad \sigma^2\beta = 3\beta. \tag{2.78}$$

As $\boldsymbol{\sigma}^2 = \sigma_x^2 + \sigma_y^2 + \sigma_z^2$ and $\sigma_z^2\alpha = \alpha$, $\sigma_z^2\beta = \beta$ we must have

$$(\sigma_x^2 + \sigma_y^2)\alpha = 2\alpha, \quad (\sigma_x^2 + \sigma_y^2)\beta = 2\beta \tag{2.79}$$

and these relations are satisfied if σ_x and σ_y are chosen so that

$$\sigma_x\alpha = \beta, \quad \sigma_x\beta = \alpha, \quad \sigma_y\alpha = \mathrm{i}\beta, \quad \sigma_y\beta = -\mathrm{i}\alpha. \tag{2.80}$$

It is usual to write σ_x, σ_y, σ_z, α and β in matrix notation. (See example 2.9.5.)†

The spin wave function of a system of two identical particles must of course be correctly symmetrized. There will be three symmetric spin functions,

$$\alpha_1\alpha_2, \quad 2^{-\frac{1}{2}}(\alpha_1\beta_2, + \alpha_2\beta_1), \quad \beta_1\beta_2, \tag{2.81}$$

and one anti-symmetric one,

$$2^{-\frac{1}{2}}(\alpha_1\beta_2 - \alpha_2\beta_1). \tag{2.82}$$

The factors $2^{-\frac{1}{2}}$ have been introduced so that all four functions are normalized in the same way. Two identical particles of spin $\frac{1}{2}$ can combine to give systems of total angular momentum $I = 1$ or $I = 0$. The former can exist in three states (magnetic quantum number $m = 1$, 0, -1) and these are given by (2.81), the latter in one state only given by (2.82). They are referred to as triplet and singlet states respectively.

We shall in the next chapter require the eigenvalues of the operator $\boldsymbol{\sigma}^{(1)} \cdot \boldsymbol{\sigma}^{(2)}$, where $\boldsymbol{\sigma}^{(1)}$ operates on one of two particles of a system and $\boldsymbol{\sigma}^{(2)}$ on the other. These are most easily obtained by direct application of the operator

$$\boldsymbol{\sigma}^{(1)} \cdot \boldsymbol{\sigma}^{(2)} = \sigma_x^{(1)}\sigma_x^{(2)} + \sigma_y^{(1)}\sigma_y^{(2)} + \sigma_z^{(1)}\sigma_z^{(2)} \tag{2.83}$$

to the spin functions (2.81) and (2.82). We find that

$$\boldsymbol{\sigma}^{(1)} \cdot \boldsymbol{\sigma}^{(2)} = 1 \text{ (triplet)}, \quad \boldsymbol{\sigma}^{(1)} \cdot \boldsymbol{\sigma}^{(2)} = -3 \text{ (singlet)}. \tag{2.84}$$

2.8 I-spin

It is frequently convenient to treat the proton and the neutron as two states of the nucleon which differ only in charge. We can then represent the wave function of the nucleon as

$$\Psi = \psi_{\text{space}} \, \psi_{\text{spin}} \, \psi_{\text{charge}}. \tag{2.85}$$

Since ψ_{charge} can be only one of two eigenfunctions corresponding to the two charge states of the nucleon, it is mathematically completely equivalent to ψ_{spin}, and our treatment of the charge operator $\boldsymbol{\tau}$ will be identical with that of the spin operator $\boldsymbol{\sigma}$ in the last section. For that reason $\boldsymbol{\tau}$ is called the *isotopic* or *isobaric spin operator*. The latter name is more correct, since neutrons and protons are isobars and not isotopes, but both names are awkwardly long. We shall follow Fermi in abbreviating either to *i-spin*. The equivalence

† Bohr reports Heisenberg as saying in 1925: " Ich weiss ja aber nicht einmal, was eine Matrix ist " (But I don't even know what a matrix is). Today, physicists *must* know about matrices.

is of course purely mathematical and i-spin has nothing whatever to do with spin physically. Further, for the concept of i-spin to be at all useful, it is necessary that nuclear forces be charge independent or at least nearly so. For if this were not so, then neutrons and protons would differ in properties other than their charge. To think of two particles that are different to such an extent as two states of the same particle would not be wrong, it would merely be profitless. This will become immediately apparent in the discussion of i-spin multiplets below.

We see then that τ has three components τ_1, τ_2, τ_3, and that τ_3 has two eigenvalues, $+ 1$, which we assign to the proton, and $- 1$, which we assign to the neutron. The charge of the nucleon is therefore given by

$$\tfrac{1}{2}(1 + \tau_3). \tag{2.86}$$

Corresponding to the two eigenvalues there are two eigenfunctions, γ for the proton and δ for the neutron. Analogously to (2.78) and (2.80) we have

$$\tau_1\gamma = \delta, \quad \tau_1\delta = \gamma, \quad \tau_2\gamma = i\delta, \quad \tau_2\delta = - i\gamma, \quad \tau_3\gamma = \gamma, \quad \tau_3\delta = - \delta. \tag{2.87}$$

It will be convenient to introduce also the operators

$$\tau_+ = \tfrac{1}{2}(\tau_1 + i\tau_2), \quad \tau_- = \tfrac{1}{2}(\tau_1 - i\tau_2). \tag{2.88}$$

We see at once that

$$\tau_+\gamma = 0, \quad \tau_+\delta = \gamma, \quad \tau_-\gamma = \delta, \quad \tau_-\delta = 0. \tag{2.89}$$

Thus τ_- is an operator which annihilates a neutron state and turns a proton state into a neutron state, and τ_+ is an operator which annihilates a proton state and turns a neutron state into a proton state.

For a two-particle system there are three symmetric and one anti-symmetric functions—

Symmetric		Anti-symmetric	
$\gamma_1\gamma_2$	two protons		
$\delta_1\delta_2$	two neutrons	$2^{-\frac{1}{2}}(\gamma_1\delta_2 - \gamma_2\delta_1)$	neutron-proton
$2^{-\frac{1}{2}}(\gamma_1\delta_2 + \gamma_2\delta_1)$	neutron-proton		(2.90)

and the eigenvalues of $\boldsymbol{\tau}^{(1)} \cdot \boldsymbol{\tau}^{(2)}$ are $+ 1$ (symmetric) and $- 3$ (anti-symmetric).

It might be thought that if we treat protons and neutrons as identical particles in different charge states, difficulties will arise, particularly in the case of the deuteron which formerly was treated as a system of two non-identical particles and now is treated as one of two identical particles. We shall see, however, that the two treatments lead to the same results.

If we denote the space and spin part of a two-nucleon wave function by $\phi(1, 2)$, then if the two nucleons are protons, which are anti-symmetric particles, we must have

$$\phi(1, 2) = - \phi(2, 1).$$

In the i-spin formalism, the complete wave function of a two-proton system will be

$$\phi(1, 2)\, \gamma_1\gamma_2$$

and this is clearly anti-symmetric as it should be. Similarly for two neutrons. For a deuteron $\phi(1, 2)$ does not need to satisfy any symmetry requirements since a proton and a neutron in this treatment are not identical. In the i-spin treatment they are identical, and are therefore represented by either of the two wave functions

$$\phi(1, 2)\, \gamma_1\delta_2 \quad \text{or} \quad \phi(2, 1)\, \gamma_2\delta_1.$$

As nucleons are now to be treated as identical particles, this function must be anti-symmetrized. Therefore the deuteron wave function in the i-spin formalism is

$$2^{-\frac{1}{2}}[\phi(1, 2)\, \gamma_1\delta_2 - \phi(2, 1)\gamma_2\delta_1].$$

It is therefore possible to obtain from a non-symmetric deuteron wave function in the old treatment an anti-symmetric one in the new, as must be possible if the two treatments are to be mutually compatible.

We now turn our attention to a system of nucleons forming a nucleus, and form the expression

$$T_3 = \tfrac{1}{2}\Sigma\tau_3 \tag{2.91}$$

where the summation is over all the nucleons in the nucleus.

Clearly $T_3 = -\tfrac{1}{2}(N - Z)$, where N and Z are the numbers of neutrons and protons respectively in the nucleus, i.e. $-2T_3$ measures the neutron excess. Now, in analogy with the spin formalism, we should expect a nucleus of total i-spin $\mathbf{T} = \tfrac{1}{2}\Sigma\boldsymbol{\tau}$ to be one of an i-spin multiplet with given T and $T_3 = T,\ T - 1,\ \ldots,\ -T$. We now assume charge-independent forces. Then if neutrons and protons had the same mass and if there were no Coulomb forces, the energy levels of the multiplet would be degenerate, and as both these effects are comparatively small, we expect the levels of a given multiplet to be fairly closely spaced, particularly in the case of light nuclei. One such level scheme which has been observed experimentally is shown in Fig. 2.8. It is that of the nuclide

$A = 14$, in which the ground states of O^{14} and C^{14} together with the first excited state of N^{14} form an i-spin triplet, with the ground state

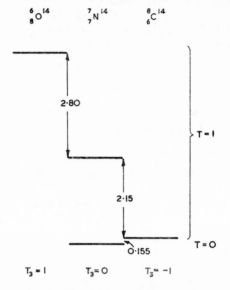

FIG. 2.8. I-SPIN TRIPLET AND SINGLET FOR $A = 14$
(ENERGIES IN MeV)

of N^{14} as an i-spin singlet below. The splitting of the $T = 1$ level is just of the order of magnitude expected.

2.9. EXAMPLES

2.9.1. Tabulate $S_n(A)$ and $S_p(A)$ for a series of values of A, using the experimentally obtained masses of nuclei. Investigate how far it is true to say that $S_n(A) = S_p(A)$ and that $S_n(A)$ and $S_p(A)$ are independent of A.

By considering the masses of heavy nuclei $(A > 210)$ show that $S_n(A) \simeq S_p(A)$ even for nuclei for which the Coulomb repulsion is important. How can this result be explained ?

2.9.2. Since the negaton scattering experiments only determine the constants c and s for the density distribution in nuclei, we can take the particle density to be given by the simple functional form

$$\rho = \begin{cases} \rho_0 & , & r < c - \tfrac{1}{2}t, \\ \rho_0 \dfrac{c + \tfrac{1}{2}t - r}{t} & , & c - \tfrac{1}{2}t < r < c + \tfrac{1}{2}t, \\ 0 & , & c + \tfrac{1}{2}t < r, \end{cases}$$

where ρ_0 is the central density (assumed to be the same for all nuclei) and $t = 1 \cdot 25s$. (Note that s is the 90 per cent to 10 per cent thickness.)

If $t \ll c$, so that terms $0(t^4/c^4)$ can be neglected and A is large, show that

$$c = aA^{\frac{1}{3}} - \frac{t^2}{12a}A^{-\frac{1}{3}}, \ R_u = aA^{\frac{1}{3}} + \frac{5t^2}{24a}A^{-\frac{1}{3}}, \text{ where } a = (\tfrac{4}{3}\pi\rho_0)^{-\frac{1}{3}}.$$

2.9.3. Use equations (2.16) and (2.43) to estimate the eccentricities and the ratios of the major to the minor axes of $_{71}\text{Lu}^{176}$ and $_{50}\text{Sn}^{119}$.

2.9.4. Prove that the anti-symmetric wave function for three identical particles is of the form
$$\psi = \phi(1, 2, 3) + \phi(2, 3, 1) + \phi(3, 1, 2) - \phi(1, 3, 2) - \phi(3, 2, 1) - \phi(2, 1, 3)$$

2.9.5. Prove that the matrices

$$\sigma_x = \begin{pmatrix} 0 & 1 \\ 1 & 0 \end{pmatrix}, \quad \sigma_y = \begin{pmatrix} 0 & -i \\ i & 0 \end{pmatrix}, \quad \sigma_z = \begin{pmatrix} 1 & 0 \\ 0 & -1 \end{pmatrix} \tag{2.92}$$

$$\alpha = \begin{pmatrix} 1 \\ 0 \end{pmatrix}, \quad \beta = \begin{pmatrix} 0 \\ 1 \end{pmatrix}$$

satisfy (2.80).

2.9.6. Use (2.80) to prove the relations

$$\sigma_x^2 = 1, \quad \sigma_y\sigma_z + \sigma_z\sigma_y = 0, \quad \sigma_y\sigma_z - \sigma_z\sigma_y = 2i\sigma_x \tag{2.93}$$

and the similar relations obtained by permuting x, y, z cyclically.

2.9.7. Interpret α^* and β^*, when α and β are given in matrix form, and hence verify (2.74).

2.9.8. By considerations similar to those used in the theory of mirror nuclei, show that the splitting of the i-spin triplet in Fig. 2.7 can be derived entirely from Coulomb effects and the neutron-proton mass difference. (Note that we must use $r_0 = 1\cdot 45$ fm. Why?)

2.9.9. Show that the i-spin of the deuteron is zero.

2.9.10. Show that $A = \pm$ B in (2.47).

[Hint : Put $A = ae^{i\alpha}$, $B = be^{i\beta}$, where a, b, α, β are real and a, $b > 0$.]

2.9.11. Show that the symmetry character of a wave function of two identical particles is a constant of motion.

[Hint : The proof is similar to that for parity. Why is the symmetry character always a constant of motion, but parity only under certain conditions?]

2.9.12. If the density distribution of protons and neutrons in nuclei is the same, show that the central density in nuclear matter is $\rho(0) = 1\cdot70$ fm^{-3}. Use this to estimate the size of an atom.

2.9.13. Use (2.9.3) to show that

$$\sigma_x\sigma_y = i\sigma_z, \text{ etc.} \tag{2.94}$$

and hence prove Dirac's identity

$$(\mathbf{a} . \boldsymbol{\sigma})(\mathbf{b} . \boldsymbol{\sigma}) = \mathbf{a} . \mathbf{b} + i\mathbf{a} \times \mathbf{b} . \boldsymbol{\sigma} \tag{2.95}$$

where $\mathbf{a}$ and $\mathbf{b}$ are vectors that commute with $\boldsymbol{\sigma}$, but not necessarily with each other.

2.9.14. Show that the wave function (2.70) describes a particle with spin in the direction given by spherical co-ordinates θ, ϕ, where

$$a = C\cos\frac{\theta}{2} e^{-\frac{1}{2}i\phi}, \ b = C\sin\frac{\theta}{2} e^{\frac{1}{2}i\phi}, \tag{2.96}$$

and C is an arbitrary constant.

[Hint: Find the spin operator which has $a\alpha + b\beta$ as an eigenfunction with eigenvalues $\pm \frac{1}{2}$.]

CHAPTER 3

Two-nucleon Systems at Low Energies

3.1 Introduction

A GREAT deal can be discovered about nuclear forces by considering the simplest nuclear systems, that is, those consisting of only two particles. We shall therefore in turn discuss the deuteron and the scattering of neutrons and protons by protons. The two other possible bound systems, the di-proton and the di-neutron, have never been observed, and neutron-neutron scattering does not lend itself to exact experimental measurements because of the difficulty of obtaining neutron targets. In the present chapter we shall confine ourselves to low energies,† and we shall also ignore the existence of the quadrupole moment of the deuteron, since it is so small. A consistent theory of nuclear forces can then be presented which will account for all the experimental facts at those energies. This theory can of course only be an approximate one, and we shall investigate the problem of nuclear forces from a more fundamental point of view in the following chapter.

Before discussing two-nucleon problems we must, however, establish two preliminary results : (a) the fact that the motion of a system of two particles under forces acting between them can be reduced to that of one particle moving in a central field of force, and (b) the way in which the scattering of particles by a centre of force can be deduced from a knowledge of the central force.

Throughout this chapter the expressions proton-proton, neutron-proton and neutron-neutron will be abbreviated to p-p, n-p and n-n.

3.2 Centre-of-mass and Laboratory Systems

We consider two masses, m_1 and m_2, moving in any way under forces between them. The co-ordinates of m_1, m_2 and their centre of mass relative to a co-ordinate system fixed in the laboratory (*lab. system*) are (x_1, y_1, z_1), (x_2, y_2, z_2) and (X, Y, Z) respectively. The co-ordinates of m_1 relative to m_2 we shall call (x, y, z). Then

$$(m_1 + m_2)X = m_1 x_1 + m_2 x_2, \quad x = x_1 - x_2 \qquad (3.1)$$

and similarly for the other co-ordinates. We next write down the

† For a discussion of what is meant by " low," see section 3.5.

Schrödinger equation for the two-particle system. If V is the potential of the force between the particles and E the total energy of the system, then the equation is

$$\left\{ \frac{\hbar^2}{2m_1} \nabla_1^2 + \frac{\hbar^2}{2m_2} \nabla_2^2 - V(x_1, y_1, z_1, x_2, y_2, z_2) \right\} \Psi + E\Psi = 0 \quad (3.2)$$

where $\nabla_1^2 = \dfrac{\partial^2}{\partial x_1^2} + \dfrac{\partial^2}{\partial y_1^2} + \dfrac{\partial^2}{\partial z_1^2}$ and similarly for ∇_2^2. This equation

is now transformed to the co-ordinates X, Y, Z, x, y, z by the use of (3.1). Clearly

$$\frac{\partial^2}{\partial x_1^2} = \left(\frac{m_1}{m_1 + m_2} \right)^2 \frac{\partial^2}{\partial X^2} + \frac{2m_1}{m_1 + m_2} \frac{\partial^2}{\partial X \partial x} + \frac{\partial^2}{\partial x^2}$$

and $\hspace{10cm} (3.3)$

$$\frac{\partial^2}{\partial x_2^2} = \left(\frac{m_2}{m_1 + m_2} \right)^2 \frac{\partial^2}{\partial X^2} - \frac{2m_2}{m_1 + m_2} \frac{\partial^2}{\partial X \partial x} + \frac{\partial^2}{\partial x^2}.$$

Hence

$$\frac{1}{m_1} \nabla_1^2 + \frac{1}{m_2} \nabla_2^2 = \frac{1}{m_1 + m_2} \nabla_X^2 + \frac{m_1 + m_2}{m_1 m_2} \nabla_x^2 \quad (3.4)$$

where ∇_X and ∇_x refer to partial differentiations with respect to (X, Y, Z) and (x, y, z) respectively, which latter we shall sometimes abbreviate to (X), (x). Now the potential in (3.2) can only be a function of the relative co-ordinates and so we shall write it $V(x)$. Then (3.2) reduces to

$$\left\{ \frac{1}{m_1 + m_2} \nabla_X^2 + \frac{m_1 + m_2}{m_1 m_2} \nabla_x^2 - \frac{2}{\hbar^2} V(x) \right\} \Psi + \frac{2}{\hbar^2} E\Psi = 0. \quad (3.5)$$

This equation can be solved by writing Ψ as a product of a function of (X, Y, Z) and one of (x, y, z)

$$\Psi = \psi(x)\chi(X). \quad (3.6)$$

This enables us to write (3.5) as follows

$$\frac{1}{\chi(X)} \left\{ \nabla_X^2 + \frac{2M}{\hbar^2} E \right\} \chi(X) = -\frac{1}{\psi(x)} \frac{M}{m} \left\{ \nabla_x^2 - \frac{2m}{\hbar^2} V(x) \right\} \psi(x), \quad (3.7)$$

where $\hspace{4cm} M = m_1 + m_2 \hspace{4cm} (3.8)$

is the total mass of the system and

$$m = \frac{m_1 m_2}{m_1 + m_2} \quad (3.9)$$

is called the *reduced mass* of the system. Now the left-hand side of (3.7) is a function of (X, Y, Z) only and the right-hand side of

(3.7) is a function of (x, y, z) only. Hence the two sides of the equation are independent of each other and must each be equal to a constant which we call $2ME_1/\hbar^2$. Equation (3.7) can then be separated into the two equations

$$\nabla_X^2 \chi + \frac{2M}{\hbar^2}(E - E_1)\chi = 0 \qquad (3.10)$$

$$\nabla_x^2 \psi + \frac{2m}{\hbar^2}(E_1 - V)\psi = 0. \qquad (3.11)$$

These are both single-particle Schrödinger equations. The first is the equation of motion of a particle of mass M under no forces, i.e. the equation of motion of the centre of mass. The second equation gives the relative motion of the two particles and is equivalent to the equation of motion of a single particle of mass m in a central field. E_1 is the energy of the internal motion and $E - E_1$ the energy of motion of the centre of mass.

Now if we take the direction of motion of the centre of mass as the x-axis, then (3.10) can be solved at once and yields for a plane wave travelling along the x-axis,

$$\chi = \exp\{iX[2M(E - E_1)/\hbar^2]^{\frac{1}{2}}\} \qquad (3.12)$$

In the system of co-ordinates in which the centre of mass is at rest (c.m. system), $E - E_1 = 0$ and hence $\chi = 1$. Therefore in the c.m. system,

$$\Psi = \psi(x, y, z), \qquad (3.13)$$

i.e. the total wave function of the system is a function only of the relative co-ordinates of the two particles, and E_1 is the total energy of the system in the c.m. system.

We have then established that the two-body problem is equivalent to a one-body problem in the c.m. system for a particle with the reduced mass. This enables us at once to solve the problem of the deuteron, where we shall only want to calculate the internal energy. Scattering problems, on the other hand, have to be referred to the lab. system, since it is in that system that experimental measurements of the energy of the incident particle and of the scattering angle between its initial and final directions of motion are made. In what follows we shall therefore consider m_2 to be the target, which is at rest in the lab. system, and m_1 to be the bombarding particle, which initially carries all the kinetic energy.

If initially the velocity of m_1 in the lab. system is v, it follows that

$$E = \tfrac{1}{2}m_1 v^2. \qquad (3.14)$$

This is the energy of the bombarding particle as measured experimentally and is denoted by E_{lab}. The initial value of the relative velocity is also v, since m_2 is initially at rest in the lab. system. Therefore in the c.m. system the initial velocities of the particles are $m_2 v/(m_1 + m_2)$ and $m_1 v/(m_1 + m_2)$. From this it follows that the total energy in the c.m. system, which is equal to E_1, is

$$E_1 = \frac{1}{2} \frac{m_1 m_2}{m_1 + m_2} v^2 = \frac{1}{2} m v^2 . \tag{3.15}$$

Therefore

$$E_1 = \frac{m_2}{m_1 + m_2} E_{\text{lab}}. \tag{3.16}$$

To find the relation between the scattering angles in the two systems we construct a vector diagram in the lab. system of the initial and final velocities of the two particles. Let the initial velocities of m_1 and m_2 be $\mathbf{u}_1$ and $\mathbf{u}_2$, and the final velocities $\mathbf{v}_1$ and $\mathbf{v}_2$. Then $\mathbf{u}_2 = 0$. On the vector diagram (Fig. 3.1) these velocities

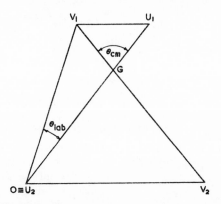

FIG. 3.1. VELOCITY DIAGRAM IN THE LAB. AND C.M. SYSTEMS

are represented by $\overrightarrow{OU_1}$, $\overrightarrow{OU_2}$, $\overrightarrow{OV_1}$, $\overrightarrow{OV_2}$, and U_2 coincides with O, which is the origin of co-ordinates in the lab. system. We first notice that if G is the intersection of $U_1 U_2$ and $V_1 V_2$ then $\overrightarrow{OG} = \mathbf{v}_G$ represents the velocity of the centre of mass. This is so because relative to the centre of mass the velocities of the particles must always be in opposite directions, and so GU_1, GV_1, GU_2, GV_2 must represent these velocities. Further, relative to the centre of mass, the velocities of the particles are inversely proportional to their masses, so that

$$\frac{GU_1}{GU_2} = \frac{GV_1}{GV_2} = \frac{m_2}{m_1},$$

i.e. U_1V_1 is parallel to U_2V_2. Lastly, since the scattering is elastic, the relative velocity of the particles is unchanged in magnitude, so that

$$U_1U_2 = V_1V_2.$$

Now in the c.m. system the initial and final velocities of m_1 are given by $\overrightarrow{GU_1}$ and $\overrightarrow{GV_1}$. The angles between the initial and final velocities of m_1 then give the scattering angles in the two systems : $\theta_{\text{lab}} = \angle U_1OV_1$, $\theta_{\text{cm}} = \angle U_1GV_1$. It then follows at once from the triangle OGV_1 that

$$\frac{OG}{GV_1} = \frac{m_1}{m_2} = \frac{\sin(\theta_{\text{cm}} - \theta_{\text{lab}})}{\sin \theta_{\text{lab}}}. \qquad (3.17)$$

To sum up. From (3.9), (3.16) and (3.17) we have for conversion from c.m. to lab. system that

$$\left. \begin{array}{c} m_{\text{cm}} = \dfrac{m_1 m_2}{m_1 + m_2}, \quad E_{\text{cm}} = \dfrac{m_2}{m_1 + m_2} E_{\text{lab}}, \\[2mm] \theta_{\text{cm}} = \theta_{\text{lab}} + \sin^{-1}\left(\dfrac{m_1}{m_2}\sin\theta_{\text{lab}}\right). \end{array} \right\} \qquad (3.18)$$

In particular, when $m_1 = m_2 = m_{\text{lab}}$, say,

$$m_{\text{cm}} = \tfrac{1}{2}m_{\text{lab}}, \quad E_{\text{cm}} = \tfrac{1}{2}E_{\text{lab}}, \quad \theta_{\text{cm}} = 2\theta_{\text{lab}}. \qquad (3.19)$$

3.3 Scattering of a Beam of Particles by a Centre of Force

We consider a beam of particles of unit cross-sectional area moving with velocity v and impinging on a scattering centre. Then the

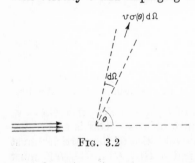

FIG. 3.2

number of particles scattered per second into a solid angle $d\Omega$ making an angle θ with the direction of incidence is proportional to v and to $d\Omega$, and the constant of proportionality is a function of θ. It is called the *scattering intensity* $\sigma(\theta)$ (see Fig. 3.2). The quantity $d\sigma = \sigma(\theta)d\Omega$ is called the *differential cross-section.†* To obtain the total number of particles scattered out of the incident beam in unit time per unit incident particle we must integrate $\sigma(\theta)$ over all solid angles. This gives the *total cross-section* σ. We shall see that

† Nuclear physicists tend to call both $d\sigma$ and $d\sigma/d\Omega$ the differential cross-section. This does not seem to cause any trouble.

the scattering can be described by a set of real parameters η_l, the so-called phase shifts.

If the beam moves along the z-axis towards the origin, then it can be represented by a plane wave e^{ikz}, where the wave number $k = mv/\hbar$ is the reciprocal of the de Broglie wavelength of the particles, whose mass is m. This wave represents a density of one particle per unit volume and thus a flow of v particles per unit cross-sectional area and unit time. The wave is scattered into an outgoing spherical wave with axial symmetry, which will be of the form $r^{-1}e^{ikr}f(\theta)$. Thus the number of particles in the scattered wave which cross an element of area dS perpendicular to the radius vector in unit time is

$$vr^{-2} \,|\, f(\theta)\,|^2 \, dS = v \,|\, f(\theta)\,|^2 \, d\Omega$$

where $d\Omega$ is the solid angle subtended by dS at the scattering centre. Hence

$$\sigma(\theta) = |\, f(\theta)\,|^2. \tag{3.20}$$

The problem then is to find a solution of the wave equation which at large distances can be written

$$\psi \sim e^{ikz} + r^{-1}\, e^{ikr}\, f(\theta). \tag{3.21}$$

Before solving the wave equation we shall obtain an expression for e^{ikz} as an expansion in partial waves of constant angular momentum. From the particle point of view this is equivalent to finding how many particles in the incident beam have a given angular momentum about the scattering centre.

Clearly e^{ikz} is a solution with axial symmetry of the equation

$$\nabla^2\psi + k^2\psi = 0. \tag{3.22}$$

This equation can be solved in spherical polar co-ordinates and solutions with axial symmetry are of the form

$$\psi_l = g_l(r)P_l(\cos\theta) \tag{3.23}$$

where l is any integer, $P_l(\cos\theta)$ is a Legendre polynomial and $g_l(r)$ is that solution of the equation

$$\frac{1}{r^2}\frac{d}{dr}\left(r^2\frac{dg}{dr}\right) + \left\{k^2 - \frac{l(l+1)}{r^2}\right\}g = 0 \tag{3.24}$$

which is bounded at the origin. This determines g_l except for an arbitrary multiplying constant. The most general solution of (3.22) with axial symmetry is then

$$\psi = \sum_{l=0}^{\infty} A_l g_l(r)P_l(\cos\theta) \tag{3.25}$$

where the A_l are arbitrary constants. Hence $e^{\mathrm{i}kz}$ can be expanded in this form and the terms in the infinite series are the partial waves. We therefore write

$$e^{\mathrm{i}kz} = e^{\mathrm{i}kr\cos\theta} = \sum_{m=0}^{\infty} A_m g_m(r) P_m(\cos\theta) \qquad (3.26)$$

multiply both sides by $P_l(\cos\theta)\sin\theta\,\mathrm{d}\theta$ and integrate from 0 to π. We obtain

$$\int_{-1}^{1} e^{\mathrm{i}krt} P_l(t)\mathrm{d}t = \frac{2}{2l+1} A_l g_l(r) \qquad (3.27)$$

where we have put $\cos\theta = t$.† This can be integrated by parts,

$$\frac{2}{2l+1} A_l g_l(r) = \frac{1}{\mathrm{i}kr}\{e^{\mathrm{i}kr} - (-1)^l\, e^{-\mathrm{i}kr}\} - \frac{1}{\mathrm{i}kr}\int_{-1}^{1} e^{\mathrm{i}krt} P_l'(t)\mathrm{d}t. \qquad (3.28)$$

The second term is $\mathrm{O}(r^{-2})$, as can be seen on integrating it by parts once more.   Hence for large r,

$$\frac{2}{2l+1} A_l g_l(r) \sim \frac{1}{\mathrm{i}kr}\{e^{\mathrm{i}kr} - e^{\mathrm{i}l\pi}\, e^{-\mathrm{i}kr}\}$$

$$= \frac{1}{\mathrm{i}kr} e^{\frac{1}{2}\mathrm{i}l\pi}\{e^{\mathrm{i}(kr-\frac{1}{2}l\pi)} - e^{-\mathrm{i}(kr-\frac{1}{2}l\pi)}\}$$

$$= 2\mathrm{i}^l(kr)^{-1}\sin(kr - \tfrac{1}{2}l\pi).$$

We now define $g_l(r)$ completely by requiring that

$$g_l(r) \sim (kr)^{-1}\sin(kr - \tfrac{1}{2}l\pi) \qquad (3.29)$$

so that

$$A_l = (2l+1)\mathrm{i}^l \qquad (3.30)$$

and

$$e^{\mathrm{i}kz} = \sum_{l=0}^{\infty} (2l+1)\mathrm{i}^l g_l(r) P_l(\cos\theta). \qquad (3.31)$$

That is the required expansion. It may be noted that (3.24) is closely related to Bessel's equation and that $g_l(r)$ is a spherical Bessel function, i.e.

$$g_l(r) = \sqrt{\frac{\pi}{2kr}}\, J_{l+\frac{1}{2}}(kr) \qquad (3.32)$$

where $J_{l+\frac{1}{2}}(kr)$ denotes the ordinary Bessel function of order $l + \frac{1}{2}$.

† We have made use here of the fact that

$$\int_{-1}^{1} P_l(t)P_m(t)\mathrm{d}t = \begin{cases} 2/(2l+1), & l = m \\ 0, & l \neq m \end{cases}$$

We can now proceed to solve the wave equation which must be satisfied by the wave function (3.21). This is

$$\nabla^2\psi + [k^2 - U(r)]\psi = 0 \qquad (3.33)$$

where $U(r) = (2m/\hbar^2)V(r)$, and $V(r)$ is the central potential. As before, the most general solution with axial symmetry can be written

$$\psi = \sum_{l=0}^{\infty} B_l L_l(r) P_l(\cos\theta) \qquad (3.34)$$

where the B_l are arbitrary constants and L_l is that solution of

$$\frac{1}{r^2}\frac{d}{dr}\left(r^2\frac{dL}{dr}\right) + \left\{k^2 - U(r) - \frac{l(l+1)}{r^2}\right\}L = 0 \qquad (3.35)$$

which is bounded at the origin. As $U(r) \to 0$ when $r \to \infty$, it is likely that for large r the solutions of (3.24) and (3.35) will be very similar. It can indeed be shown rigorously (Mott and Massey, *Theory of Atomic Collisions*, Ch. II) that, provided $rU(r) \to 0$ when $r \to \infty$, the asymptotic form of $L_l(r)$ is

$$L_l(r) \sim (kr)^{-1}\sin(kr - \tfrac{1}{2}l\pi + \eta_l) \qquad (3.36)$$

where η_l is a constant which depends on k and on the shape of the potential. Thus the asymptotic forms of $L_l(r)$ and $g_l(r)$ are sine waves, identical in shape but displaced relative to each other through a constant phase shift. It may be noted that (3.36) is not true for the Coulomb potential.

To determine the B_l, we remember that ψ must have the asymptotic form (3.21), i.e. there must be no terms proportional to $r^{-1}e^{-1kr}$ in the asymptotic expansion of the scattered wave since these can be shown to correspond to incident waves. Therefore

$$\{B_l L_l(r) - (2l+1)i^l g_l(r)\}P_l(\cos\theta) \sim C_l r^{-1}e^{1kr}P_l(\cos\theta). \qquad (3.37)$$

On substituting the asymptotic expressions (3.29) and (3.36) into (3.37) we obtain

$$\{B_l e^{1\eta_l} - (2l+1)i^l\}e^{1(kr - \frac{1}{2}l\pi)}$$
$$- \{B_l e^{-1\eta_l} - (2l+1)i^l\}e^{-1(kr - \frac{1}{2}l\pi)} = 2ikC_l e^{1kr} \qquad (3.38)$$

and hence by equating the coefficients of e^{1kr} and e^{-1kr},

$$\left.\begin{array}{l} B_l = (2l+1)i^l e^{1\eta_l} \\[2mm] C_l = \dfrac{1}{2ik}(2l+1)(e^{2l\eta_l}-1). \end{array}\right\} \qquad (3.39)$$

Thus the solution of (3.33) with the correct asymptotic form is

$$\psi = \sum_{l=0}^{\infty}(2l+1)i^l e^{1\eta} L_l(r)P_l(\cos\theta). \qquad (3.40)$$

Also (3.38) and (3.39) give

$$f(\theta) = \frac{1}{2ik} \sum_{l=0}^{\infty} (2l+1)(e^{2i\eta} - 1)P_l(\cos\theta). \qquad (3.41)$$

From (3.41) we can obtain the total cross-section, since

$$\sigma = \int \sigma(\theta)d\Omega = 2\pi \int_0^{\pi} |f(\theta)|^2 \sin\theta d\theta. \qquad (3.42)$$

When we evaluate this expression we can ignore all cross-terms of the type $P_l(\cos\theta)P_m(\cos\theta)$, since these vanish on integration. Hence

$$\sigma = \frac{\pi}{2k^2} \int_0^{\pi} \sum_0^{\infty} (2l+1)^2 \{(\cos 2\eta_l - 1)^2$$

$$+ (\sin 2\eta_l)^2\}\{P_l(\cos\theta)\}^2 \sin\theta d\theta$$

$$= \frac{\pi}{2k^2} \int_0^{\pi} \sum_0^{\infty} (2l+1)^2(2 - 2\cos 2\eta_l)\{P_l(\cos\theta)\}^2 \sin\theta d\theta$$

$$= \frac{4\pi}{k^2} \sum_0^{\infty} (2l+1) \sin^2\eta_l. \qquad (3.43)$$

We proceed to investigate the quantities η_l, and we first show by means of a semi-classical argument that if the range of the scattering potential is finite, then only a finite number of the η_l need to be taken into account in the infinite sums (3.41) and (3.43).

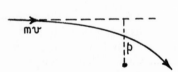

If mv is the momentum and p the impact parameter of a particle in the beam (see Fig. 3.3), then the classical angular momentum of the particle is

FIG. 3.3. LINEAR MOMENTUM AND IMPACT PARAMETER OF A CLASSICAL PARTICLE

pmv and, when this is equated to the quantum mechanical expression for the angular momentum, we have

$$pmv = \hbar[l(l+1)]^{\frac{1}{2}}. \qquad (3.43')$$

Now an interaction can only take place if $p < b$, where b is the range of the potential. Hence

$$[l(l+1)]^{\frac{1}{2}} < kb. \qquad (3.44)$$

Thus for a given energy of the incident particles, i.e. for a given k, the lth partial wave is unaffected by the scattering potential if $[l(l+1)]^{\frac{1}{2}} > kb$, and for such l, η_l must be negligible. The quantum mechanical argument leads to exactly the same result.

It is possible to attach a physical meaning to η_l. Asymptotically the difference between an undisturbed wave (3.29) and a scattered one (3.36) lies purely in the phase shift η_l. This means that the only effect of the scattering potential on the incident wave is to advance or retard it. The absolute value of the amplitude is unchanged as can be seen on comparing (3.30) and (3.39). Further, the undisturbed wave is given by $\eta_l = 0$, i.e. it is a solution of

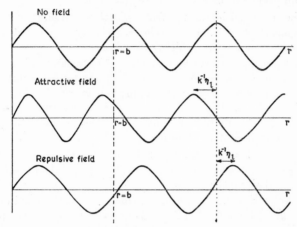

FIG. 3.4. RADIAL WAVE FUNCTION FOR AN ATTRACTIVE AND A REPULSIVE FIELD

(3.22) and has wavelength $2\pi/k$. The disturbed wave is a solution of (3.33). If we divide space into two regions, an outer one for which $r > b$, say, and where $U = 0$, and an inner one for which $r < b$ and $U \neq 0$, then in the outer region the wavelength is unchanged. In the inner region we can define a local wavelength $2\pi/\sqrt{(k^2 - U)}$, which will vary from point to point, as U is not constant. It is usual to assume that U does not change sign. Then, for an attractive potential ($U < 0$) the wavelength is reduced and $\eta_l > 0$; for a repulsive potential ($U > 0$) the wavelength is increased and $\eta_l < 0$. This is illustrated in Fig. 3.4.

3.4 The Ground State of the Deuteron

Of the preceding two sections the latter will not be required for the treatment of a bound state. It will of course be needed in the later sections, when we deal with free states.

In discussing the ground state of the deuteron we shall make the following assumptions—

(a) The deuteron consists of two particles of roughly equal mass M, so that the reduced mass of the system is $\frac{1}{2}M$.

(b) The force between the particles is short-range and attractive, and acts along the line joining the two particles, i.e. it is a central force. This assumption is not quite correct, since a central force cannot account for the quadrupole moment of the deuteron. This will be discussed in section 4.2. As the quadrupole moment is small, the assumption will be approximately correct.

(c) The force can be derived from a *local* potential. [See remarks after equation (4.86).] This excludes velocity dependent forces, which may be important at higher energies.

Since the force is everywhere attractive, the potential is negative and decreases with decreasing r, and since the force is short-range, the potential vanishes for practical purposes for $r > b$, where b is of the order of 3 fm. We shall show in section 3.9 that low-energy results are practically independent of the exact shape of the potential and so at present we shall use a square well potential,

$$V = -V_0, r < b \; ; \quad V = 0, r > b \tag{3.45}$$

as this is the easiest to use mathematically. V_0 is called the *depth* of the potential and b is its *range*.

Now we showed at the end of section 2.3 that the total angular momentum of the deuteron $I = 1$ is due effectively to the spins of the two nucleons which compose it. Hence the nucleons in the ground state of the deuteron have zero orbital angular momentum, i.e. the ground state is an S-state which is spherically symmetric. Its wave function can therefore be written as $\psi(r) = u(r)/r$, where $u(r)$ satisfies the equation

$$\frac{\mathrm{d}^2 u}{\mathrm{d}r^2} + \frac{M}{\hbar^2}(E - V)u = 0. \tag{3.46}$$

In view of (3.45) this can be written

$$\left.\begin{array}{l} \dfrac{\mathrm{d}^2 u}{\mathrm{d}r^2} + \kappa^2 u = 0, r < b \\[2ex] \dfrac{\mathrm{d}^2 u}{\mathrm{d}r^2} - \alpha^2 u = 0, r > b \end{array}\right\} \tag{3.47}$$

where we have put

$$\alpha^2 = \frac{MB}{\hbar^2}, \quad \kappa^2 = \frac{M}{\hbar^2}(V_0 - B).$$

The total energy E of the system is of course the negative of the binding energy B of the deuteron. Its experimental value is (Knowles, 1962)

$$B = 2 \cdot 2245 \pm 0 \cdot 0002 \text{ MeV}. \tag{3.48}$$

We require that solution of (3.47) which vanishes at the origin and at infinity. Hence

$$u = A_1 \sin \kappa r, \ r < b \ ; \ \ u = A_2 e^{-\alpha r}, \ r > b \tag{3.49}$$

where A_1 and A_2 are normalization constants. Since u and du/dr must be continuous at $r = b$, we have

$$\left. \begin{aligned} A_1 \sin \kappa b &= A_2 e^{-\alpha b} \\ A_1 \kappa \cos \kappa b &= -A_2 \alpha e^{-\alpha b}. \end{aligned} \right\} \tag{3.50}$$

From these relations A_1 and A_2 can be eliminated and we obtain a relation between κ and b, i.e. a relation between the depth and range of the potential

$$\kappa \cot \kappa b = -\alpha. \tag{3.51}$$

The constants A_1 and A_2 are obtained from the requirement that the integral of $|\psi|^2$ over all space must equal unity,

$$4\pi \int_0^\infty |\psi|^2 r^2 dr = 4\pi \int_0^\infty u^2 dr = 1. \tag{3.52}$$

Using (3.49), we have after a little simplification,

$$\frac{A_1^2}{2\kappa} (2\kappa b - \sin 2\kappa b) + \frac{A_2^2}{\alpha} e^{-2\alpha b} = \frac{1}{2\pi}. \tag{3.53}$$

A_1 and A_2 can then be obtained from (3.53) and either of the equations (3.50).

We next show that the deuteron cannot exist in an excited state. To do this we observe that (3.51) can be written

$$x \cot x = -\alpha b \tag{3.54}$$

where $x = \kappa b$. Now $b \lesssim 3$ fm, and using (3.48) we find that $\alpha = 0{\cdot}232$ fm^{-1}. Therefore $\alpha b \lesssim 0{\cdot}7$. If we then draw the curves $y = \cot x$ and $y = -\alpha b/x$, the intersections give the roots of (3.54), and from Fig. 3.5 it is clear that the roots are approximately equal to, but slightly larger than $(n + \frac{1}{2})\pi$, where $n = 0, 1, \ldots$ The correct solution to take is $\kappa b \simeq \frac{1}{2}\pi$, since if κb were greater than π, the wave function would have a node at $\kappa r = \pi$ and thus would not be the wave function of the ground state. We therefore have the very important result

$$\tfrac{1}{2}\pi \lesssim \kappa b < \pi. \tag{3.55}$$

To obtain a better approximation for κb we put $\kappa b = \frac{1}{2}\pi + \epsilon$ and substitute in (3.51),

$$(\tfrac{1}{2}\pi + \epsilon) \cot (\tfrac{1}{2}\pi + \epsilon) = -\alpha b.$$

If ϵ is small, $\cot(\tfrac{1}{2}\pi + \epsilon) \simeq -\epsilon$, so that $\epsilon \simeq 2\alpha b/\pi$. Hence

$$\kappa b \simeq \frac{\pi}{2} + \frac{2\alpha b}{\pi}. \tag{3.55'}$$

Therefore $\kappa \gtrsim 0{\cdot}6\ \text{fm}^{-1}$, so that $\kappa^2 \gg \alpha^2$, i.e. the depth of the potential is very much greater than the binding energy.

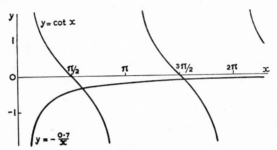

FIG. 3.5. SOLUTION OF THE EQUATION $x \cot x = -0{\cdot}7$

From (3.55') it follows at once that there cannot be any excited S-states. Since the ground state binding energy is so very much smaller than the depth of the potential, we deduce from (3.55') that

$$\tfrac{1}{2}\pi \lesssim k_0 b < \pi \tag{3.56}$$

where we have put $MV_0/\hbar^2 = k_0{}^2$. But if the binding energy of the first excited S-state is given by $\hbar^2\beta^2/M$, then we must have

$$b\sqrt{(k_0{}^2 - \beta^2)} > \tfrac{3}{2}\pi$$

and this contradicts (3.56).

To see that there cannot be any bound states with higher angular momenta we first write down the radial equation for any angular momentum,

$$\frac{\mathrm{d}^2 u}{\mathrm{d}r^2} + \frac{M}{\hbar^2}(E - V)u - \frac{l(l+1)}{r^2}u = 0. \tag{3.57}$$

This is a generalization of (3.46) for $l \neq 0$. On comparing it with (3.46) we see that it is equivalent to an S-wave radial equation with the potential

$$V_{\text{eff}}(r) = V(r) + \frac{\hbar^2 l(l+1)}{Mr^2}. \tag{3.58}$$

The second term on the right-hand side is the potential of the centrifugal force (see example 3.10.10). This is positive and therefore repulsive and, as it increases with l, the binding energy of the lowest bound state for a given l decreases as l increases. All that is needed therefore is to show that there is no bound P-state.

We rewrite (3.57) for $l = 1$ as

$$\left.\begin{array}{l} \dfrac{d^2u}{dr^2} + \kappa^2 u - \dfrac{2}{r^2}u = 0,\ r < b \\[3mm] \dfrac{d^2u}{dr^2} - a^2 u - \dfrac{2}{r^2}u = 0,\ r > b \end{array}\right\} \quad (3.59)$$

where κ and α now refer to the binding energy of the lowest P-state. The least well depth is required when this state is only just bound, i.e. when $\alpha = 0$, $\kappa = k_0$. If we put $k_0 r = x$, the wave equation is

$$\left.\begin{array}{l} \dfrac{d^2u}{dx^2} + u - \dfrac{2u}{x^2} = 0,\ x < k_0 b \\[3mm] \dfrac{d^2u}{dx^2} - \dfrac{2u}{x^2} = 0,\ x > k_0 b. \end{array}\right\} \quad (3.60)$$

The solution of the second of these with the correct boundary conditions is easily seen to be

$$u = A_2 x^{-1}, \quad x > k_0 b,$$

but that of the first is not so easily found. The equation can be rewritten

$$\frac{d^2v}{dx^2} - \frac{2}{x}\frac{dv}{dx} + v = 0, \quad x < k_0 b$$

where $v = xu$, and, if this is differentiated, we have

$$\frac{d^2}{dx^2}\left(\frac{1}{x}\frac{dv}{dx}\right) + \frac{1}{x}\frac{dv}{dx} = 0, \quad x < k_0 b$$

after some rearrangement. As $u = x^{-1}v$ must vanish for $x = 0$, the correct solution is

$$\frac{1}{x}\frac{dv}{dx} = A_1 \sin x, \quad x < k_0 b$$

which yields after integration

$$v = xu = A_1 (\sin x - x \cos x), \quad x < k_0 b. \quad (3.61)$$

(Those with a knowledge of Bessel functions could have obtained this result much more quickly.) Matching of the function xu on the boundary $x = k_0 b$ then yields the continuity equation

$$\frac{d}{dx}(\sin x - x \cos x) = 0, \quad x = k_0 b,$$

or

$$k_0 b \sin k_0 b = 0. \quad (3.62)$$

The smallest positive root of this equation is $k_0 b = \pi$.

Hence a bound state for $l \neq 0$ can exist only if $k_0 b > \pi$, and that contradicts (3.56). The deuteron therefore has no excited states.

Qualitatively, the reason why excited states of the deuteron are unlikely to exist is that even the ground state is not very firmly bound. Our present figures lead to a well depth V_0 greater than about 15 MeV. Actually we shall see later [see (3.108)] that $b = 1 \cdot 93$ fm and that $V_0 = 38 \cdot 5$ MeV.

All the states of the deuteron discussed so far have been triplet states, i.e. states with parallel spins of the nucleons. The question arises whether there is a bound singlet state, in which the spins are anti-parallel. It has never been observed and strong evidence against its existence will be presented in section 3.7.

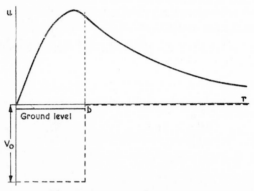

FIG. 3.6. RADIAL WAVE FUNCTION OF THE DEUTERON, ASSUMING
A SQUARE WELL POTENTIAL

In consequence of the very weak binding, the two nucleons that make up the deuteron spend more than half their time a distance apart which is greater than the range of the forces between them. This can be seen from (3.49) or from Fig. 3.6 where u is plotted against r. $4\pi u^2 \mathrm{d}r$ is of course the probability of finding the particles a distance apart between r and $r + \mathrm{d}r$. The potential well and the position of the ground level have been drawn on the same figure. (See also ex. 3.10.3.)

3.5 Scattering of Neutrons by Free Protons

In n-p scattering we have to distinguish between the case where the protons are free and the case where they are bound in molecules. In practice the protons are of course always bound in molecules, but the molecular binding energy is so small—about 0·1 eV—that for energies of the incident neutrons greater than about 1 eV the protons can be considered to be free. This sets a lower limit to the neutron energy, as below it a much more complicated theory would have to be used. An upper limit is set by the requirement that only the first phase shift η_0 should be significant (S-wave scattering). In the remainder of this chapter we shall omit the suffix in η_0 since we shall not be concerned with phase shifts for higher angular momenta.

From (3.44), the maximum allowed energy in the c.m. system is given by $kb = \sqrt{2}$. Since the reduced mass is $\frac{1}{2}M$, we have $k = Mv/2\hbar$, and therefore

$$E_{\text{lab}} = 2E_{\text{cm}} = \frac{2k^2\hbar^2}{M} = \frac{4\hbar^2}{Mb^2} = 2\cdot8 \times 10^{-5} \text{ ergs} = 17 \text{ MeV.}$$

To be on the safe side, we shall actually restrict ourselves to laboratory energies below 5 MeV.

It might be thought that a single experimental scattering cross-section, together with a knowledge of the deuteron binding energy would be enough to determine the range and depth of the nuclear potential. The reason why this is not so is that the ground state of the deuteron is a triplet state, while n-p scattering occurs in a statistical mixture of triplet and singlet states in the ratio 3 : 1. It would therefore be necessary for the scattering to be coherent, i.e. all triplet or all singlet, if it is to be correlated with the bound state of the deuteron. This will be discussed in section 3.7. In the present section we shall confine ourselves to incoherent scattering.

Since we are concerned with only S-wave scattering, the scattering amplitude is given by [see (3.41)]

$$f(\theta) = \frac{1}{2ik} (e^{2i\eta} - 1) P_0(\cos \theta) \tag{3.63}$$

and since $P_0(\cos \theta) = 1$, the scattering is spherically symmetric in the c.m. system. This has been verified experimentally. The total cross-section is obtained from (3.43) and is

$$\sigma = \frac{4\pi}{k^2} \sin^2 \eta. \tag{3.64}$$

These formulae as well as what follows apply equally to triplet and to singlet scattering, and we shall distinguish between the two only towards the end of this section.

The wave equation is again (3.46), where E is now the energy of the scattering system and is therefore positive. We put

$$k^2 = ME/\hbar^2, \ K^2 = M(V_0 + E)/\hbar^2, \ k_0^2 = MV_0/\hbar^2, \tag{3.65}$$

and obtain the solution, corresponding to (3.49)

$$\left.\begin{array}{ll} u = A_1 \sin Kr, & r < b \\ u = A_2 \sin (kr + \eta), & r > b. \end{array}\right\} \tag{3.66}$$

This ensures that u has the correct asymptotic form (3.36). The continuity condition then gives

$$k \cot (kb + \eta) = K \cot Kb. \tag{3.67}$$

This equation gives η in terms of k_0 and b. However, we cannot measure k_0 directly by experiment and we therefore proceed to express η in terms of b and a new quantity a, called the *scattering length*, which is defined by the equation

$$\sigma_0 = 4\pi a^2. \tag{3.68}$$

Here σ_0 is the scattering cross-section (3.64) in the limit $k \to 0$, i.e. at zero incident energy. This can be measured experimentally with great accuracy.

From (3.67) we have after a little rearrangement,

$$k \cot \eta = \frac{K \cot Kb + k \tan kb}{1 - (K/k) \cot Kb \tan kb} \tag{3.69}$$

and therefore, when $k \to 0$,

$$k \cot \eta \to \frac{k_0 \cot k_0 b}{1 - k_0 b \cot k_0 b}. \tag{3.69'}$$

But, from (3.64), in the limit when $k \to 0$,

$$k^2 \cot^2 \eta = k^2 \operatorname{cosec}^2 \eta = 4\pi/\sigma_0 = a^{-2}. \tag{3.70}$$

So far the sign of a is undetermined and we shall now fix it by putting

$$k \cot \eta \to - a^{-1} \quad \text{as } k \to 0. \tag{3.71}$$

We shall see later that this leads to a more useful interpretation of scattering length than if we had chosen the opposite sign. We have then

$$\frac{k_0 \cot k_0 b}{1 - k_0 b \cot k_0 b} = -\frac{1}{a}, \quad \text{i.e.} \quad k_0 \cot k_0 b = \frac{1}{b - a}. \tag{3.72}$$

Using (3.56), it is clear that for triplet scattering $a > 0$.

We now return to (3.69) and expand the right-hand side in powers of k. For accurate calculations we must of course solve the simultaneous equations (3.69) and (3.72) exactly by numerical methods if we want the energy dependence of η, but it is instructive to obtain an explicit expression of this dependence on the assumption that the energies are small. Neglecting third powers in k we have

$$K = \sqrt{(k_0^2 + k^2)} \simeq k_0 + k^2/2k_0$$

and, expanding $K \cot Kb$ in a Taylor series about $K = k_0$,

$$K \cot Kb \simeq k_0 \cot k_0 b + (k^2/2k_0)(\cot k_0 b - k_0 b \operatorname{cosec}^2 k_0 b)$$

$$= \frac{1}{b-a} - \tfrac{1}{2} b k^2 - \frac{ak^2}{2k_0^2(b-a)^2}$$

using (3.72). Hence

$$k \cot \eta \simeq \left\{ \frac{1}{b-a} + \tfrac{1}{2} b k^2 - \frac{ak^2}{2k_0^2(b-a)^2} \right\}$$

$$\times \left\{ 1 - \frac{b}{b-a} + \tfrac{1}{2} b^2 k^2 + \frac{abk^2}{2k_0^2(b-a)^2} - \frac{k^2 b^3}{3(b-a)} \right\}^{-1}$$

$$\simeq -\frac{1}{a} + \tfrac{1}{2} k^2 \left(b - \frac{b^3}{3a^2} - \frac{1}{k_0^2 a} \right) \tag{3.73}$$

if the second bracket is expanded by the binomial theorem. This expression is substituted in (3·64) and we finally obtain

$$\sigma \simeq 4\pi a^2 \left\{ 1 - k^2 \left[a(a-b) + \frac{b^3}{3a} - \frac{1}{k_0^2} \right] \right\}. \tag{3.74}$$

Lastly we express the scattering length in terms of the binding energy of the bound state, i.e. in terms of α, on the assumption that $\alpha \ll k_0$. The algebra is the same as above, except that we must replace K^2, k_0^2 and k^2 by k_0^2, κ^2 and α^2 respectively. We then obtain

$$k_0 \cot k_0 b \simeq \kappa \cot \kappa b + (\alpha^2/2\kappa)(\cot \kappa b - \kappa b \operatorname{cosec}^2 \kappa b)$$

$$= -\alpha - \tfrac{1}{2} \alpha^2 b$$

using (3.51). This is substituted in (3.72) and yields

$$\frac{1}{a} \simeq \alpha(1 - \tfrac{1}{2} \alpha b). \tag{3.75}$$

Thus $a \to \infty$, as $\alpha \to 0$. Therefore, to a small binding energy of the bound state corresponds a large zero-energy scattering cross-section of the free state.

It is possible to give both a mathematical and a physical interpretation of the scattering length. From (3.71) we have

$$\lim_{k \to 0} \eta = n\pi - ka, \tag{3.76}$$

where n is any integer. If this value of η is substituted in (3.66), we see that apart from a multiplying constant the wave function for $r > b$ is

$$u = \sin k(a - r), \quad r > b. \tag{3.77}$$

Thus $r = a$ is the position of the first node outside the potential well of the radial wave function for zero-energy scattering. Also, for zero energy $K = k_0$, and we know from our discussion of the deuteron that only about a quarter of a wave of wave number $\simeq k_0$ can be fitted into the potential well. Thus there can be no node inside the well, and $r = a$ is the first node of the radial wave function altogether. Hence, in (3.76), $n = 1$. The wave function for some values of k is plotted in Fig. 3.7.

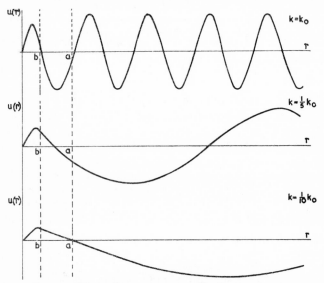

Fig. 3.7. Radial Wave Function $u(r)$ for Various Values of k
Triplet-state scattering data have been used.

The physical interpretation is that $4\pi a^2$ is just exactly the zero-energy scattering cross-section of an impenetrable sphere of radius a. This will not be proved here, but it is worth noting that the wave function of a particle scattered by such a sphere must vanish at the surface of the sphere and be a free particle wave function outside the sphere, and that is just what we have found to be the case for our wave function. Note also that the quantum mechanical cross-section for zero-energy scattering by an impenetrable sphere is four times the classical one, which is πa^2.

So far we have not distinguished between triplet and singlet scattering and all our formulae are equally valid for both. As the three triplet states and the singlet state are all equally likely, the complete cross-section for incoherent scattering is

$$\sigma = \tfrac{3}{4}\sigma_t + \tfrac{1}{4}\sigma_s \tag{3.78}$$

where suffixes t and s will refer to triplet and singlet scattering. We can calculate σ_{0t} from (3.68) and (3.75) or by a numerical solution of the exact equations, since we know α_t very accurately and b_t fairly accurately, say $b_t = 1 - 3$ fm. We obtain

$$2\cdot8 \text{ barns} < \sigma_{0t} < 4\cdot5 \text{ barns}. \tag{3.79}$$

The experimental cross-section for zero-energy incoherent scattering is (Melkonian, 1949)

$$\sigma_0 = 20\cdot36 \pm 0\cdot05 \text{ barns}. \tag{3.80}$$

Hence the singlet cross-section must lie within the limits

$$68 \text{ barns} < \sigma_{0s} < 73 \text{ barns}. \tag{3.81}$$

The singlet cross-section is thus enormously large, and this is only possible if $|a_s|$ is very large, much larger than a_t. In fact, from (3.81), $|a_s| \simeq 24$ fm. The experiments so far give no indication of the sign of a_s. This we shall discuss in the next section.

3.6 Singlet State of the Deuteron

We must now investigate more closely the possibility of a bound singlet state of the deuteron. We know that if it exists, then its energy B_s must be higher than the deuteron ground state energy, since that is known from experiment to be a triplet state. This is confirmed by the fact that if a bound singlet state exists, its energy is given by (3.75). To fit the experimental results we must have $|B_s| \simeq 100$ keV.

The radial wave equation of a bound singlet S-state is

$$\left. \begin{aligned} \frac{\mathrm{d}^2 u}{\mathrm{d}r^2} + (k_{0s}^2 - \alpha_s^2)\, u &= 0, \quad r < b_s \\ \frac{\mathrm{d}^2 u}{\mathrm{d}r^2} - \alpha_s^2 u &= 0, \qquad\quad r > b_s. \end{aligned} \right\} \tag{3.82}$$

Since α_s is so small, we can neglect it to a first approximation, and the solution of (3.82) is then

$$\left. \begin{aligned} u &= A_1 \sin k_{0s} r, \quad r < b_s \\ u &= A_2(r - c), \quad\ \ r > b_s. \end{aligned} \right\} \tag{3.83}$$

If instead we consider low energy scattering in the singlet state, then the wave equation is identical with (3.82) except that α_s^2 must be replaced by $-k^2$. In the low energy limit, as $k \to 0$, the solution is therefore just exactly (3.83), and since that wave function has its first node at $r = c$, c must be the singlet scattering length a_s. The wave function is sketched in Fig. 3.8 for the two cases (a) $a_s > 0$, (b) $a_s < 0$. In the first the binding is sufficiently strong for just over a quarter of a wave to be inside the potential well. In that case the line $u = A_2(r - a_s)$ is the limit of either an exponentially decreasing wave function as $\alpha_s \to 0$ or of a sine wave as $k \to 0$.

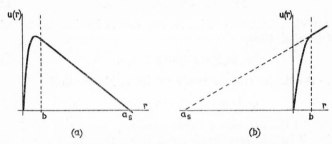

FIG. 3.8. RADIAL WAVE FUNCTION (3.83)
FOR (a) $a_s > 0$, (b) $a_s < 0$

These correspond to bound and free states respectively. In the second case just under a quarter of a wave is inside the well, and so the line is the limit of either an exponentially increasing wave function as $\alpha_s \to 0$ or of a sine wave as $k \to 0$. Because an exponentially increasing wave function is physically inadmissible, there is then no bound state, although a free state of course exists. As $|a_s|$ is so very large, the deuteron is either just bound or just not bound in the singlet state.

In principle it is possible to decide between the two cases $a_s > 0$ and $a_s < 0$ by using (3.74) for non-zero energy scattering. However, the difference between the results in the two cases is so small that the experimental n-p scattering results are not sufficiently accurate to distinguish between them. A better method will be described in the next section, where we shall see that there is indeed no bound singlet state. Because the singlet state of the deuteron is so nearly bound, it is sometimes referred to as a virtual bound state.

3.7 Coherent Scattering of Neutrons by Protons bound in Molecules

If the energy of the incident neutrons is very low, then their wavelength is so large that, as we shall see, scattering takes place coherently from neighbouring nuclei in the target. Neutrons with such low energies are called thermal neutrons, since their energies are such that they are in equilibrium with their surrounding medium of temperature T °K, and their energies are frequently expressed in terms of the temperature by means of the relation $E = kT$, where k is Boltzmann's constant. Thus

$$T = 11,600 \, E \text{ °K, where } E \text{ is in eV.} \tag{3.84}$$

The use of such very slow neutrons makes it possible to distinguish between singlet and triplet scattering. A hydrogen molecule can exist in two possible ground states, one in which the spins of the two protons are parallel (ortho-hydrogen) and one in which they are anti-parallel (para-hydrogen). Although the energy of ortho-hydrogen is greater, conversion to para-hydrogen is very slow and at ordinary temperatures hydrogen gas consists of a mixture of the two in proportion $3 : 1$. At very low temperatures (about $20°$ K), however, we have nearly pure para-hydrogen. Now at $20°$ K the de Broglie wavelength of a neutron is $\lambda = 7 \times 10^{-8}$ cm, which considerably exceeds the distance between the atoms of a hydrogen molecule (0.74×10^{-8} cm). Hence, if such neutrons are scattered by para-hydrogen, the waves scattered by the two protons in the molecule are coherent and interference phenomena will be observed. Results for pure ortho-hydrogen can then be deduced from a knowledge of the incoherent scattering by hydrogen at higher temperatures. The results for ortho-hydrogen and para-hydrogen will be quite different because the scattering by para-hydrogen is triplet for one proton and singlet for the other, while that by ortho-hydrogen is triplet for both or singlet for both.

The scattering lengths for triplet and singlet scattering can be expressed by means of a single formula in the following way,

$$a_{t,s} = \tfrac{1}{4}(3a_t + a_s) + (a_t - a_s)\mathbf{s}_n \cdot \mathbf{s}_p \tag{3.85}$$

where $\mathbf{s}_n$ and $\mathbf{s}_p$ refer to the spins of the neutron and the proton in units of $\hbar$. This is because we have shown [see (2.84)] that

$$\mathbf{s}_n \cdot \mathbf{s}_p = \tfrac{1}{4} \text{ (triplet) and } \mathbf{s}_n \cdot \mathbf{s}_p = -\tfrac{3}{4} \text{ (singlet).} \tag{3.86}$$

Since the scattering by the two protons in the molecule is in phase we can add the scattering lengths for the two protons† to obtain the scattering length for the molecule,

$$a = \tfrac{1}{2}(3a_t + a_s) + (a_t - a_s)\mathbf{s}_n \cdot (\mathbf{s}_{p1} + \mathbf{s}_{p2}) \tag{3.87}$$

---

† This is strictly correct only if the scattering phases due to the two scatterings are the same, which is the case for ortho-hydrogen. However, even for para-hydrogen the phases are not very different from each other.

and the cross-section $\sigma = 4\pi a^2$ is given by

$$a^2 = \tfrac{1}{4}(3a_t + a_s)^2 + (3a_t + a_s)(a_t - a_s)\mathbf{s}_n . \mathbf{S}_{\mathrm{H}}$$
$$+ (a_t - a_s)^2(\mathbf{s}_n . \mathbf{S}_{\mathrm{H}})^2 \quad (3.88)$$

where

$$\mathbf{S}_{\mathrm{H}} = \mathbf{s}_{p1} + \mathbf{s}_{p2} \quad (3.89)$$

is the total angular momentum of the molecule. The neutron spin must be averaged over all directions and clearly

$$\text{average of } \mathbf{s}_n . \mathbf{S}_{\mathrm{H}} = 0. \quad (3.90)$$

Also

$$(\mathbf{s}_n . \mathbf{S}_{\mathrm{H}})^2 = s_{nx}^2 S_{\mathrm{H}x}^2 + \ldots + 2s_{nx}s_{ny}S_{\mathrm{H}x}S_{\mathrm{H}y} + \ldots$$

and, since $s_{nx}^2 = s_{ny}^2 = s_{nz}^2 = \tfrac{1}{4}$, and average of $s_{nx}s_{ny} = 0$, etc., we have

$$\text{average of } (\mathbf{s}_n . \mathbf{S}_{\mathrm{H}})^2 = \tfrac{1}{4}\mathbf{S}_{\mathrm{H}}^2 = \tfrac{1}{4}S_{\mathrm{H}}(S_{\mathrm{H}} + 1). \quad (3.91)$$

Therefore after averaging,

$$a^2 = \tfrac{1}{4}(3a_t + a_s)^2 + \tfrac{1}{4}(a_t - a_s)^2 \, S_{\mathrm{H}}(S_{\mathrm{H}} + 1). \quad (3.92)$$

Now for orthohydrogen, $S_{\mathrm{H}} = 1$, for para-hydrogen $S_{\mathrm{H}} = 0$. Therefore

$$a_{\text{ortho}}^2 = \tfrac{1}{4}(3a_t + a_s)^2 + \tfrac{1}{2}(a_t - a_s)^2 \quad (3.93)$$

$$a_{\text{para}}^2 = \tfrac{1}{4}(3a_t + a_s)^2. \quad (3.94)$$

From the experimental values (3.79) and (3.81) for σ_t and σ_s we have

$$a_t \simeq 5 \,\text{fm}, \quad | a_s | \simeq 24 \,\text{fm}. \quad (3.95)$$

Because of the fortunate accident that $| 3a_t + a_s |$ is very much smaller than $| a_t - a_s |$ when $a_s < 0$, but very much larger when $a_s > 0$, we have

$$\sigma_{\text{para}} \ll \sigma_{\text{ortho}} \text{ if } a_s < 0, \quad \sigma_{\text{para}} \simeq \sigma_{\text{ortho}} \text{ if } a_s > 0. \quad (3.96)$$

This in itself is sufficient to distinguish between the two cases, since the experimental results are (Sutton, 1947)

$$\sigma_{\text{para}} = 4 \cdot 0 \text{ barns}, \sigma_{\text{ortho}} = 125 \text{ barns}. \quad (3.97)$$

Thus $a_s < 0$ and the singlet state of the deuteron is virtual.

For more accurate comparison with experiment (3.93) and (3.94) must be modified because of the changed reduced mass when the protons are bound in molecules and because of the velocity of the molecules.

The experimental results (3.97) then lead to

$$a_t = 5 \cdot 2 \text{ fm}, \quad a_s = -23 \cdot 4 \text{ fm} \qquad (3.98)$$

and this checks very well with (3.95). The quantity which we shall have to employ later, however, is the para-hydrogen scattering length, which from (3.94) is

$$a_{\text{para}} = \tfrac{1}{2}(3a_t + a_s). \qquad (3.99)$$

We find that

$$a_{\text{para}} = -3 \cdot 93 \text{ fm}. \qquad (3.100)$$

There are two other methods which will give values for a_{para}. The first depends on the scattering of neutrons by hydrogen atoms in crystals, which is similar to X-ray scattering. The second involves the total reflexion of neutrons by a liquid mirror containing protons. This is probably the most accurate method, and the value of a_{para} obtained from it (Burgy, 1951) is

$$a_{\text{para}} = -(3 \cdot 78 \pm 0 \cdot 02) \text{ fm}. \qquad (3.100')$$

The discrepancy with the result obtained from para-hydrogen scattering is almost certainly due to the admixture of a small amount of ortho-hydrogen. This would change the result in the right direction. A weighted mean for a_{para} has recently been given by Wilson (1963) and we shall use this as the best value

$$a_{\text{para}} = -(3 \cdot 744 \pm 0 \cdot 010) \text{ fm}. \qquad (3.101)$$

The results (3.97) also yield further evidence that the spin of the neutron is $\tfrac{1}{2}$. For if $s_n = \tfrac{3}{2}$, then (3.85) must be replaced by

$$a_{t,q} = \tfrac{1}{8}(3a_t + 5a_q) + \tfrac{1}{2}(a_q - a_t)\mathbf{s}_n \cdot \mathbf{s}_p \qquad (3.102)$$

since a neutron-proton pair can now exist in a quintuplet ($S = 2$) or a triplet ($S = 1$) state and (see example 3.10.6)

$$\mathbf{s}_n \cdot \mathbf{s}_p = \tfrac{3}{4}(\text{quintuplet}), \mathbf{s}_n \cdot \mathbf{s}_p = -\tfrac{5}{4} \text{ (triplet)}. \qquad (3.103)$$

Hence (3.92) becomes

$$a^2 = \tfrac{1}{16}(3a_t + 5a_q)^2 + \tfrac{1}{16}(a_q - a_t)^2 S_{\text{H}}(S_{\text{H}} + 1), \qquad (3.104)$$

where $S_{\text{H}} = 0$ for para and 1 for ortho as before. Since (3.95) remains true except that a_s must be replaced by a_q, it is clear that now $|3a_t + 5a_q|$ is large compared with $|a_q - a_t|$, whether $a_q > 0$ or $a_q < 0$. Hence $\sigma_{\text{ortho}} \simeq \sigma_{\text{para}}$, and this contradicts the experimental results.

To sum up. The whole problem has been reduced to that of finding four lengths. Two of these, the scattering lengths a_t and a_s, together with the binding energies of the bound states, determine the depths of the potentials V_t and V_s. The other two are the ranges b_t and b_s of the potentials, which need not necessarily be the same.

We thus require four experimental results. For three of them we take—

(a) Binding energy of the deuteron,

$$B_t = 2 \cdot 2245 \pm 0 \cdot 0002 \text{ MeV} \qquad (3.48)$$

(b) Incoherent zero-energy scattering cross-section,

$$\sigma_0 = 20 \cdot 36 \pm 0 \cdot 05 \text{ barns} \qquad (3.80)$$

(c) Para-hydrogen scattering length,

$$a_{\text{para}} = - (3 \cdot 744 \pm 0 \cdot 010) \text{ fm.} \qquad (3.101)$$

For the fourth we take a cross-section for n-p scattering at higher energy. This has been determined with great accuracy for 4·75 MeV (lab. system) neutrons by Hafner (1953).

(d) Scattering cross-section at 4·75 MeV (lab. system),

$$\sigma = 1 \cdot 690 \pm 0 \cdot 008 \text{ barns.} \qquad (3.105)$$

From (b) and (c) we find

(e) $\qquad\qquad a_t = 5 \cdot 397 \text{ fm.} \qquad\qquad (3.106)$

(f) $\qquad\qquad a_s = - 23 \cdot 68 \text{ fm.} \qquad\qquad (3.107)$

(e) together with (a) are then used to obtain b_t and V_{0t} from (3.51) and (3.72)

$$b_t = 1 \cdot 93 \text{ fm,} \quad V_{0t} = 38 \cdot 5 \text{ MeV.} \qquad (3.108)$$

Next b_s and V_{0s} are calculated. The triplet cross-section at 4·75 MeV (lab. system) is evaluated from (3·64) and (3·67). (3.78) then gives the singlet cross-section, and this in turn determines the corresponding phase shift. This and (f) are then substituted into (3.67) and (3.72) and yield

$$b_s = 2 \cdot 50 \text{ fm,} \quad V_{0s} = 14 \cdot 3 \text{ MeV.} \qquad (3.109)$$

Lastly the binding energy of the virtual singlet state can be calculated from (3.51) and (3.72). It is

$$| B_s | = 92 \text{ keV.} \qquad (3.110)$$

The errors are unlikely to exceed a few per cent except in (3.109) where the values are accurate to probably only 20 per cent or even less, since the calculation is very sensitive there to small changes in the experimental values.

The most important conclusion we can draw from these results is that the nuclear forces are clearly spin-dependent, since $b_t \neq b_s$, $V_{0t} \neq V_{0s}$.

3.8 Proton-proton Scattering

The scattering of protons by protons is mathematically a good deal more complicated than n-p scattering, because (*a*) the Coulomb scattering due to the charges on the protons is superimposed on the nuclear scattering, and (*b*) we are now dealing with identical particles. We shall see, however, that it is just those two facts that make p-p scattering particularly interesting. The fact that the Coulomb scattering interferes with the nuclear scattering leads to much greater sensitivity in determining the parameters of the nuclear potential. Also since protons are identical particles obeying the exclusion principle, they cannot exist in a state that has a symmetric wave function. This means that at energies at which the nuclear part of the scattering is pure S-wave, the nuclear interaction is pure singlet. We thus have only one phase shift instead of the two in n-p scattering, and with this we must fit not just a total cross-section, but a differential cross-section for all scattering angles, since the scattering due to the combined Coulomb and nuclear forces is certainly not spherically symmetrical. Further, p-p scattering can be measured much more accurately than n-p scattering, since well-collimated monochromatic beams of protons can easily be obtained and the scattered protons can easily be detected by their ionization.

We first treat the scattering by a pure Coulomb field. This is discussed in full in Mott and Massey, *Theory of Atomic Collisions*, Chapter 3. If in the radial equation (3.35) $U(r) = (M/\hbar^2)(e^2/r)$, then $rU(r) \nrightarrow 0$ as $r \to \infty$. In that case it can be shown that (3.36) has to be modified to

$$L_l(r) \sim (kr)^{-1} \sin(kr - \gamma \ln 2kr - \tfrac{1}{2}l\pi + \delta_l) \qquad (3.111)$$

where $\gamma = e^2/\hbar v$, v is the relative velocity and $\delta_l = \arg\Gamma(l + 1 + i\gamma)$. Equation (3.41) remains true, however, and can be summed in this case. The result is

$$f_c(\theta) = \frac{e^2}{Mv^2} \operatorname{cosec}^2 \frac{\theta}{2} \exp\{- i\gamma \ln(1 - \cos\theta) + i\pi + 2i\delta_0\}. \quad (3.112)$$

Now the nuclear potential only influences the S-wave, the phase shift of which it changes to $\delta_0 + \zeta$, say. The splitting up of the phase shift into two terms is purely a matter of convenience. Phase shifts are not simply additive, and so ζ is certainly not the phase shift that would arise from pure nuclear scattering. We then have to modify only the first term of the sum (3.41) and obtain

$$f(\theta) = f_c(\theta) + \frac{1}{2ik} e^{2i\delta_0}(e^{2i\zeta} - 1). \qquad (3.113)$$

From this expression the differential cross-section can be calculated.

4

So far we have neglected the fact that the two protons are identical particles and must therefore be described by an anti-symmetric wave function. If the protons are in a singlet state, the spin wave function is anti-symmetric and so the space wave function must be symmetric and is given by

$$\psi(\mathbf{r}) + \psi(-\mathbf{r})$$

where $\mathbf{r}$ is the relative position vector of the protons. Similarly, in a triplet state the space wave function is

$$\psi(\mathbf{r}) - \psi(-\mathbf{r}).$$

Now in scattering problems we have

$$\psi(\mathbf{r}) = I_+ + Sf(\theta), \qquad \psi(-\mathbf{r}) = I_- + Sf(\pi - \theta), \qquad (3.114)$$

where I and S are the incident plane wave and the radial part of the scattered wave. Hence for incoherent scattering, in which triplet is three times as frequent as singlet scattering, the scattering intensity is

$$\sigma(\theta) = \tfrac{3}{4} \, | \, f(\theta) - f(\pi - \theta) \, |^2 + \tfrac{1}{4} \, | \, f(\theta) + f(\pi - \theta) \, |^2. \qquad (3.115)$$

If (3.113) is substituted into this expression, we obtain, after a good deal of simplification,

$$\sigma(\theta) = \frac{\gamma^2}{4k^2}\left\{ \operatorname{cosec}^4 \frac{\theta}{2} + \sec^4 \frac{\theta}{2} - \sec^2 \frac{\theta}{2} \operatorname{cosec}^2 \frac{\theta}{2} \cos\left(\gamma \ln \tan^2 \frac{\theta}{2}\right) \right\}$$

$$- \frac{\gamma}{2k^2} \sin \zeta \left\{ \operatorname{cosec}^2 \frac{\theta}{2} \cos\left(\gamma \ln \sin^2 \frac{\theta}{2} + \zeta\right) \right.$$

$$\left. + \sec^2 \frac{\theta}{2} \cos\left(\gamma \ln \cos^2 \frac{\theta}{2} + \zeta\right) \right\} + \frac{1}{k^2} \sin^2 \zeta. \qquad (3.116)$$

In this expression the first term is the pure Coulomb scattering, the third the pure nuclear scattering and the second the interference between the two, which depends linearly on ζ. Because of this linear dependence, we can find the sign of ζ from the scattering and this in turn leads to the sign of the scattering length corresponding to it. This turns out to be negative, so that there is no bound state of the p-p system. (It was just because the scattering of neutrons by free protons only gives η^2, that we had to scatter neutrons by bound protons in order to determine the sign of the singlet scattering length.)

The Coulomb term in (3.116) can be further analysed. It consists of three parts, of which the first is the well-known Rutherford scattering, which gives the complete scattering of non-identical particles. The result was derived originally classically by Rutherford but is equally correct in quantum mechanics. The second part also arises classically from the fact that it is impossible in the case of identical particles to distinguish experimentally between the scattered particle and the recoil of the target particle. (The angle between the two particles in the c.m. system is 180°.) The last part is purely quantum mechanical and arises from the interference between the waves of the two identical particles.

The quantity which is measured experimentally is the differential cross-section in the lab. system

$$\mathrm{d}\sigma = \sigma_{\mathrm{lab}}(\theta_{\mathrm{lab}})\mathrm{d}\Omega_{\mathrm{lab}}. \tag{3.117}$$

Since the flux of particles out of corresponding solid angles in the lab. and c.m. systems must be the same, we have

$$2\pi\,\sigma_{\mathrm{lab}}\,(\theta_{\mathrm{lab}})\sin\theta_{\mathrm{lab}}\,\mathrm{d}\theta_{\mathrm{lab}} = 2\pi\,\sigma_{\mathrm{cm}}\,(\theta_{\mathrm{cm}})\sin\theta_{\mathrm{cm}}\,\mathrm{d}\theta_{\mathrm{cm}}. \tag{3.118}$$

For identical particles, $\theta_{\mathrm{cm}} = 2\theta_{\mathrm{lab}}$, and hence

$$\sigma_{\mathrm{lab}}(\theta_{\mathrm{lab}}) = 4\sigma_{\mathrm{cm}}(2\theta_{\mathrm{lab}})\cos\theta_{\mathrm{lab}} \tag{3.119}$$

Thus to convert (3.116) into the lab. system, we must change θ to 2θ and then multiply by $4\cos\theta$.

Formula (3.116) clearly gives a very sensitive test of the correctness of the theory on which it is based, and the fact that the experimentally obtained differential cross-section at all angles really can be fitted by a single parameter ζ is strong confirmation for the theory. For a square well the range and depth are found to be (Jackson and Blatt, 1950)

$$b = 2\cdot58\;\mathrm{fm}, \quad V_0 = 13\cdot3\;\mathrm{MeV} \tag{3.120}$$

and these values should be accurate to a few per cent. They can be compared with (3.109) and clearly the values for the n-p and the p-p forces differ by very little if at all. The fact that the difference in the binding energy of mirror nuclei can be satisfactorily accounted for by the Coulomb repulsion of the protons (see section 2.2) shows that the p-p forces are also approximately equal to the n-n forces. These facts have led to the hypothesis that nuclear forces, at least at low energy, are charge independent.†

3.9 Shape Independence of Nuclear Potential

Up to now we have assumed a square well shape for the nuclear potential. This was done for the sake of mathematical simplicity and not of physical correctness, and the physical justification of

†See *Note* on p. 85.

this choice of shape is that the results obtained are to a high degree of accuracy independent of the shape chosen. This we now show.

Let u_a and u_b be the radial wave functions corresponding to two energies E_a and E_b. Then from (3.46) we have

$$\frac{d^2 u_a}{dr^2} + k_a^2 u_a - U(r)u_a = 0 \tag{3.121}$$

$$\frac{d^2 u_b}{dr^2} + k_b^2 u_b - U(r)u_b = 0 \tag{3.122}$$

where we have written $U = MV/\hbar^2$, and $V(r)$ is the nuclear potential. We multiply (3.121) by u_b, (3.122) by u_a, subtract and integrate from 0 to ∞. Then

$$\left[u_b u_a' - u_a u_b' \right]_0^\infty = (k_b^2 - k_a^2)\int_0^\infty u_a u_b dr. \tag{3.123}$$

Next, we introduce a comparison function v which represents the asymptotic behaviour of u, i.e.

$$v_a = A_a \sin (k_a r + \eta_a). \tag{3.124}$$

We choose the normalization factor A_a for the sake of convenience so that $v_a(0) = 1$. Therefore

$$v_a = \sin (k_a r + \eta_a)/\sin \eta_a \tag{3.125}$$

and similarly for v_b. Then in the same way as for (3.123),

$$\left[v_b v_a' - v_a v_b' \right]_0^\infty = (k_b^2 - k_a^2)\int_0^\infty v_a v_b dr. \tag{3.126}$$

We now subtract (3.126) from (3.123). For $r = 0$, u_a and u_b vanish, and their asymptotic forms are equal to those of v_a and v_b. Hence

$$[v_a v_b' - v_b v_a']_{r=0} = (k_b^2 - k_a^2)\int_0^\infty (v_a v_b - u_a u_b)dr. \tag{3.127}$$

If we substitute from (3.125), this reduces to

$$k_b \cot \eta_b - k_a \cot \eta_a = (k_b^2 - k_a^2)\int_0^\infty (v_a v_b - u_a u_b)dr. \tag{3.128}$$

We now apply this formula to the special case $k_a = 0$. Then

$$k_a \cot \eta_a = k_a \csc \eta_a = -a^{-1} \tag{3.129}$$

where a is the scattering length defined by (3.68) and (3.71). This quantity is quite independent of the shape of the potential since it depends purely on the experimental value of σ_0. (3.128) can there-fore now be written

$$k \cot \eta = -a^{-1} + \tfrac{1}{2}k^2 \rho(0, E) \tag{3.130}$$

where

$$\tfrac{1}{2}\rho(0, E) = \int_0^\infty (v_a v - u_a u)dr. \tag{3.131}$$

Here we have dropped the suffix b, and the suffix a refers to the zero energy wave functions.

So far we have made no approximations. Now u and v differ only inside the range of nuclear forces. Therefore the integrand in (3.131) vanishes outside the force range. Inside the range, the wave functions are almost independent of the energy, because for all the energies that we consider the depth of the potential is so much larger than the energy of the system. [See (3.66) for the square well wave function, which illustrates this very well.] It will therefore be a good approximation to replace u and v by u_a and v_a. We then have

$$\tfrac{1}{2}\rho(0, E) \simeq \tfrac{1}{2}\rho(0, 0) = \int_0^\infty (v_a^2 - u_a^2)\mathrm{d}r = \tfrac{1}{2}r_0. \qquad (3.132)$$

The quantity r_0, which is constant, is called the *effective range*. We substitute this in (3.130) and obtain

$$k \cot \eta \simeq - a^{-1} + \tfrac{1}{2}r_0 k^2. \qquad (3.133)$$

This is just exactly equivalent to (3.73) for the square well. We see that $r_0 \to b$, as $a \to \infty$, i.e. as $\alpha \to 0$. The effective range is therefore equal to the actual square well range in the limit of zero binding energy of the bound state. The values of r_0 for both the singlet and triplet n-p scattering can be derived from the experimental results (3.48), (3.80), (3.101) and (3.105). The most recent determination is that of Noyes (1963), who finds

$$r_{0s} = 2 \cdot 51 \pm 0 \cdot 11 \text{ fm}, \quad r_{0t} = 1 \cdot 727 \pm 0 \cdot 014 \text{ fm}.$$

The singlet effective range definitely differs from that for p-p scattering (Noyes, 1964), which is

$$r_{pp} = 2 \cdot 746 \pm 0 \cdot 014 \text{ fm}.$$

The nuclear forces are therefore not completely charge independent.

To this approximation the scattering cross-section at any energy is thus given by two parameters, the scattering length a and the effective range r_0. We can therefore fit the experimental results to a high degree of accuracy to any potential shape which is given by two parameters. These two parameters are usually called the depth and the range of the potential.

The potentials most commonly employed are :

Square well, $\qquad V = - V_\mathrm{S}, r < b_\mathrm{S}, V = 0, r > b_\mathrm{S} \qquad (3.134)$

Gaussian well, $\qquad V = - V_\mathrm{G} \exp (- r^2/b_\mathrm{G}^2) \qquad\qquad (3.135)$

Exponential well, $\quad V = - V_\mathrm{E} \exp (- r/b_\mathrm{E}) \qquad\qquad (3.136)$

Yukawa well, $\qquad V = - V_\mathrm{Y}(r/b_\mathrm{Y})^{-1} \exp (- r/b_\mathrm{Y}). \qquad (3.137)$

Of these only the Yukawa well has any theoretical justification (see section 10.1), the others are chosen for their mathematical simplicity. The first two are so-called short-tail potentials, i.e. they decay very rapidly for $r > b$, the other two are long-tail potentials.

The constants in the above expressions must be adjusted so as to give the same scattering length and effective range. This adjustment is a function of the scattering length, and we give below the values

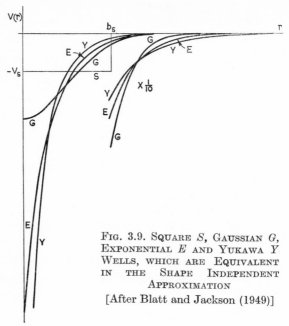

FIG. 3.9. SQUARE S, GAUSSIAN G, EXPONENTIAL E AND YUKAWA Y WELLS, WHICH ARE EQUIVALENT IN THE SHAPE INDEPENDENT APPROXIMATION

[After Blatt and Jackson (1949)]

for an infinite scattering length, corresponding to zero binding energy of the bound state. This is a very good approximation for the singlet state and quite good for the triplet state. The values in terms of the square well constants are

$$V_G = 2.24\ V_S, \qquad b_G = 0.706\ b_S$$
$$V_E = 7.36\ V_S, \qquad b_E = 0.282\ b_S \qquad (3.138)$$
$$V_Y = 3.07\ V_S, \qquad b_Y = 0.472\ b_S.$$

The wells are plotted in Fig. 3.9.

The fact that zero energy scattering depends only on one parameter, the scattering length, which is independent of the shape of the scattering potential, indicates that, if we consider only very low energies, there must be a relationship between the range and the depth of the potential which is independent of its functional form.

To show this, we write down the wave equation (3.121)

$$u'' + k^2 u - U(r)u = 0 \qquad (3.139)$$

and compare it with the free wave equation at the same energy,

$$u_0'' + k^2 u_0 = 0. \qquad (3.140)$$

The boundary conditions on the wave functions are

$$u(0) = 0, \quad u_0(0) = 0,$$

$$u(r) \sim A \sin(kr + \eta), \quad u_0(r) \sim A \sin kr. \qquad (3.141)$$

We now multiply (3.139) by u_0, (3.140) by u and subtract.

$$u_0 u'' - u u_0'' = u U_0 u.$$

Integrating and using the boundary conditions we have

$$\int_0^\infty u_0 U u \, dr = \Big[u_0 u' - u u_0' \Big]_0^\infty = - A^2 k \sin \eta. \qquad (3.142)$$

So far this is exact. Now $U(r) \to 0$ rapidly as r increases, so that we require $u(r)$ and $u_0(r)$ only for small r. If we restrict our considerations to small energies, then we can clearly put $u_0(r) = Akr$ for small r. To find $u(r)$, we note that it essentially consists of just over a quarter of a wave of average wavenumber $k_0 = [- \text{Av. } U(r)]^{\frac{1}{2}}$, which joins onto the free wave just beyond its first maximum, i.e.

$$u(r) = A' \sin k_0 r \simeq A' k_0 r \text{ for small } r,$$

where $A' = A \sin \eta$. We have assumed here that at the joining distance $k_0 r \simeq \frac{1}{2}\pi$, $kr \ll \eta$. This is equivalent to assuming that the force range is much smaller than the scattering length and, as we have seen, this is only a fair approximation for triplet scattering, although an excellent one for singlet scattering.

Substituting in (3.142) we obtain

$$\int_0^\infty r^2 U(r) dr = - \frac{1}{k_0}. \qquad (3.143)$$

Thus the low energy scattering determines the volume integral of the scattering potential or, alternatively, the average wavelength of the scattered wave inside the potential. These conclusions can be checked for the singlet state against the values quoted for different potentials in (3.138). Agreement is found to be good.

The next step in obtaining further information about the nuclear force is clearly to take into account the existence of the quadrupole moment of the deuteron and then to turn to the results obtained from n-p and p-p scattering at higher energies. This will be the task of the next chapter.

3.10. EXAMPLES

3.10.1. Show that if deuterons are scattered by protons, the maximum scattering angles in the c.m. and lab. systems are 120° and 30° respectively, but that if protons are scattered by deuterons, the maximum angle is 180° in both systems.

3.10.2. Show that if a particle m_1 is scattered by a particle m_2, then the angle between the final directions of motion in the lab. system is

$$\frac{\pi}{2} + \tfrac{1}{2}\theta_{\text{lab}} - \tfrac{1}{2}\sin^{-1}\left(\frac{m_1}{m_2}\sin\theta_{\text{lab}}\right). \tag{3.144}$$

Hence show that if the particles have equal mass, the angle between their final directions of motion is always 90°.

3.10.3. Prove that A_1 and A_2 in (3.53) are given approximately by

$$A_1 \simeq (\alpha/2\pi)^{\frac{1}{2}}(1 - \tfrac{1}{2}\alpha b), \quad A_2 \simeq (\alpha/2\pi)^{\frac{1}{2}}(1 + \tfrac{1}{2}\alpha b).$$

Use the experimental values (3.48) and (3.108) to show that the probability of the two nucleons in a deuteron being within the range of their forces is about 0·3.

3.10.4. By solving (3.57) for $l = 1$, as on p. 64, but using the boundary conditions for scattering, show that

$$
\begin{aligned}
u &= A_1\{(Kr)^{-1}\sin Kr - \cos Kr\}, & r < b \\
u &= A_2\{(kr)^{-1}\sin(kr + \eta_1) - \cos(kr + \eta_1)\}, & r > b
\end{aligned}
\tag{3.145}
$$

is the radial wave function for P-wave scattering with a square well potential. Show also that the continuity condition for $r = b$ is

$$K^2[kb\cot(kb + \eta_1) - 1] = k^2[Kb\cot Kb - 1]. \tag{3.146}$$

3.10.5. Using (3.67) (3.108) and (3.146), evaluate η_0 and η_1 for a range of scattering energies $E_{\text{cm}} = 0 - 10$ MeV. Hence plot a graph of

$$\sigma_{l=0} = 4\pi k^{-2}\sin^2\eta_0 \text{ and of } \sigma_{l=1} = 12\pi k^{-2}\sin^2\eta_1$$

against E_{cm} and find the energy at which $\sigma_{l=1}$ contributes 1 per cent of the total cross-section.

3.10.6. Prove (3.103) by using the identity

$$(\mathbf{s}_n + \mathbf{s}_p)^2 = \mathbf{s}_n^2 + \mathbf{s}_p^2 + 2\mathbf{s}_n . \mathbf{s}_p.$$

[Hint : Remember the rule for angular momenta, $\mathbf{L}^2 = L(L + 1)$.]

3.10.7. Verify (3.73) by expanding (3.131) in powers of k for the special case of the square well.

3.10.8. With the help of (3.118) show that the differential cross-sections in the c.m. and lab. systems are related by the equation

$$\left(\frac{d\sigma}{d\Omega}\right)_{\text{lab}} = \frac{(m_1^2 + m_2^2 + 2m_1m_2\cos\theta_{\text{cm}})^{3/2}}{m_2^2 \mid m_2 + m_1\cos\theta_{\text{cm}}\mid}\left(\frac{d\sigma}{d\Omega}\right)_{\text{cm}} \tag{3.147}$$

where m_1 and m_2 are the masses of the bombarding and target particles respectively.

3.10.9. Prove that the i-spin of the ground state of the deuteron is $T = 0$.

[Hint : Use the symmetry property of the deuteron wave function.]

3.10.10. Show that the potential corresponding to the centrifugal force on a particle of mass m can be put quantum mechanically as

$$V = \frac{\hbar^2 l(l + 1)}{2mr^2}.$$

[Hint: Use (3.43′) to transfer from classical to quantum mechanics.]

3.10.11. Show that the binding energy of the deuteron determines the volume integral of the triplet n-p potential.

[Hint : Use (3.55′) and the argument following (3.138).]

3.10.12. Show that for a system of two particles the momentum of the relative motion is equal to the actual momentum of either particle in the c.m. system.

Note added in proof.

Recently [Haddock *et al.*, *Phys. Rev. Let.*, **14**, 318 (1965)] the neutron-neutron scattering length has been measured, using the reaction

$$\pi^- + d \to 2n + \gamma.$$

The result was

$$a_{nn} - (16{\cdot}4 \pm 1{\cdot}9) \text{ fm.}$$

Because of the nearly bound nature of the singlet state, this yields a very sensitive test of charge independence, and the difference between this value and that of the singlet neutron-proton scattering length, $a_s = -23{\cdot}68$ fm, shows that nuclear forces are not entirely charge-independent.

CHAPTER 4

Nuclear Forces

4.1 Central and Non-central Forces

It was pointed out in section 3.1 that the whole theory of two-body forces built up in the last chapter ignored the existence of the quadrupole moment and the anomalous magnetic moment of the deuteron. This is so because on the assumptions made at the beginning of section 3.4 the ground state of the deuteron is a spherically symmetric S-state and such a state cannot produce a quadrupole moment. We therefore now remove restriction (*b*) at the beginning of section 3.4, that the forces are central. As we shall still only be concerned with low energies for the time being, we shall not yet remove restriction (*c*), that the forces are velocity independent. We shall see later that velocity dependent forces do in fact become important at higher energies.

Now it was seen in section 3.7 that the potential was different in triplet and singlet states, i.e. it depended on the spins of the particles. Let us then see whether we can construct a potential which depends not only on the relative position vector of the particles **r**, but also on their spin co-ordinates $\boldsymbol{\sigma}_1$ and $\boldsymbol{\sigma}_2$, and which can account for the quadrupole moment.† The form which such a potential can take is very much circumscribed by the requirement that it must be invariant under rotations and reflexions of the co-ordinate system which we use to describe it. Hence it must be a scalar. It might be thought that a very large number of such potentials could be constructed, but this is not so for the following reasons—

1. The vector **r** changes to $-\,$**r** under reflexion and thus must occur in even powers only.

2. The vectors $\boldsymbol{\sigma}_1$, $\boldsymbol{\sigma}_2$ do not change sign under reflexion, since they transform like an angular momentum and

$$\mathbf{r} \times \mathbf{p} \to (-\,\mathbf{r}) \times (-\,\mathbf{p})$$

under reflexion.

---

† We shall use subscripts to denote particles 1 and 2 rather than the clumsy bracketed superscripts which we needed in Chapter 2 to avoid confusion.

3. Higher powers of σ_1 and σ_2 can always be reduced to the first power by the commutation relations (2.93).

4. Derivatives of $\mathbf{r}$ cannot occur since these lead to velocity dependent forces.

The only scalars which satisfy all these conditions are

$$V(r), \quad \sigma_1 . \sigma_2, \quad (\sigma_1 . \mathbf{r})(\sigma_2 . \mathbf{r}), \quad (\sigma_1 \times \mathbf{r}) . (\sigma_2 \times \mathbf{r}) \tag{4.1}$$

or products of these. The last can be simplified to

$$(\sigma_1 \times \mathbf{r}) . (\sigma_2 \times \mathbf{r}) = \mathbf{r}^2 \sigma_1 . \sigma_2 - (\sigma_1 . \mathbf{r})(\sigma_2 . \mathbf{r}) \tag{4.2}$$

and thus can be represented in terms of the other three.

The first two of the potentials in (4.1) are clearly invariant not only under a combined rotation of space and spin co-ordinates, but also under separate rotations of these co-ordinates. Such potentials are called *central*, and it can be shown quite generally that for any two-body system under purely central forces the S-state is lower than the D-state, which is the lowest angular momentum state that can lead to a quadrupole moment. The third potential in (4.1) is not of this kind. It is called *tensor* and is non-central. Such a potential couples the space and spin co-ordinates of the particles of a two-body system, and hence couples their orbital and spin angular momenta. The result of this is, as will be seen more clearly later, that the orbital angular momentum is no longer a constant of motion, although the total angular momentum is, and that any state of given total angular momentum will be a linear combination of states of different orbital angular momenta. The ground state of the two-body system will then no longer be a pure S-state, but a mixture of S- and D-states, and this will lead to a quadrupole moment.

It is usual to define the non-central potential in such a way that its average over all directions $\mathbf{r}$ vanishes. Now

$$\frac{1}{4\pi}\int (\sigma_1 . \mathbf{r})(\sigma_2 . \mathbf{r}) \mathrm{d}\Omega = \tfrac{1}{3} r^2 \sigma_1 . \sigma_2 \tag{4.3}$$

and hence we define the tensor operator S_{12} by

$$S_{12} = \frac{3}{r^2}(\sigma_1 . \mathbf{r})(\sigma_2 . \mathbf{r}) - \sigma_1 . \sigma_2. \tag{4.4}$$

The non-central force is then derivable from a potential

$$V = V_T(r)S_{12}. \tag{4.5}$$

The potential which we shall employ to account for two-body forces at low energies is therefore of the form

$$V = V_R(r) + V_\sigma(r)\,\sigma_1 . \sigma_2 + V_T(r)S_{12}. \tag{4.6}$$

It would appear that in Chapter 3 only a special type of central potential, $V(r)$, was employed instead of the more general one

$$V_C = V_R(r) + V_\sigma(r)\boldsymbol{\sigma}_1 \cdot \boldsymbol{\sigma}_2. \qquad (4.7)$$

This however is not so. It was found there that the potential was different in the triplet and singlet states ; i.e. that it was *spin-dependent*, and this is just exactly the result that follows for V_C on substituting (2.84) into (4.7). In fact,

$$\left.\begin{array}{l} V_C^{\text{trip}} = V_R(r) + V_\sigma(r) \\ V_C^{\text{sing}} = V_R(r) - 3V_\sigma(r) \end{array}\right\} \qquad (4.8)$$

and by a suitable choice of $V_R(r)$ and $V_\sigma(r)$ potentials equivalent to (3.108) and (3.109) in the low-energy region can be obtained.

We next turn our attention to the constants of motion of the two-body system under central and non-central forces. As central forces are invariant under separate rotations of space and spin co-ordinates, the orbital and spin angular momenta are separately constants of motion, i.e.

$$L^2, S^2, L_z, S_z \text{ are constants of motion.} \qquad (4.9)$$

Non-central forces are invariant only under coupled rotations of space and spin, and so only the total angular momentum

$$\mathbf{I} = \mathbf{L} + \mathbf{S}$$

and its z-component I_z are conserved. Another constant of motion is the parity P (S_{12} has been constructed so as to be invariant under space reversal !) ; and, in the particular case of a system consisting of two particles of spin $\frac{1}{2}$, the total spin angular momentum S^2 is also conserved. This is because V in (4.6) and hence the Hamiltonian of the system is invariant under the exchange of $\boldsymbol{\sigma}_1$ and $\boldsymbol{\sigma}_2$. It then follows, analogously to the argument in section 2.5, that the spin wave function of the system is either symmetric or anti-symmetric. But there are only two possible spin states for two particles of spin $\frac{1}{2}$, the triplet which is the symmetric state and the singlet which is the anti-symmetric state. Thus our argument has proved that the system is either in a triplet ($S = 1$) state or in a singlet ($S = 0$) state, so that S^2 is a constant of motion. S_z of course is not, and so we have for tensor forces that

$$I^2, I_z, P, S^2 \text{ are constants of motion.} \qquad (4.10)$$

Furthermore, for two particles (but not for more than two particles!) space inversion is equivalent to the exchange of the position of the particles. This was treated in section 2.5, where it was found that the wave function of such a system was even under inversion for even orbital angular momenta and odd for old angular momenta [see equation (2.58)]. Hence a state of even parity will consist of a linear combination of even L states, and similarly for odd parity. [See (4.12) below.]

It is now possible to classify the states of the neutron-proton system.

4.1.1 SINGLET STATES $(S = 0)$. For these $L^2 = I^2$ and thus L is a constant of motion. Hence non-central forces do not affect singlet states. (This can also be seen directly, by observing that when $\sigma_1 = -\sigma_2$, then $S_{12} = -(3/r^2)(\sigma_1 . \mathbf{r})^2 + \sigma_1^2 = -3 + 3 = 0$.) Therefore possible states are—

$$I = 0 : {}^1S_0 \ ; \ I = 1 : {}^1P_1 \ ; \ I = 2 : {}^1D_2 \ ; \ \text{etc.}\dagger \qquad (4.11)$$

4.1.2 TRIPLET STATES $(S = 1)$. Since states of even and odd L do not mix, the following states are possible :

$$\left. \begin{array}{ll} I = 0, L = 1 \quad : {}^3P_0 \ ; \\ I = 1, L = 0, 2 : {}^3S_1 + {}^3D_1 \ ; \quad I = 1, L = 1 : {}^3P_1 \\ I = 2, L = 1, 3 : {}^3P_2 + {}^3F_2 \ ; \quad I = 2, L = 2 : {}^3D_2, \text{etc.} \end{array} \right\} \qquad (4.12)$$

In Chapter 3 it was shown that the ground state of the deuteron was well represented by a ${}^3S_1$ state, and so we now conclude that the ground state of the deuteron is really a ${}^3S_1$ state with a small admixture of a ${}^3D_1$ state.

Lastly we have to determine the constants of the potentials V_R, V_σ, V_T in (4.6). This is no longer uniquely possible from the low energy data. There are in fact many potentials which fit the experimentally determined binding energy, quadrupole moment and magnetic moment of the deuteron, as well as the low energy n-p and p-p scattering data. This will be discussed further in the next section.

4.2 Ground State of the Deuteron under Non-central Forces

The ground state of the deuteron will now be investigated in detail. Its total angular momentum is $I = 1$. Since it is a bound state with no preferred direction, and since I_z is a constant of motion, we can arbitrarily put $I_z = 1$. The correctly normalized angle and spin dependent part of the total ${}^3S_1(I_z = 1)$ wave function ψ_S is

$$X_S = (4\pi)^{-\frac{1}{2}}\alpha_1\alpha_2 \qquad (4.13)$$

where α_1, α_2 are the spin wave functions introduced in section 2.7.

† The symbol ${}^\sigma L_I$ indicates a state of orbital angular momentum L, total angular momentum I and spin multiplet σ.

We operate on this function with

$$S_{12} = 3(\sigma_{1x} \sin\theta \cos\phi + \sigma_{1y} \sin\theta \sin\phi + \sigma_{1z} \cos\theta)$$
$$(\sigma_{2x} \sin\theta \cos\phi + \sigma_{2y} \sin\theta \sin\phi + \sigma_{2z} \cos\theta)$$
$$- (\sigma_{1x}\sigma_{2x} + \sigma_{1y}\sigma_{2y} + \sigma_{1z}\sigma_{2z}) \tag{4.14}$$

and obtain

$$S_{12}X_S = (4\pi)^{-\frac{1}{2}}\{(3\cos^2\theta - 1)\alpha_1\alpha_2 + 3\sin\theta\cos\theta\, e^{i\phi}(\alpha_1\beta_2 + \beta_1\alpha_2)$$
$$+ 3\sin^2\theta\, e^{2i\phi}\beta_1\beta_2\}$$
$$= (4\pi)^{-\frac{1}{2}}\{2P_2^0(\cos\theta)\alpha_1\alpha_2 + \sqrt{2}P_2^1(\cos\theta)e^{i\phi}.$$
$$2^{-\frac{1}{2}}(\alpha_1\beta_2 + \beta_1\alpha_2) + P_2^2(\cos\theta)e^{2i\phi}\beta_1\beta_2\} \tag{4.15}$$

where the $P_l^m(\cos\theta)$ are the associated Legendre polynomials. But, because of (4.12), there must exist constants A and B such that

$$S_{12}X_S = AX_S + BX_D \tag{4.16}$$

where X_D is the angle and spin dependent part of the corresponding $^3D_1(I_z = 1)$ wave function ψ_D. Also, on averaging over all directions of space,

$$\text{av. } S_{12} = 0, \quad \text{av. } X_S \neq 0, \quad \text{av. } X_D = 0$$

and X_S is independent of the direction of space. Hence $A = 0$, and apart from a normalizing factor, the brace in (4.15) must be X_D. Integrating its square over all space, we find that

$$\int |\{\quad\}|^2 d\Omega = 32\pi$$

and so that

$$S_{12}X_S = 8^{\frac{1}{2}}X_D \tag{4.17}$$

where

$$X_D = (32\pi)^{-\frac{1}{2}}\{2P_2^0(\cos\theta)\alpha_1\alpha_2 + \sqrt{2}P_2^1(\cos\theta)e^{i\phi}.$$
$$2^{-\frac{1}{2}}(\alpha_1\beta_2 + \beta_1\alpha_2) + P_2^2(\cos\theta)e^{2i\phi}\beta_1\beta_2\}. \tag{4.18}$$

(It is easily verified that each term of X_D corresponds to $L = 2$, $I_z = 1$, as of course it must. Thus the first term is made up of $P_2^0(\cos\theta)$, which gives $L = 2$, $L_z = 0$, and $\alpha_1\alpha_2$, which gives $S = 1$, $S_z = 1$, and similarly for the other terms.)

Similarly to (4.16) we must have

$$S_{12}X_D = CX_S + DX_D. \tag{4.19}$$

We find the constants C and D by taking $\mathbf{r}$ in a particular direction. Choosing the x-direction, we have

$$\theta = \tfrac{1}{2}\pi,\ \phi = 0,\ S_{12} = 3\sigma_{1x}\sigma_{2x} - \boldsymbol{\sigma}_1 \cdot \boldsymbol{\sigma}_2$$
$$X_S = (4\pi)^{-\frac{1}{2}}\alpha_1\alpha_2,\ X_D = (32\pi)^{-\frac{1}{2}}(-\alpha_1\alpha_2 + 3\beta_1\beta_2). \tag{4.20}$$

Therefore

$$S_{12}X_D = (32\pi)^{-\frac{1}{2}}(10\alpha_1\alpha_2 - 6\beta_1\beta_2). \tag{4.21}$$

We eliminate $\alpha_1\alpha_2$ and $\beta_1\beta_2$ between (4.20) and (4.21) and obtain

$$S_{12}X_D = 8^{\frac{1}{2}}X_S - 2X_D. \tag{4.22}$$

(4.17) and (4.22) thus show the effect of operating with the tensor operator S_{12} on the angle and spin dependent parts of the deuteron wave function.

It is now possible to establish the wave equations for the radial parts of the wave function. The separately normalized wave functions ψ_S and ψ_D can be written

$$\psi_S = r^{-1}u(r)X_S, \quad \psi_D = r^{-1}v(r)X_D, \tag{4.23}$$

and their most general linear combination, also correctly normalized, is

$$\Psi = \psi_S \cos w + \psi_D \sin w. \tag{4.24}$$

This is now substituted into the wave equation of the deuteron,

$$\{(\hbar^2/M)\nabla^2 + E - V_R - V_\sigma\ \boldsymbol{\sigma}_1 . \boldsymbol{\sigma}_2 - V_T S_{12}\}\Psi = 0. \tag{4.25}$$

As before, we write for the central potential

$$V_R + V_\sigma\ \boldsymbol{\sigma}_1 . \boldsymbol{\sigma}_2 = V_C \tag{4.26}$$

and remember that when operating on states with angular dependence $P_l^m (\cos\theta)e^{im\phi}$, the operator ∇^2 reduces to

$$\nabla^2 = \frac{1}{r}\frac{d^2}{dr^2}r - \frac{l(l+1)}{r^2} . \tag{4.27}$$

Therefore

$$\left\{\left[\frac{\hbar^2}{M}\frac{d^2}{dr^2} + E - V_C\right]uX_S - V_T\ 8^{\frac{1}{2}}uX_D\right\}\cos w$$
$$+ \left\{\left[\frac{\hbar^2}{M}\left(\frac{d^2}{dr^2} - \frac{6}{r^2}\right) + E - V_C\right]vX_D - V_T(8^{\frac{1}{2}}vX_S - 2vX_D)\right\}\sin w$$
$$= 0. \tag{4.28}$$

This leads to two simultaneous differential equations for $u(r)$ and $v(r)$

$$\left.\begin{aligned}
(\hbar^2/M)\ u'' + (E - V_C)u - 8^{\frac{1}{2}}V_T v \tan w = 0 \\
(\hbar^2/M)\left(v'' - \frac{6v}{r^2}\right) + (E - V_C + 2V_T)v - 8^{\frac{1}{2}}V_T u \cot w = 0.
\end{aligned}\right\} \tag{4.29}$$

These equations can only be solved numerically.

When evaluating the quadrupole moment of the deuteron, we must remember that only the proton contributes to it, and that its distance from the centre of mass of the system is half that of the neutron-proton distance r. Hence from (2.42) it follows that

$$Q = \int \tfrac{1}{4}(3z^2 - r^2) \mid \Psi \mid^2 d\tau = \int \tfrac{1}{2} r^2 P_2^0 (\cos \theta) \mid \Psi \mid^2 d\tau. \quad (4.30)$$

Substituting from (4.24) for Ψ we have

$$Q = Q_1 \cos^2 w + 2Q_2 \cos w \sin w + Q_3 \sin^2 w \quad (4.31)$$

where

$$Q_1 = \int \tfrac{1}{2} r^2 P_2^0 (\cos \theta) \mid \psi_S \mid^2 d\tau = 0 \quad (4.32)$$

since a pure S-state cannot have a quadrupole moment,

$$Q_2 = \frac{1}{4\pi} \int_0^\infty \tfrac{1}{2} u(r)v(r)r^2 dr \int_0^\pi P_2^0 (\cos \theta) . 2^{-\frac{1}{2}} P_2^0 (\cos \theta) \sin \theta d\theta \int_0^{2\pi} d\phi$$

$$= \frac{1}{2\sqrt{50}} \int_0^\infty r^2 u(r)v(r)dr \quad (4.33)$$

since the terms with different spin functions drop out because of the orthogonality of the spin functions, and

$$Q_3 = -\frac{1}{20} \int_0^\infty r^2 [v(r)]^2 dr. \quad (4.34)$$

(This is much more difficult to work out !) As we know that the D-admixture must be small, since the experimental value of Q is so small, it follows that w is small and that

$$Q \simeq w . \frac{1}{\sqrt{50}} \int_0^\infty r^2 u(r)v(r)dr \quad (4.35)$$

$$\Psi \simeq \psi_S + w\psi_D. \quad (4.36)$$

The magnitude of Q depends not only on w, but also on the shape of the radial D-wave, $v(r)$. In particular, the longer the range of the tensor force, the further away from the origin will be the maximum of $v(r)$, and hence, because of the r^2 factor, the larger will be the integral in (4.35). Thus for a given Q, the D-state probability w depends strongly on the assumed range of the tensor force.

A value of w can be obtained directly from the magnetic moment of the deuteron μ_d. If magnetic moments are expressed in nuclear magnetons, then clearly

$$\mu_d = \mu_n \sigma_n + \mu_p \sigma_p + \mathbf{L}_p$$
$$= \tfrac{1}{2}(\mu_n + \mu_p)(\sigma_n + \sigma_p) + \tfrac{1}{2}(\mu_n - \mu_p)(\sigma_n - \sigma_p) + \mathbf{L}_p \quad (4.37)$$

where $\mathbf{L}_p = \tfrac{1}{2}\mathbf{L}$ is the angular momentum of the proton relative to the centre of mass of the system. The neutron, being uncharged, does not contribute to μ_d except through its intrinsic magnetic moment μ_n. (Note that the z-components of σ_n and σ_p have eigenvalues

± 1, not $\pm \frac{1}{2}$.) The total spin angular momentum is $\mathbf{S} = \frac{1}{2}(\boldsymbol{\sigma}_n + \boldsymbol{\sigma}_p)$ and in triplet states the eigenvalue of $\boldsymbol{\sigma}_n - \boldsymbol{\sigma}_p$ is zero. Thus

$$\boldsymbol{\mu}_d = (\mu_n + \mu_p)\mathbf{S} + \tfrac{1}{2}\mathbf{L}$$
$$= (\mu_n + \mu_p)\mathbf{I} - (\mu_n + \mu_p - \tfrac{1}{2})\mathbf{L}, \qquad (4.38)$$

since $\mathbf{I} = \mathbf{L} + \mathbf{S}$. Now the experimentally measured magnetic moment (see section 2.3) is the actual magnetic moment in the state $I_z = I$. In that case

$$L_z = \frac{\mathbf{L} \cdot \mathbf{I}}{I^2} I_z = \frac{I(I + 1) + L(L + 1) - S(S + 1)}{2I(I + 1)} I_z. \quad (4.39)$$

For the deuteron, $I = 1$, $S = 1$, and $L(L + 1)$ has the appropriate value for the correct mixture of S- and D-states, i.e.

$$L(L + 1) = 0(0 + 1)\cos^2 w + 2(2 + 1)\sin^2 w \simeq 6w^2.$$

Hence

$$\mu_d = \mu_n + \mu_p - \tfrac{3}{2}(\mu_n + \mu_p - \tfrac{1}{2})w^2. \qquad (4.40)$$

On inserting the values for the magnetic moments quoted in section 2.3, we find that $w^2 = 0.04$.† Thus the D-state admixture is 4 per cent. in probability or 20 per cent. in amplitude.

As has been stated, there are many potentials which fit all the experimental facts. The procedure consists of postulating a reasonable potential with several arbitrary constants, and then integrating equations (4.29) numerically for a variety of values of the arbitrary constants. The experimental facts can then be fitted. There seems little to choose between the various results obtained.

4.3 Forces Depending on i-Spin

If nuclear forces depend on $\boldsymbol{\sigma}_1$ and $\boldsymbol{\sigma}_2$, might they not also depend on the i-spin co-ordinates $\boldsymbol{\tau}_1$ and $\boldsymbol{\tau}_2$? The answer is yes, but this fortunately does not lead to quite such complications as might be imagined. It is important to remember that $\boldsymbol{\tau}$ and $\boldsymbol{\sigma}$ are only mathematically similar, and not physically so. Thus the spin operator σ_z has eigenvalues corresponding to " up " and " down " in our real everyday space, but the space in which " up " means proton and " down " neutron, i.e. the i-spin space, is a purely mathematical device and is in no way related to the space in which we measure distances and spin directions. For that reason products between i-spin vectors on the one hand and spin or space vectors on the other, such as $\boldsymbol{\sigma} \cdot \boldsymbol{\tau}$ and $\mathbf{r} \cdot \boldsymbol{\tau}$, are completely meaningless.

It might be thought now that the only possible i-spin dependent term must be of the form $\boldsymbol{\tau}_1 \cdot \boldsymbol{\tau}_2$. But this would be too simple. The analogy with spin breaks down here, because there is no reason

† Relativistic effects may make this result uncertain by as much as ± 0.02.

why there should be any invariance with respect to rotations in the purely mathematical i-space. On the other hand we do know that charge is conserved, so that all energy terms must commute with the charge operator which, from (2.86), is $\frac{1}{2}(1 + \tau_{3,1} + 1 + \tau_{3,2})$. Also all terms must be unchanged under exchange of the identical particles 1 and 2. (This requirement is clearly satisfied by all the potential terms discussed so far.) With these restrictions we have the following possible terms only

$$\tau_1 \cdot \tau_2, \quad \tau_{3,1}\, \tau_{3,2}, \quad \tau_{3,1} + \tau_{3,2}$$

and any other possible term can be reduced to a combination of the above three.

The eigenvalues of these operators are easily calculated from (2.87) and they are given in Table 4.1. On examining the i-spin triplet, we see that the eigenvalues of $\tau_1 \cdot \tau_2$ are charge independent, while those of the others are not. Since at low energies at least, nuclear forces are charge independent, we shall assume that our potential contains only the $\tau_1 \cdot \tau_2$ operator and so is of the form

$$V = V_{\mathrm{R}}(r) + V_\sigma(r)(\sigma_1 \cdot \sigma_2) + V_\tau(r)(\tau_1 \cdot \tau_2) + V_{\sigma\tau}(r)(\sigma_1 \cdot \sigma_2)(\tau_1 \cdot \tau_2)$$
$$+ V_{\mathrm{T}}(r)S_{12} + V_{\mathrm{T}\tau}(r)S_{12}(\tau_1 \cdot \tau_2). \quad (4.41)$$

If nuclear forces are only charge symmetric, i.e. if the n-n and p-p forces are equal to each other, but the n-p forces are different, then the $\tau_{3,1}\, \tau_{3,2}$ operator will have to be employed. Lastly, the $\tau_{3,1}+\tau_{3,2}$ operator enables us to write down expressions which are different for n-n, p-p and n-p forces respectively.

TABLE 4.1. EIGENVALUES OF $\tau_1 \cdot \tau_2$, $\tau_{3,1}\, \tau_{3,2}$, $\tau_{3,1} + \tau_{3,2}$

	I-spin triplet			I-spin singlet
	n-n	p-p	n-p	n-p
$\tau_1 \cdot \tau_2$	1	1	1	-3
$\tau_{3,1}\, \tau_{3,2}$	1	1	-1	-1
$\tau_{3,1} + \tau_{3,2}$	2	-2	0	0

4.4 Exchange Forces

Historically, forces of the type (4.41) were derived in quite a different manner, to account for the two most important properties of nuclei. These are

(a) the approximately constant density of nuclear matter, which leads to the relation $R \propto A^{1/3}$ for the nuclear radius, and

(b) the approximately constant binding fraction of medium and heavy nuclei.

These properties are referred to as the saturation properties of nuclear matter. Similar saturation phenomena in molecules are accounted for by forces arising out of the exchange of negatons between atoms in the molecule. Heisenberg (1932) therefore postulated that nuclear forces were of the exchange type, which, as we shall see later, is just exactly equivalent to postulating forces of the type (4.41). We now have good direct evidence from high energy n-p and p-p scattering (see below and section 4.6) for the existence of exchange forces, but this evidence also shows that by themselves exchange forces cannot account for the saturation properties of nuclei. Possible other explanations of these will however be given there and in section 4.6.

When Heisenberg originally made this suggestion, mesons had not been thought of and it was not at all clear what was being exchanged between nucleons. However, if pions are an integral part of nuclear forces, such an exchange could take place via a pion, by any of the following processes

(1) n p	(2) p n	(3) n p	(4) p p	(5) n n
p $\xrightarrow{\pi^-}$ p	n $\xrightarrow{\pi^+}$ n	n $\xrightarrow{\pi^\circ}$ p	p $\xrightarrow{\pi^\circ}$ p	n $\xrightarrow{\pi^\circ}$ n
p n	n p	n p	p p	n n

The exchange of a pion can thus be equivalent to an exchange of charge, and if the emission and absorption of a pion by a nucleon is coupled to the spin of the nucleon, the pion exchange can also exchange spin. Alternatively we can think of the nucleons as exchanging their space and spin co-ordinates. The introduction of exchange of charge co-ordinates will not then lead to anything further, as can easily be seen. The advantage of describing the process through the exchange of space and spin co-ordinates is that we then do not need to write down the charge co-ordinates of our wave functions. These are in any case irrelevant, since we assume the forces to be charge independent.

The wave equation of the two-body system is

$$[(\hbar^2/M)\nabla^2 + E]\Psi(\mathbf{r_1}\mathbf{r_2}s_1s_2) = V_{12}\Psi(\mathbf{r_1}\mathbf{r_2}s_1s_2) \qquad (4.42)$$

where $\mathbf{r_1}, \mathbf{r_2}$, s_1, s_2 refer to the positions and spins of the two particles, and V_{12} is a two-body potential which includes a purely distance dependent attractive potential $V(r)$, negative for all r, as well as an exchange operator. We now split up the wave function Ψ into a space dependent part $\psi(\mathbf{r})$ and a spin dependent part χ_{12} where $\mathbf{r}$ is the relative position vector of the two particles. Thus

$$\Psi(\mathbf{r_1}\mathbf{r_2}s_1s_2) = \psi(\mathbf{r})\chi_{12}. \qquad (4.43)$$

The four possible types of two-body exchange interaction, which are usually named after the scientists who first investigated them, and the corresponding wave equations can then be written—

(a) No exchange (Wigner)

$$V_{12} = V(r)W_{12} \qquad (4.44)$$

where W_{12} is the unit operator. Hence the wave equation is

$$[(\hbar^2/M)\nabla^2 + E]\psi(\mathbf{r}) = V(r)\psi(\mathbf{r}). \qquad (4.45)$$

The forces are always attractive.

(b) Spin exchange (Bartlett)

$$V_{12} = V(r)B_{12} \qquad (4.46)$$

where B_{12} exchanges spins, i.e. $B_{12}\chi_{12} = \chi_{21}$. Hence

$$[(\hbar^2/M)\nabla^2 + E]\psi(\mathbf{r})\chi_{12} = V(r)\psi(\mathbf{r})\chi_{21}. \qquad (4.47)$$

Now for triplet states ($S = 1$) χ_{12} is symmetric, so that $\chi_{12} = \chi_{21}$, and for singlet states ($S = 0$) χ_{12} is antisymmetric, so that $\chi_{12} = -\chi_{21}$. Equation (4.47) reduces to

$$[(\hbar^2 M)\nabla^2 + E]\psi(\mathbf{r}) = (-1)^{S+1}V(r)\psi(\mathbf{r}). \qquad (4.48)$$

Bartlett forces are thus attractive for triplet states and repulsive for singlet states.

(c) Space exchange (Majorana)

$$V_{12} = V(r)M_{12} \qquad (4.49)$$

where M_{12} exchanges the spatial co-ordinates, i.e. $M_{12}\psi(\mathbf{r}) = \psi(-\mathbf{r})$. The exchange of the spatial co-ordinates of the particles is therefore equivalent to a space inversion of the co-ordinate system, which is the parity operation. [See (2.65).] Hence

$$\psi(-\mathbf{r}) = (-1)^{\frac{1}{2}(1-K)}\psi(\mathbf{r}) \qquad (4.50)$$

where $K = \pm 1$ is the parity eigenvalue of the system. This leads to the equation

$$[(\hbar^2/M)\nabla^2 + E]\psi(\mathbf{r}) = (-1)^{\frac{1}{2}(1-K)}V(r)\psi(\mathbf{r}) \qquad (4.51)$$

so that Majorana forces are attractive for even parity states (S, D, . . . states) and repulsive for odd parity states (P, F,· · · states).

(d) Space and spin exchange (Heisenberg)

$$V_{12} = V(r)H_{12} \qquad (4.52)$$

where H_{12} exchanges space and spin co-ordinates. Clearly

$$H_{12} = M_{12}B_{12}$$

and we have

$$[(\hbar^2/M)\nabla^2 + E]\psi(\mathbf{r}) = (-1)^{\frac{1}{2}(1-K)+S+1}V(r)\psi(\mathbf{r}). \qquad (4.53)$$

The potential here is attractive for even triplet states and odd singlet states, i.e. for states for which the wave function

$$\Psi(\mathbf{r}_1\mathbf{r}_2 s_1 s_2)$$

is symmetric, and is repulsive for odd triplet and even singlet states, i.e. for states for which Ψ is anti-symmetric. Since the complete wave function $\psi_{\text{space}}\psi_{\text{spin}}\psi_{\text{charge}}$ must be anti-symmetric, ψ_{charge} is anti-symmetric in the first case (potential attractive) and symmetric in the second case (potential repulsive).

We can express the four exchange operators W_{12}, B_{12}, M_{12}, H_{12} in terms of the spin and i-spin operators $\boldsymbol{\sigma}_1 . \boldsymbol{\sigma}_2$ and $\boldsymbol{\tau}_1 . \boldsymbol{\tau}_2$, making use of (2.84) and the corresponding expression for $\boldsymbol{\tau}_1 . \boldsymbol{\tau}_2$. These lead to

$$\tfrac{1}{2}(1 + \boldsymbol{\sigma}_1 . \boldsymbol{\sigma}_2) = \begin{cases} + 1, \text{ if } \psi_{\text{spin}} \text{ symmetric} \\ - 1, \text{ if } \psi_{\text{spin}} \text{ anti-symmetric} \end{cases} \qquad (4.54)$$

$$\tfrac{1}{2}(1 + \boldsymbol{\tau}_1 . \boldsymbol{\tau}_2) = \begin{cases} + 1, \text{ if } \psi_{\text{charge}} \text{ symmetric} \\ - 1, \text{ if } \psi_{\text{charge}} \text{ anti-symmetric.} \end{cases} \qquad (4.55)$$

The four operators can then be written—

(a) $$W_{12} = 1. \qquad (4.56)$$

(b) $B_{12} = + 1$ for ψ_{spin} symmetric, $- 1$ for ψ_{spin} anti-symmetric. Hence

$$B_{12} = \tfrac{1}{2}(1 + \boldsymbol{\sigma}_1 . \boldsymbol{\sigma}_2). \qquad (4.57)$$

(c) $M_{12} = + 1$ for ψ_{space} symmetric, $- 1$ for ψ_{space} anti-symmetric, i.e. $M_{12} = + 1$ for $\psi_{\text{spin}}\psi_{\text{charge}}$ anti-symmetric, $- 1$ for $\psi_{\text{spin}}\psi_{\text{charge}}$ symmetric. Hence

$$M_{12} = - \tfrac{1}{4}(1 + \boldsymbol{\sigma}_1 . \boldsymbol{\sigma}_2)(1 + \boldsymbol{\tau}_1 . \boldsymbol{\tau}_2). \qquad (4.58)$$

(d) $H_{12} = + 1$ for ψ_{charge} anti-symmetric, $- 1$ for ψ_{charge} symmetric. Hence

$$H_{12} = - \tfrac{1}{2}(1 + \boldsymbol{\tau}_1 . \boldsymbol{\tau}_2). \qquad (4.59)$$

This shows that any one of the four exchange potentials or any linear combination of them can be described by the potential (4.41) with a suitable choice of the distance dependent parts of that potential.

The way in which exchange forces could lead to saturation is now clear. What is required is that as more and more nucleons enter the nucleus, repulsive forces should tend to balance the attractive forces and prevent the collapse of the nucleus into a very small volume indeed. Since in any nucleus there will be about as many nucleons in odd angular momentum states as in even ones, a large predominance of Majorana over Wigner forces would lead to saturation. Unfortunately, as we shall see in the next section, there is strong evidence against such a large predominance. Bartlett or Heisenberg forces cannot be dominant since they lead to repulsion in the singlet S-state of the deuteron, and we know that this state, although not as attractive as the triplet state, is still attractive.

The exchange character of the n-p forces should become apparent as soon as partial waves other than S-waves enter the picture. We first discuss this, for the sake of simplicity, on the assumption of purely central forces and restrict ourselves to triplet scattering, since at high energies the effect of the large singlet scattering length is unimportant, and so the weight factor [see (3.78)] makes triplet scattering dominant. When waves above the D-wave can be neglected, the scattering amplitude is [see (3.41)]

$$f(\theta) = \frac{1}{2ik} \{(e^{2i\eta_0} - 1) + 3(e^{2i\eta_1} - 1) \cos\theta$$
$$+ \tfrac{5}{2}(e^{2i\eta_2} - 1)(3\cos^2\theta - 1)\} \quad (4.60)$$

and as η_1 and η_2 are small compared with η_0,† we can write

$$f(\theta) = \frac{1}{2ik} \{(e^{2i\eta_0} - 1) + 6i\eta_1 \cos\theta + 5i\eta_2(3\cos^2\theta - 1)\} \quad (4.61)$$

neglecting terms of the second order in η_1 and η_2. The scattering intensity to the same order is, after some reduction,

$$I(\theta) = k^{-2}\{\sin^2\eta_0 + \sin 2\eta_0[3\eta_1 \cos\theta + \tfrac{5}{2}\eta_2(3\cos^2\theta - 1)]\}. \quad (4.62)$$

For ordinary (Wigner) forces η_0, η_1 and η_2 are all positive, but for Majorana exchange forces the sign of η_1 is changed (and also the magnitude). Hence clearly

$$I(180°) < I(0°) \text{ for Wigner forces} \quad (4.63)$$

$$I(180°) > I(0°) \text{ for Majorana forces} \quad (4.64)$$

and in general forward scattering (scattering into small angles) predominates for ordinary forces and backward scattering (scattering into large angles) for Majorana exchange forces.

Experiments at energies up to 90 MeV showed that the n-p differential scattering cross-section was almost symmetric about 90° with a deep minimum at 90°, a clear indication that exchange forces exist. Such a cross-section can be fitted with a potential that allows scattering mainly for even angular momenta, since $P_l(\cos\theta)$

† This approximation has been made for the sake of simplicity. The conclusions drawn from (4.62) and (4.66) are just as true when no approximations are made.

is symmetric about 90° for even l, but not for odd l, i.e. a potential of the form

$$V_{12} = \tfrac{1}{2}\{(1-a)W_{12} + aM_{12}\}V(r) \tag{4.65}$$

where $a \simeq \tfrac{1}{2}$. The potential with $a = \tfrac{1}{2}$ is called the Serber potential. For odd angular momentum states, for which $M_{12} = -W_{12}$, such a potential gives no interaction, and so η_1, η_3, . . . all vanish. Hence from (4.62),

$$I(\theta) = k^{-2}\{\sin^2 \eta_0 + \tfrac{5}{2}\eta_2 \sin 2\eta_0(3 \cos^2 \theta - 1)\} \tag{4.66}$$

so that $I(\theta) = I(\pi - \theta)$. Because of its simplicity, this potential is still frequently employed at comparatively low energies, although it is now known that it cannot fit the data at higher energies.

4.5 Polarization

The usual impact parameter considerations [see (3.44)] show that we must go to higher energies if we wish to investigate the effect of higher angular momentum components in the scattered wave. When this was done in the early 1950s, it became apparent that nuclear forces were very complicated indeed and simplifying restrictions had to be removed one after another. However, because successive partial waves do not become important until a certain threshold energy is reached, it should be possible to fit all the experimental facts at a given energy with a restricted set of phase shifts. Further these phase shifts should vary reasonably with energy. The technique has therefore been to break the problem down into two parts.

(*a*) To find sets of phase shifts to fit experiments at given energies. If, as is often the case, several very different sets fit the results within the experimental error, then those are chosen that have a smooth variation with energy.

(*b*) To find potentials which give the type of phase shifts found under (*a*).

The number of phase shifts which are relevant increases rapidly with energy and a knowledge of differential and total cross-sections is then no longer sufficient to determine them. Fortunately a great deal of information can be obtained by scattering polarized beams in which the spins of the nucleons are not randomly oriented, but have some preferred direction. For spin-$\tfrac{1}{2}$ particles there are of course only two directions, " up " and " down," and if the number of particles in the beam with spins along and opposite to the preferred direction are $N \uparrow$ and $N \downarrow$, then the polarization of the beam is defined as

$$P = \frac{N \uparrow - N \downarrow}{N \uparrow + N \downarrow}. \qquad (4.67)$$

Experimentally it turns out that partially polarized beams can be obtained by scattering unpolarized nucleon beams by unpolarized hydrogen targets. The extent of polarization can then be determined by a second scattering. Thus, let the wave vector of the beam

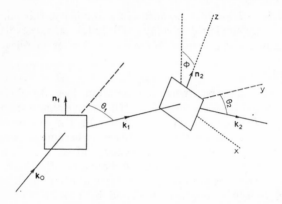

FIG. 4.1. DOUBLE SCATTERING TO DETECT POLARIZATION

before the scattering and after the first and second scattering be $\mathbf{k_0}$, $\mathbf{k_1}$ and $\mathbf{k_2}$ respectively and let the two scattering angles be θ_1 and θ_2 (see Fig. 4.1). Then we shall show that the polarization induced in the first scattering can be measured by the variation of the intensity of the final beam as a function of the azimuthal angle ϕ.

The spin part of the wave function of a particle in a beam before scattering is, from (2.70),

$$\chi = a\alpha + b\beta = \begin{pmatrix} a \\ b \end{pmatrix} \qquad (4.68)$$

in matrix notation. The intensity $|a|^2 + |b|^2$ is not necessarily normalized to unity, and the polarization along the z-axis is, from (4.67),

$$P_z = \frac{|a|^2 - |b|^2}{|a|^2 + |b|^2}. \qquad (4.69)$$

Asymptotically the wave function for the whole scattering process may be written, by an obvious generalization of (3.21),

$$\Psi = \left[e^{i\mathbf{k} \cdot \mathbf{r}} + \frac{e^{ikr}}{r} M(\theta,\phi) \right] \binom{a}{b} \tag{4.70}$$

where $M(\theta, \phi)$ must now be a 2×2 matrix, the elements of which depend on the scattering angle, as well as on the incident energy. Now the most general 2×2 matrix can be expressed as a linear combination of the unit matrix $\mathbf{1}$, and the three Pauli spin matrices σ [see (2.92)], i.e.

$$M = g\mathbf{1} + \mathbf{h} \cdot \boldsymbol{\sigma} \tag{4.71}$$

where g and $\mathbf{h}$ are functions of scattering angle and incident energy. (For scattering by a purely central force, $h = 0$.) As M is a scalar in ordinary space and $\boldsymbol{\sigma}$ an axial vector, which does not change sign under space reflection, $\mathbf{h}$ must also be an axial vector. Further, it must be derived from vectors which describe the scattering process and, for unpolarized targets, the only vectors available are the momenta of the particle before and after scattering. From these we can form the two unit axial vectors

$$\mathbf{n}_1 = \frac{\mathbf{k}_0 \times \mathbf{k}_1}{|\mathbf{k}_0 \times \mathbf{k}_1|}, \quad \mathbf{n}_2 = \frac{\mathbf{k}_1 \times \mathbf{k}_2}{|\mathbf{k}_1 \times \mathbf{k}_2|}, \tag{4.72}$$

one respectively for each scattering, and no others. Hence we can put

$$M_j = g_j \mathbf{1} + h_j \mathbf{n}_j \cdot \boldsymbol{\sigma}, \quad j = 1, 2, \tag{4.73}$$

for the two scatterings. In what follows, suffixes 1 and 2 always denote the first and second scattering.

We take the z-axis along $\mathbf{n}_2$ and the xz-plane in the plane of $\mathbf{n}_1$ and $\mathbf{n}_2$. Clearly $\mathbf{n}_1 \cdot \mathbf{n}_2 = \cos \phi$, where ϕ is the azimuthal angle of Fig. 4.1. Then

$$M_1 = g_1 \mathbf{1} + h_1 (\sin \phi \cdot \sigma_x + \cos \phi \cdot \sigma_z)$$

so that

$$M_1 \binom{a_1}{b_1} = \binom{(g_1 + h_1 \cos \phi)a_1 + h_1 \sin \phi \cdot b_1}{h_1 \sin \phi \cdot a_1 + (g_1 - h_1 \cos \phi)b_1}. \tag{4.74}$$

The differential cross-section is given by the ratio of the beam intensities after and before scattering, i.e.

$$\frac{d\sigma_1}{d\Omega} = \{ \, | \, (g_1 + h_1 \cos \phi)a_1 + h_1 \sin \phi \cdot b_1 \, |^2 + | \, h_1 \sin \phi \cdot a_1 +$$
$$(g_1 - h_1 \cos \phi)b_1 \, |^2 \}/\{ \, | \, a_1 \, |^2 + | \, b_1 \, |^2 \}$$
$$= | \, g_1 \, |^2 + | \, h_1 \, |^2 +$$
$$\frac{(g_1^* h_1 + g_1 h_1^*)[(\, | \, a_1 \, |^2 - | \, b_1 \, |^2) \cos \phi + (a_1^* b_1 + a_1 b_1^*) \sin \phi]}{| \, a_1 \, |^2 + | \, b_1 \, |^2}. \tag{4.75}$$

Now if a measurement of spin orientation is made on an unpolarized beam, then it is found to consist of equal numbers of particles with spin up and spin down, i.e. for half the particles $a_1 = 1$, $b_1 = 0$ and for the other half $a_1 = 0$, $b_1 = 1$. Thus on average

$$\text{av.}(|\,a_1\,|^2 - |\,b_1\,|^2) = 0, \quad \text{av.}(a_1^* b_1 + a_1 b_1^*) = 0, \quad (4.76)$$

so that

$$\frac{d\sigma_1}{d\Omega} = |\,g_1\,|^2 + |\,h_1\,|^2. \quad (4.77)$$

The polarization of the scattered beam along the z-axis is given by (4.69), where a and b now refer to the two components of the spin wave function (4.74). Hence

$$P_{1z} = \frac{g_1^* h_1 + g_1 h_1^*}{|\,g_1\,|^2 + |\,h_1\,|^2} \cos \phi \quad (4.78)$$

where we have averaged over the incident beam. Thus, if $h \neq 0$, the beam is polarized after one scattering. As the polarization cannot depend on the direction $\mathbf{n}_2$, this shows that the polarization vector is

$$\mathbf{P}_1 = P_1 \mathbf{n}_1 \quad \text{where} \quad P_1 = \frac{g_1^* h_1 + g_1 h_1^*}{|\,g_1\,|^2 + |\,h_1\,|^2}. \quad (4.79)$$

For the second scattering we have

$$\left. \begin{array}{l} a_2 = (g_1 + h_1 \cos \phi) a_1 + h_1 \sin \phi \cdot b_1 \\ b_2 = h_1 \sin \phi \cdot a_1 + (g_1 - h_1 \cos \phi) b_1. \end{array} \right\} \quad (4.80)$$

Averaging again over the incident beam, we have

$$\text{av.} \frac{|\,a_2\,|^2 - |\,b_2\,|^2}{|\,a_2\,|^2 + |\,b_2\,|^2} = \frac{g_1^* h_1 + g_1 h_1^*}{|\,g_1\,|^2 + |\,h_1\,|^2} \cos \phi = P_1 \cos \phi. \quad (4.81)$$

The differential scattering cross-section is obtained from (4.75) on replacing 1 by 2 and putting $\phi = 0$. Then

$$\frac{d\sigma_2}{d\Omega} = |\,g_2\,|^2 + |\,h_2\,|^2 + (g_2^* h_2 + g_2 h_2^*) P_1 \cos \phi$$

$$= (|\,g_2\,|^2 + |\,h_2\,|^2)(1 + P_1 P_2\, \mathbf{n}_1 \cdot \mathbf{n}_2) \quad (4.82)$$

where P_2 is the polarization produced by the second scatterer. Thus the second cross-section depends on the azimuthal angle ϕ, which is what we set out to prove.

If the two scatterings are in the same plane, then

$$\frac{d\sigma_2}{d\Omega} = (|\,g\,|^2 + |\,h\,|^2)(1 \pm P_1 P_2), \quad (4.83)$$

the sign depending on whether the angle θ_2 is taken on the right or left of $\mathbf{k}_1$, the angle θ_1 being taken on the right of $\mathbf{k}_0$. From this right-left asymmetry we at once obtain the polarization

$$e_{r-l} = \frac{d\sigma_2^r - d\sigma_2^l}{d\sigma_2^r + d\sigma_2^l} = P_1 P_2 \qquad (4.84)$$

If the scattering angles are the same, and if the energy loss in the first scattering, due to target recoil, is negligible, then we have

$$P_1 = P_2 = \sqrt{e_{r-l}} \qquad (4.85)$$

In this way it is possible to obtain the magnitude, although not the sign, of the polarization due to single scattering by means of a double scattering experiment. Other double and triple scattering experiments yield further parameters, but it would be beyond the scope of this book to go into these. All can be expressed in terms of the usual scattering phase shifts for the partial waves.

Polarization can be produced by a tensor force, for S_{12} has opposite signs depending on whether the spins of incident and target nucleons are parallel or anti-parallel (see ex. 4.8.3), but detailed analysis of the experimental results at high energies shows that these cannot be fitted with such a force alone. It is therefore now necessary (Case and Pais, 1950) to introduce velocity dependent forces, which, as we explained at the beginning of the chapter, would not be expected to be important at low energies. A rather special potential of this kind is a spin-orbit coupling potential of the form

$$V_{LS} = V(r)\, \mathbf{L} \cdot \mathbf{S} = V(r)\, \mathbf{r} \times \mathbf{p} \cdot (\mathbf{s}_1 + \mathbf{s}_2). \qquad (4.86)$$

Such a potential satisfies the general invariance conditions laid down in section 4.1 (see ex. 4.8.7), but it does of course introduce a velocity dependence through $\mathbf{p}$. Further, since $\mathbf{p}$ is the gradient operator, this potential affects the wave function at one point through the values of the wave functions at other points. For this reason it is called *non-local*.

The potential (4.86) vanishes in singlet states, and in triplet states is equal to

$$\mathbf{L} \cdot \mathbf{S} \text{ (triplet)} = \tfrac{1}{2}[(\mathbf{L} + \mathbf{S})^2 - \mathbf{L}^2 - \mathbf{S}^2]$$
$$= \tfrac{1}{2}(\mathbf{I}^2 - \mathbf{L}^2 - \mathbf{S}^2)$$
$$= \tfrac{1}{2}\{I(I + 1) - L(L + 1) - 2\}. \qquad (4.87)$$

It is easily shown that both $\mathbf{I}$ and $\mathbf{L}$ are constants of motion for this potential (see ex. 4.8.9), so that, unlike the tensor force potential, it does not mix states of different L, but it follows from (4.87) that it is different and hence scatters differently for states with the same L

and different I. The phase shifts will therefore depend on both L and I, so that for instance the phase shifts for the three triplet P-states, $^3P_0$, $^3P_1$ and $^3P_2$, will be different from each other.

4.6 Two-body Scattering at High Energies

The experimental results for energies up to about 400 MeV are shown in Figs. 4.2 – 4.6. Beyond this energy meson production becomes important so that treatments using potentials become inapplicable. The main features can be characterized as follows :

(*a*) The n-p differential cross-section has a large backward peak. At high energies scattering at 180° exceeds that at 0°.

(*b*) Except for small angles where Coulomb scattering is important, the p-p differential cross-section is almost isotropic, i.e. independent of scattering angle.

(*c*) The p-p and n-n differential cross-sections are very similar.

. (*d*) The p-p total cross-section is remarkably constant over a wide energy range.

(*e*) The p-p and n-n total cross-sections are very similar.

(*f*) The n-p and p-n total cross-sections are very similar.

(*g*) There is substantial polarization, both for p-p and for n-p scattering.

Points (*c*), (*e*) and (*f*) confirm our hypothesis of charge symmetry of nuclear forces. The p-n and n-n experiments were conducted by bombarding deuterium targets and assume that the waves from the neutron and proton interfere incoherently. This may not be entirely justified.

Let us now turn to the other points, which are less easy to deal with. It can be shown that, irrespective of the nature of the interaction, when a high energy particle is scattered by a stationary target, then in general there will only be a small amount of energy transferred to the target. The point is that it requires an almost head-on collision to transfer a large amount of energy, and such an event is rare. This means that the incident particle will as a rule be scattered in the forward direction. If therefore, in high energy n-p scattering, we detect large numbers of neutrons in the backward direction, then these must be due to an exchange process in which the incident neutron has exchanged charge with the target proton so that the recoiling target particle is now a neutron. The conclusion, that there must be exchange forces, which we had already drawn from (*a*) for central forces, is therefore generally valid. However, the conclusion that the symmetric shape of the cross-section is due to an absence of P-wave is no longer valid. We now have three

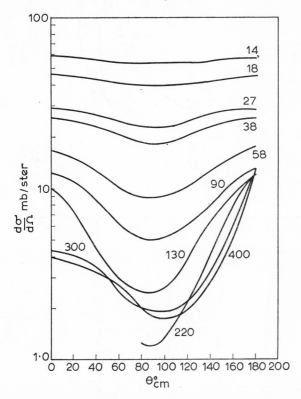

Fig. 4.2. Neutron-Proton Differential Cross-section

[From Moravcsik, M. J., *The Two-Nucleon Interaction* (Oxford, 1963)]

P-phase shifts, corresponding to the states $^3P_0$, $^3P_1$ and $^3P_2$, and these all enter into the coefficient of $\cos \theta$ in the expression (4.61) for $f(\theta)$. It in any case follows from the fact that at comparatively low energies there is substantial polarization, that there must be a P-wave contribution.

The analysis of the high energy p-p scattering is no more satisfactory. An isotropic angular distribution generally implies pure

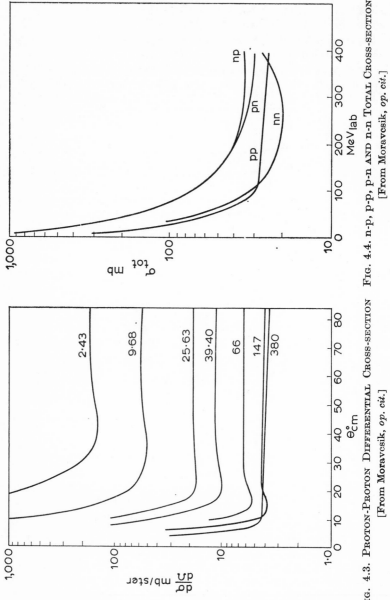

Fig. 4.3. PROTON-PROTON DIFFERENTIAL CROSS-SECTION
[From Moravcsik, *op. cit.*]

Fig. 4.4. n-p, p-p, p-n AND n-n TOTAL CROSS-SECTIONS
[From Moravcsik, *op. cit.*]

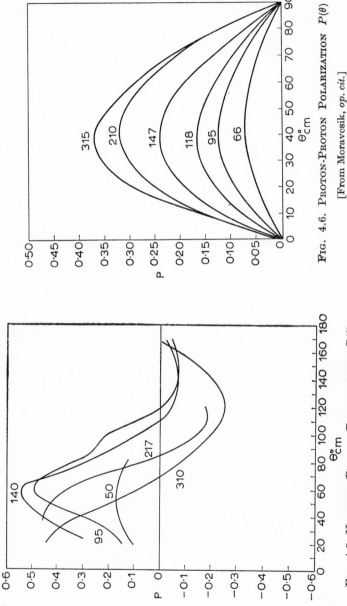

FIG. 4.6. PROTON-PROTON POLARIZATION $P(\theta)$

[From Moravcsik, *op. cit.*]

FIG. 4.5. NEUTRON-PROTON POLARIZATION $P(\theta)$

[From Moravcsik, *op. cit.*]

S-wave scattering, but apart from the intrinsic improbability that p-p scattering at 400 MeV should be pure S-wave, it can in fact not be so, because the total cross-section is almost twice as large as the maximum possible for pure S-wave scattering. This latter is obtained from (3.43) and is clearly $4\pi/k^2$. On the other hand, an interference of the P, D, . . . waves to give an isotropic distribution, while possible at one particular energy, is most unlikely to occur over a range of energies.

The energy dependence of the total cross-section is equally puzzling. It requires a potential very different from the ones usually considered, all of which would require the cross-section to decrease as the energy increases.

An interesting explanation of these strange results has been suggested by Jastrow (1951). For any conventional potential the S-phase decreases to zero with increasing energy, and it is then not possible to obtain an even approximately isotropic differential cross-section when phases other than S-phases are involved. This can only be achieved by letting the S-phase become negative, which corresponds to a repulsive potential. (See example 4.8.4 for a simple illustration of this.) Now at high energies, the S-wave is strongly influenced by the behaviour of the potential at very short distances, so that what we require is a potential that is attractive at larger distances, but has a strongly repulsive core. This core would have no effect on higher angular momentum waves, since their amplitudes vanish at the origin. It turns out that the distance at which the potential changes sign must be about 0·4 fm. Since the total cross-section depends only on the magnitude of the phase shifts, but not on their signs, a repulsive core leading to an S-phase that first decreases and then again increases in absolute magnitude, might also account for the constancy of the total cross-sections over a wide energy range.

It is clear that a repulsive core would also materially aid the problem of saturation of nuclear forces. Although by itself it is too small to account for it completely (the inter-nucleon distance in nuclei is about 1·2 fm), it is probable that saturation is not due to any one cause, but can be produced by a combination of exchange forces, repulsive core and perhaps many-body forces, which will be discussed in section 4.7. It turns out that a repulsive core is also suggested by meson theory (section 10.3). Unfortunately there the repulsive core would appear in both singlet and triplet interactions, while we require it only in singlet states, since the n-p results, which are due predominantly to triplet scattering, do not after all show the peculiar properties of the p-p results.

At a first glance it would appear that the n-p and p-p results are so different that charge independence of nuclear forces could not possibly be maintained. This is not true. Because of the anti-symmetric nature of the wave function the p-p system can exist in only half as many states as the n-p system (see example 4.8.5), and

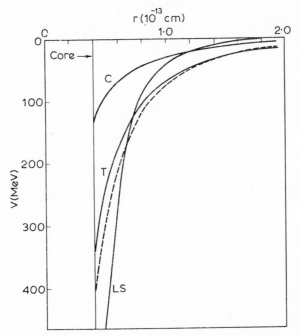

FIG. 4.7. GAMMEL-THALER POTENTIAL IN EVEN-PARITY STATES
- - - - - Singlet
————— Triplet : C, T and LS
[Phillips, R. J. N., *Rep. Prog. Phys.*, **22**, 562 (1959)]

so the corresponding scattering cross-sections may well be very different. It is in fact still possible to maintain the hypothesis of charge independence at high energies, although the evidence from scattering is neutral rather than in favour of it. It should be added, however, that the strongest evidence for the charge independence of nuclear forces at high energies comes from the properties of the pion-nucleon interaction. This will be treated in section 10.2.

Our treatment of the experimental data has been entirely qualita-tive, and detailed phase shift analyses require extensive numerical computations. These have been performed for a large number of energies, the most complete results being at 150 and 300 MeV.

They have been fitted independently by Gammel and Thaler (1957), and by Signell and Marshak (1958), who used potentials of the form

$$V = V_C + V_\sigma \boldsymbol{\sigma}_1 . \boldsymbol{\sigma}_2 + V_T S_{12} + V_{LS} \mathbf{L} . \mathbf{S} \qquad (4.88)$$

where each V-function is of the form

$$V_1(r) + V_2(r) \, \boldsymbol{\tau}_1 . \boldsymbol{\tau}_2 \qquad (4.89)$$

and has a repulsive core. The inclusion of the spin-orbit term made it possible for the first time to obtain fits with an energy independent

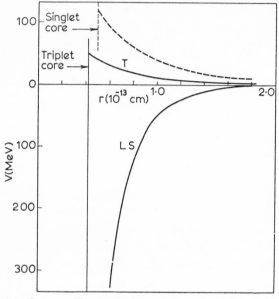

FIG. 4.8. GAMMEL-THALER POTENTIAL IN ODD-PARITY STATES

- - - - - Singlet
——— Triplet : T and LS
[Phillips, R. J. N., *op. cit.*]

potential over a wide range of energies. Even then it was found necessary to use different potentials for states of even and odd spatial parity.

The Gammel-Thaler potentials for both even- and odd-parity states are shown in Figs. 4.7 and 4.8. For singlet states there is of course only a central interaction. For triplet states, the tensor force is substantially stronger than the central force and in odd-parity states there is no central force at all. The spin-orbit force has a much shorter range than the other forces and thus becomes important only at higher energies.

4.7 Many-body Forces

It was stated in section 4.4 that the nuclear interaction is thought to take place through the exchange of pions. This statement will be amplified in Chapter 10, but for the moment it is sufficient that such a description is possible. There is then no reason to suppose that only one pion is exchanged, and the observed forces between two nucleons may well be the result of the superposition of exchanges of one, two, or more pions. For the sake of simplicity we shall restrict our discussion to the exchange of one or two pions and see how this affects the forces between three nucleons.

If only one pion is exchanged between any pair of nucleons, then the interaction energy of the three-body system 1-2-3 is simply the sum of the interaction energies of the three two-body systems 1-2, 2-3, 3-1. Now let us assume that sometimes two pions are exchanged. Then there are four possibilities in the three-body system—

(*a*) A nucleon emits two pions which are absorbed by one other nucleon.

(*b*) A nucleon absorbs two pions which had been emitted by one other nucleon.

(*c*) A nucleon emits two pions which are absorbed one by each of the other nucleons.

(*d*) A nucleon absorbs two pions which had been emitted one by each of the other nucleons.

Cases (*a*) and (*b*) can also occur in the two-body system, but cases (*c*) and (*d*) clearly cannot. The result is that if two pions can be exchanged, then the interaction energy of the three-body system is not simply the sum of the energies of its three two-body interactions. Forces which are such that they depend on the number of particles present in a system are called many-body forces. They are quite negligible in electromagnetic interactions, but it is very possible that they are important in nuclear interactions.

With this in mind it is now possible to investigate the problem of nuclear saturation. If the forces between nucleons in a nucleus are purely attractive, then the total potential energy will be proportional to the total number of pairs in the nucleus, i.e. to $\frac{1}{2}A(A-1)$, so that the binding fraction will be proportional to A and not constant. This is strictly speaking only true of a classical system. In a quantum mechanical system, the exclusion principle leads to the result that the probability of a nucleon being in the immediate neighbourhood of another nucleon is much reduced compared with the same probability in a classical system. Hence the total energy is reduced too, but not sufficiently to account for saturation. Further, for increasing A, the nuclear matter will become more and more concentrated, as each nucleon is attracted by more and more linkages. This again is not observed ; on the contrary, the nuclear density remains remarkably constant. It is clear then that any mechanism which is to account for saturation must introduce repulsions between the nucleons.

The treatment of many-body systems is exceedingly complicated, and no exact calculations are possible. However, an approximate calculation of many-body forces, which may at least be qualitatively correct has yielded the following results (Drell, 1953)—

1. n-body forces are attractive for even n and repulsive for odd n.

2. The range of n-body forces decreases with increasing n.

3. The importance of n-body forces decreases rapidly with increasing n. This is a result of the exclusion principle which prevents more than a few nucleons being sufficiently near to each other to interact with each other.

4. n-body forces are likely to be negligible for $n > 3$.

Whether more exact calculations will uphold these conclusions is not at all certain. However, we now have three possible mechanisms leading to saturation, and it is not unreasonable to hope that between them they should achieve it.

4.8. EXAMPLES

4.8.1. Prove that $(\sigma_1 . \sigma_2)^2 = 3 - 2\sigma_1 . \sigma_2$ and that $(\sigma_1 \times \sigma_2)^2 = 6 - 2\sigma_1 . \sigma_2.$

4.8.2. Given that the angular part of the wave function of a ${}^3P_1 (I_z = 1)$ state is a linear combination of
$$P_1^0 (\cos \theta) = \cos \theta \text{ and } P_1^1 (\cos \theta) e^{i\phi} = \sin \theta e^{i\phi},$$
show that the correctly normalized wave function of the state is given by
$$X_P = \sqrt{\frac{3}{16\pi}} \{2P_1^0 (\cos \theta) \alpha_1\alpha_2 + P_1^1 (\cos \theta) e^{i\phi}(\alpha_1\beta_2 + \beta_1\alpha_2)\}.$$

[Hint : $S_{12}X_P = cX_P$, where c is a constant. Why?]

4.8.3. If we treat the neutron and proton spins classically, then the triplet state of the deuteron is represented by either of the following configurations—

(a)   (b)

Show that in this classical picture S_{12} has the values 2 and -1 for (a) and (b) respectively. Hence show that the tensor force must be attractive to give the correct sign of the quadrupole moment (prolate spheroid).

[Hint : The ground state is the state of least energy.]

4.8.4. Evaluate $|f(\theta)|^2$ in (4.60) exactly, on the assumption of pure Serber forces, and contrast the differential cross-sections for (a) $\eta_0 = +\ 45°$, $\eta_2 = +\ 15°$, (b) $\eta_0 = -\ 45°$, $\eta_2 = +\ 15°$.

4.8.5. Show that p-p scattering can take place only in ^1S, ^3P, ^1D, $\ldots$ states. What can you say about the total i-spin of the n-p system in these states?

[Hint : The total wave function must be anti-symmetric.]

4.8.6. Prove that scattering at 90° in the c.m. system is due to even angular momenta only, and hence that at 90°,

$$\frac{d\sigma^{\,p-p}}{d\Omega} = \sum_{\text{even } l} \left| \frac{^1 d\sigma^{\,p-p}}{d\Omega_l} \right|^2,$$

$$\frac{d\sigma^{\,n-p}}{d\Omega} = \frac{3}{4} \sum_{\text{even } l} \left| \frac{^3 d\sigma^{\,n-p}}{d\Omega_l} \right|^2 + 1\tfrac{1}{4} \sum_{\text{even } l} \left| \frac{^1 d\sigma^{\,n-p}}{d\Omega_l} \right|$$

where the affixes 1 and 3 refer to singlet and triplet scattering respectively. Hence show that a criterion for charge independence of nuclear forces is that at 90°

$$\frac{d\sigma^{\,p-p}}{d\Omega} \leqslant 4 \frac{d\sigma^{\,n-p}}{d\Omega}.$$

(This criterion is satisfied wherever it has been tested.)

4.8.7. Show that the spin-orbit terms $\mathbf{L . S}$ satisfies all the requirements for a potential listed in section 4.1.

4.8.8. Show that for a given total angular momentum I of the two-body system in a triplet state under tensor forces, the spin-orbit term is different in both magnitude and sign for the two orbital angular parts of the state.

4.8.9. Show that both $\mathbf{I}^2$ and $\mathbf{L}^2$ are constants of motion for a spin-orbit potential.

[Hint : Use the commutation rules for angular momentum to show that $\mathbf{I}^2$ and $\mathbf{L}^2$ commute with $\mathbf{L . S}$.]

CHAPTER 5

Nuclear Models

5.1 Introduction

THE detailed knowledge of nuclear forces which has been gained from consideration of the two-body system cannot unfortunately, because of the immense mathematical complexity, be applied directly to the many-body system. This problem is not of course peculiar to nuclear physics, but arises similarly in the consideration of a drop of liquid, a volume of gas, a heavy atom, the planetary system and of many other cases. In some of these, e.g. the first two mentioned above, the number of particles is so large that statistical methods can be employed and give excellent results. In others, e.g. the last two mentioned above, there is a centre of force, which is such that the forces between it and the particles of the system are very much stronger than the forces between any two of the particles, and these latter can then be treated as small perturbations on the main force. In a nucleus—and this makes the problem so difficult—there are too few particles for a statistical treatment, and there is no overriding centre of force which would enable us to treat the forces between nucleons as small perturbations. For this reason physicists have fallen back on the " as if " methods of attack, also known here as the method of nuclear models. This method consists of looking round for a physical system, the " model ", with which we are familiar and which in some of its properties resembles a nucleus. The physics of the model are then investigated and it is hoped that any properties thus discovered will also be properties of the nucleus. This extrapolation procedure must of course break down sooner or later, but it is surprising how far it can sometimes be taken. Even when it does break down, the very cause of the breakdown may often indicate in which way the original model was defective and has to be modified. In this way the nucleus had been treated " as if " it were a gas, a liquid drop, an atom and several other things. No single model can account for all the known facts about nuclei and so these models will now be discussed in turn.

5.2 Degenerate Gas Model

If the forces between pairs of nucleons are neglected, but the overall force on each nucleon is simulated by requiring that all nucleons should be contained in a sphere of definite volume Ω, radius $R = r_0 A^{1/3}$, then the nucleus can be treated as a gas, the particles of which move freely inside an enclosure. Treated as such, the nucleus is found to be almost completely degenerate, even in the first few excited states, i.e. unlike a classical gas it occupies almost all the lowest energy states available. The reason for this is that in a gas which is confined to so small a volume as that of a nucleus the spacing of the energy levels turns out to be of the order of several MeV. As the excitation energies of the first few excited states are no larger than this, the ground state and probably the first few excited states must be almost completely degenerate. Such a gas must then be treated according to quantum statistics and, as the particles are anti-symmetric (see section 2.5), according to Fermi-Dirac statistics. Since we assume the particles to be non-interacting, the exclusion principle is strictly valid so that no two particles have exactly the same quantum numbers. As the particles can exist in two spin states this means that there are at most two in each momentum state. It is clear that this model completely ignores surface effects, which are very important. While it gives a good qualitative picture of the nucleus, actual numerical results, therefore, e.g. energy levels, are likely to be inaccurate.

It should be noted here that a degenerate Fermi-Dirac gas is very different indeed from a classical gas. If in a classical gas the temperature is lowered at constant pressure, collisions between particles become more frequent, so that the mean-free-path of the particles becomes short compared with the volume dimensions of the gas. In a degenerate Fermi-Dirac gas, on the other hand, all the lowest available states of the system are occupied. Hence the transfer of momentum and energy between particles which would be the normal consequence of the strong forces acting between the particles is prevented by the exclusion principle. For if a particle transferred momentum and energy to another, it would find itself in another state, and that state in a completely degenerate gas is already occupied. Thus the mean-free-path of a particle in a degenerate Fermi-Dirac gas is long compared with the volume dimensions. This may be the justification for neglecting the interactions between particles in this model.

We first calculate the number of states available to particles of one kind (neutrons or protons) in the gas with momentum less than a given momentum p. The result is most easily proved if we assume the particles to move in a cubical box, volume Ω, length of side L, with perfectly reflecting walls. The corresponding result for a spherical box of the same volume is some 25 per cent lower for medium and heavy nuclei (see examples 5.8.1 and 5.8.2), but as we are only interested in orders of magnitude we shall employ a cubical box, for which closed formulae can be obtained.

The wave equation of each particle is

$$- \nabla^2 u = \frac{2ME}{\hbar^2} u = \frac{1}{\hbar^2}(p_x^2 + p_y^2 + p_z^2)u \qquad (5.1)$$

and any solution must vanish for $x = y = z = 0$ and for $x = y = z = L$. Hence

$$u = A \sin\frac{p_x x}{\hbar} \sin\frac{p_y y}{\hbar} \sin\frac{p_z z}{\hbar} \qquad (5.2)$$

where

$$p_x = n_x \hbar\pi/L, \quad p_y = n_y \hbar\pi/L, \quad p_z = n_z \hbar\pi/L \qquad (5.3)$$

and n_x, n_y, n_z are positive integers. (Negative integers do not lead to new solutions.) States with momentum less than p are given by

$$p_x^2 + p_y^2 + p_z^2 < p^2, \text{ i.e. } n_x^2 + n_y^2 + n_x^2 < \frac{p^2 L^2}{\pi^2 \hbar^2}. \qquad (5.4)$$

The number of different combinations (n_x, n_y, n_z) which satisfy this inequality is given by the number of lattice points of a cubic lattice of unit interval, contained in one octant of a sphere of radius $pL/\pi\hbar$, where the octant arises from the fact that n_x, n_y, $n_z > 0$. But that is the volume of the octant. Remembering that there can be two particles with spin $\frac{1}{2}$ in each momentum state, we find that the number of possible states with momentum less than p is

$$n = \frac{\pi\Omega}{3}\left(\frac{p}{\pi\hbar}\right)^3 \qquad (5.5)$$

and the number of possible states with momenta between p and $p + \mathrm{d}p$ is

$$\mathrm{d}n = \frac{\Omega p^2 \mathrm{d}p}{\pi^2 \hbar^3}. \qquad (5.6)$$

Here we have used the fact that $\Omega = L^3$.

In the ground state of a nucleus the gas is completely degenerate and so all the states up to a certain one are filled. The maximum momenta of neutrons and protons are then obtained by putting n equal to N or Z in (5.5). Hence, since now $\Omega = \frac{4}{3}\pi r_0^3 A$, where we take $r_0 \simeq 1 \cdot 2$ fm,

$$p^{\text{prot}}_{\text{max}} = \frac{\hbar}{r_0}\left(\frac{9\pi Z}{4A}\right)^{1/3}, \quad p^{\text{neut}}_{\text{max}} = \frac{\hbar}{r_0}\left(\frac{9\pi N}{4A}\right)^{1/3}. \qquad (5.7)$$

If we put $C = \hbar^2(9\pi/4)^{2/3}/2Mr_0^2 \simeq 0{\cdot}056$ u, then the corresponding kinetic energies are

$$E^{\text{prot}}_{\max} = C\left(\frac{Z}{A}\right)^{2/3}, \; E^{\text{neut}}_{\max} = C\left(\frac{N}{A}\right)^{2/3}. \tag{5.8}$$

The total kinetic energy of all the protons in the gas is given by

$$E_Z = \int_0^Z E\mathrm{d}n \tag{5.9}$$

where $\mathrm{d}n$ is given by (5.6). Hence

$$\begin{aligned}
E_Z &= \int_0^{p^{\text{prot}}_{\max}} \frac{p^2}{2M} \frac{p^2 \Omega \mathrm{d}p}{\pi^2 \; \hbar^3} \\
&= \frac{\Omega}{10M\pi^2\hbar^3}\left(p^{\text{prot}}_{\max}\right)^5 \\
&= \tfrac{3}{5}Z\, E^{\text{prot}}_{\max}, \tag{5.10}
\end{aligned}$$

using (5.7) and (5.8). Similarly $E_N = \tfrac{3}{5}NE^{\text{neut}}_{\max}$.

We now can derive some results about the kinetic energy of a nucleus, $E(N, Z)$. As our standard nucleus we shall take the one with $N = Z = \tfrac{1}{2}A$. For this nucleus, using (5·8) and (5·9) we have

$$E(\tfrac{1}{2}A, \tfrac{1}{2}A) = \tfrac{3}{5}AC2^{-2/3} \simeq 0{\cdot}021A \text{ u.} \tag{5.11}$$

Thus the average kinetic energy of a nucleon in such a nucleus is about 20 MeV, and the maximum kinetic energy, from (5.10), is about 33 MeV. This value is somewhat larger than the one obtained from wavelength considerations (see 2.9). If we use the fact that the binding energy of the last nucleon in a medium or heavy nucleus is about 8 MeV, then we see that the depth of the averaged potential well in which we assume the nucleons to move is about 41 MeV.

We next show that for a given A our standard nucleus is the most stable by computing the increase in the kinetic energy of an isobar with neutron or proton excess. This is clearly

$$E(N, 0) + E(0, Z) - E(\tfrac{1}{2}A, \tfrac{1}{2}A) = \tfrac{3}{5}CA^{-2/3}[N^{5/3} + Z^{5/3} - 2(\tfrac{1}{2}A)^{5/3}]$$

$$= \tfrac{3}{5}CA^{-2/3}\left[\left(\frac{A}{2} + \triangle\right)^{5/3} + \left(\frac{A}{2} - \triangle\right)^{5/3} - 2\left(\frac{A}{2}\right)^{5/3}\right]$$

where $\triangle = N - \tfrac{1}{2}A = \tfrac{1}{2}A - Z$. As for any real nucleus $\triangle$ is small, we can expand this expression as far as $\triangle^2$ and obtain for the increase in kinetic energy

$$E(N, 0) + E(0, Z) - E(\tfrac{1}{2}A, \tfrac{1}{2}A) = \tfrac{1}{3}2^{4/3}C\frac{(\tfrac{1}{2}A - Z)^2}{A}$$

$$= 0{\cdot}407\frac{(\tfrac{1}{2}A - Z)^2}{A} \tag{5.12}$$

in atomic mass units. This is always positive and as the depth of the potential well is independent of N, Z and A, it follows that the standard nucleus is the isobar with least energy.

So far we have neglected the Coulomb interaction between the protons. This results in raising the bottom of the proton well by eV over that of the neutron well, where V is the electrostatic potential inside the nucleus.

From (2.14),

$$eV = \frac{Ze^2}{2r_0 A^{1/3}} \left(3 - \frac{r^2}{r_0^2 A^{2/3}} \right). \qquad (5.13)$$

For a heavy nucleus this is quite appreciable. Thus for Pb^{208} the electrostatic potential varies from 25 MeV at the centre of the nucleus to 16 MeV at the surface. In a heavy nucleus there are therefore less protons than neutrons.

The above argument brings out the not always appreciated fact that it is only the exclusion principle which makes it possible for stable nuclei to contain protons at all. Without this, it would always be energetically more favourable to add another neutron rather than a proton to the nucleus, so that the most stable nuclei would consist entirely of neutrons.

5.3 The Semi-empirical Mass Formula

The virtue of the gas model is that it brings out the peculiar quantum effects of a highly degenerate system. It is not a suitable model for investigating the energetics of a nucleus.

The total energy of a nucleus is governed largely by the saturation properties of the nuclear forces (see section 4.4), and these are very similar to the properties of intermolecular forces in a liquid. A formula for the total energy of a nucleus can be developed in which the most important terms are obtained from the analogy with a liquid drop, and the finer detail, due to the quantum nature of the nucleus, from the gas model. A few numerical constants have to be fitted experimentally, although we shall see that to an order of magnitude at least they too follow from the theory.

The parallel with the liquid drop gives the first three terms of the formula. There is first the total mass energy (we shall again consider the masses of neutral atoms and work in atomic mass units)

$$M_1 = M_p Z + M_n(A - Z) = 1{\cdot}008658A - 0{\cdot}000839Z. \qquad (5.14)$$

From this must be subtracted the binding energy of the nucleons (heat of condensation in the liquid drop), which is proportional to the number of particles in the nucleus

$$M_2 = -a_1 A. \qquad (5.15)$$

The correction M_2 is actually an overestimate because the nucleons near the surface are less firmly bound than those inside the volume. This surface tension effect is proportional to the surface area and is positive

$$M_3 = a_2 A^{2/3}. \qquad (5.16)$$

A numerical estimate of a_1 and a_2 can be obtained from the experimental fact that the binding fraction of medium and heavy nuclei is approximately constant and equal to about 12 MeV, if the Coulomb repulsion energy is allowed for. This can be fitted with

$$a_1 \simeq a_2 \simeq 0.015 \text{ u.}$$

The next term to be added is the electrostatic repulsion energy of the protons. Quite independently of the charge distribution within the nucleus, this will be inversely proportional to the radius of the nucleus and, on a classical calculation, directly proportional to $Z(Z-1)$. Quantum mechanical considerations, analogous to those used in connexion with the Coulomb energy of mirror nuclei in section 2.2, will change this last factor to Z^2. Thus we put

$$M_4 = a_3 Z^2 A^{-1/3}. \qquad (5.17)$$

If the charge distribution is uniform, then it is easily shown (see (2.15)) that

$$a_3 = \frac{3e^2}{5r_0}. \qquad (5.18)$$

This can be written as

$$\begin{aligned}
a_3 &= \frac{3}{5} \cdot \frac{e^2}{\hbar c} \cdot \frac{\hbar}{m_e c} \cdot \frac{1}{r_0} \cdot \frac{m_e}{M} \cdot M c^2 \\
&= \frac{3}{5} \cdot \frac{1}{137} \cdot \frac{386}{1.2} \cdot \frac{1}{1837} \text{ u} \qquad (5.19) \\
&= 0.000763 \text{ u}
\end{aligned}$$

where use has been made of the following constants,

$$\text{fine structure constant,} \quad \frac{e^2}{\hbar c} = \frac{1}{137}$$

$$\text{reduced Compton wavelength,} \quad \frac{\hbar}{m_e c} = 386 \text{ fm}$$

$$\text{ratio of nucleon to negaton mass} \quad \frac{M}{m_e} = 1837.$$

The last two terms are derived from the gas model. We saw there (see 5.12) that a nucleus was particularly stable if it had equal numbers of neutrons and protons, so that we shall have to add a correction term for the neutron or proton excess. This we saw was of the form

$$M_5 = a_4 \frac{(\frac{1}{2}A - Z)^2}{A}. \tag{5.20}$$

All the terms considered so far are continuous functions of N and Z. However, if there is an odd number of neutrons in the nucleus, then the highest energy state is only half filled and so the next neutron will go into it. This means that the energy of the nucleus does not increase smoothly with N, as had been assumed, but rather in steps. In other words, compared with the smooth increase, an even-even nucleus will have less energy and an odd-odd nucleus more. This step-like increase of the energy is ensured by a sixth term which is of the form

$$\delta(A, Z) = \begin{cases} + f(A) & A \text{ even, } Z \text{ odd} \\ \quad 0 & A \text{ odd} \\ - f(A) & A \text{ even, } Z \text{ even.} \end{cases} \tag{5.21}$$

A possible form of $f(A)$ follows naturally from the gas model. It is clear that the energy of an even-even nucleus (N, Z) has been overestimated in comparison with the nucleus $(N - 1, Z)$ by

$$E_{\max}^{\text{neut}}(N) - E_{\max}^{\text{neut}}(N - 1)$$

and so this is $f(A)$. On substituting (5.8) and expanding to the first order we have

$$f(A) = CA^{-2/3}[N^{2/3} - (N - 1)^{2/3}]$$
$$\simeq \tfrac{2}{3} CA^{-2/3} N^{-1/3}. \tag{5.22}$$

As $N \simeq \frac{1}{2}A$,

$$f(A) = \tfrac{1}{3} 2^{4/3} CA^{-1} = 0 \cdot 047 \, A^{-1} \text{ u.} \tag{5.23}$$

We would expect then that

$$f(A) = a_5 \, A^{-1}. \tag{5.24}$$

It is too much to hope that this fine adjustment should actually be given correctly by the gas model, and we shall therefore fit the whole function $f(A)$ empirically and not just a_5.

On combining all the terms we have

$$M(A, Z) = M_p Z + M_n(A - Z) - a_1 A + a_2 A^{2/3}$$
$$+ a_3 \frac{Z^2}{A^{1/3}} + a_4 \frac{(\frac{1}{2}A - Z)^2}{A} + \delta(A, Z). \tag{5.25}$$

The constants a_1, a_2, a_3, a_4 and the function $f(A)$ are now fitted to the experimental data. The numerical values given below are those of Green (1954).

For a given A the minimum of $M(A, Z)$ as a function of Z must correspond to the stable isobar. Hence stable isobars are given by

$$\frac{\partial M}{\partial Z} = 0 = -0{\cdot}00084 - a_4 \frac{A - 2Z}{A} + 2a_3 ZA^{-1/3}. \quad (5.26)$$

As (5.12) underestimates a_4, it is certainly permissible to neglect $0{\cdot}00084$ compared with a_4. Then

$$Z = \frac{A}{2 + \left(\dfrac{2a_3}{a_4}\right) A^{2/3}}. \quad (5.27)$$

This is the nuclear stability curve which was drawn in Fig. 1.1. The best fit is obtained for

$$\frac{2a_3}{a_4} = 0{\cdot}014989. \quad (5.28)$$

The remaining three constants are then adjusted to give the best fit to the odd-A stable elements. It is found that

$$a_1 = 0{\cdot}0169172,\ a_2 = 0{\cdot}019115,\ a_3 = 0{\cdot}0007626,\ a_4 = 0{\cdot}10175 \quad (5.29)$$

all in u. The value obtained for a_3 checks very well with that of (5.19) which was obtained on the assumptions that the nucleus has a uniform charge distribution and that $r_0 = 1{\cdot}2$ fm.

The even-A stable elements are then used to determine $f(A)$. If $f(A)$ is to be of the form (5.24), then

$$a_5 = 0{\cdot}140 \text{ u} \quad (5.30)$$

but if the function itself is fitted to the available data, then the best fit is obtained either with

$$f(A) = 0{\cdot}010\ A^{-1/2} \quad (5.31)$$

or with

$$f(A) = 0{\cdot}036\ A^{-3/4}. \quad (5.32)$$

The complete expression for $M(A, Z)$ then reads

$$M(A, Z) = 1{\cdot}008658A - 0{\cdot}000839Z - 0{\cdot}016917A + 0{\cdot}019115A^{2/3}$$
$$+ 0{\cdot}0007626 \frac{Z^2}{A^{1/3}} + 0{\cdot}10175 \frac{(\tfrac{1}{2}A - Z)^2}{A} + \delta(A, Z). \quad (5.33)$$

Sometimes it is more useful to have a formula for the binding energy.

This, in MeV, is

$$B(A, Z) = 15 \cdot 753A - 17 \cdot 804A^{2/3} - 0 \cdot 7103 \frac{Z^2}{A^{1/3}} - 94 \cdot 77 \frac{(\frac{1}{2}A - Z)}{A}$$
$$- \delta(A, Z) \quad (5.34)$$

where $\delta(A, Z) = \pm 33 \cdot 6A^{-3/4}$ or 0. Clearly the formula to be tested for good agreement with experiment is (5.34) and not (5.33) where any small disagreement would be masked by the dominant first two terms, which are obviously correct. It is found that (5.34)

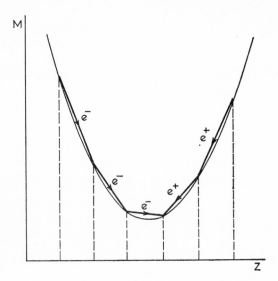

FIG. 5.1. MASSES OF ISOBARS FOR ODD A

Only one isobar can be stable.

agrees with the experimental values to better than 1 per cent. for $A > 15$, and the difference in binding energies of nuclei of not too different A is often given correctly to 0·1 per cent.

The $\delta(A, Z)$ term also ensures that there is the possibility of more than one stable nuclide for a given even A, but not for a given odd A. This can be seen from Figs. 5.1 and 5.2 where $M(A, Z)$ is plotted against Z for a given A. The curves are parabolae, and in Fig. 5.2 the dashed line represents $M(A, Z) - \delta(A, Z)$, while the full lines give $M(A, Z)$ for even Z and odd Z nuclides. It is clear that for odd A, only one isobar can be stable, but that for even A, two or even more isobars can be stable. Fig. 5.3 illustrates the hypothetical

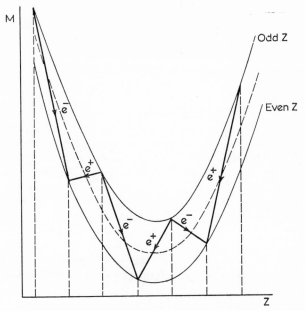

FIG. 5.2. MASSES OF ISOBARS FOR EVEN A
The diagram illustrates the possibility of three even-even isobars
being stable.

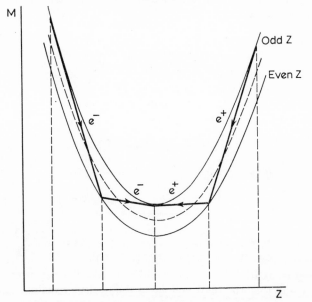

FIG. 5.3. MASSES OF ISOBARS FOR EVEN A
The diagram illustrates the possibility of one odd-odd isobar being
stable. (This does not occur in nature.)

case of an odd-odd nuclide being stable. As this does not occur in nature for $A > 15$, a lower limit is placed on $\delta(A, Z)$, which must give a splitting between the parabolae sufficiently large to prevent this case from occurring. Fig. 5.2 also illustrates the occurrence of nuclides which are both positon and negaton emitters.

5.4 The Liquid Drop Model

The success of the semi-empirical mass formula encourages us to take the idea of the liquid drop model a little further. As has already been pointed out this model should be suitable for investigating nuclear energies and so should be useful when considering the stability of nuclei.

Up to now we have confined ourselves entirely to the ground states of nuclei. In such a state a liquid drop is of course perfectly spherical. The liquid drop model, in a much more sophisticated form, has also been used to account for some of the excited states of nuclei, but we shall leave a discussion of this until section 5.7. Instead, we investigate how severe deformations of the drop could lead to nuclear fission.

We assume that in the ground state the nucleus is a sphere with a sharp surface, radius R_0. Then in an excited state the nucleus is deformed, but in the lowest excitations the surface will still have axial symmetry, so that it can be expressed in terms of spherical harmonics,

$$R(\theta) = R_0 \left\{ 1 + \sum_{l=0}^{\infty} b_l P_l(\cos \theta) \right\}. \tag{5.35}$$

Now this formula can give both a deformation of the sphere and a translation of the sphere as a whole, which latter is of no interest to us. If the sphere is moved undeformed through a distance $b_1 R_0$ along the line $\theta = 0$, then

$$R_0^2 = R^2 + b_1^2 R_0^2 - 2R b_1 R_0 \cos \theta \tag{5.36}$$

i.e.

$$R = R_0 \{ [1 - b_1^2 (1 - \cos^2 \theta)]^{\frac{1}{2}} + b_1 \cos \theta \}$$
$$= R_0 \left\{ 1 + b_1 \cos \theta + \sum_{l=0}^{\infty} c_{2l} P_{2l}(\cos \theta) \right\} \tag{5.37}$$

where the c_{2l} arise from the expansion of the square root. Thus the coefficient of $P_1(\cos \theta)$ in (5.35) gives the distance through which the centre of mass of the nucleus has moved, and for a pure deformation without translation we must have $b_1 = 0$. Also b_0 must be chosen in such a way that the total volume of the nucleus remains constant.

The lowest excited states are given by $b_2 \neq 0$, $b_l = 0$ for $l > 2$, and in that case it is easily shown that

$$R(\theta) = R_0\{1 - \tfrac{1}{5}b_2^2 + b_2 P_2(\cos\theta)\}. \tag{5.38}$$

For sufficiently large excitations, vibrations with $b_2 \neq 0$ may lead to fission into two parts, as is shown schematically in Fig. 5.4. As

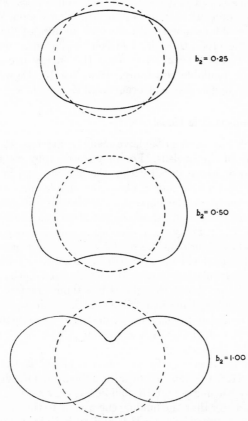

$b_2 = 0.25$

$b_2 = 0.50$

$b_2 = 1.00$

Fig. 5.4. Surface (5.38) for Various Deformations

the surface is deformed, the surface energy increases and the Coulomb energy decreases, the changes in energy being

$$\triangle E_S = \tfrac{2}{5}a_2 b_2^2, \tag{5.39}$$

and

$$\triangle E_C = -\tfrac{1}{5}a_3\frac{Z^2}{A}b_2^2 \tag{5.40}$$

where a_2 and a_3 are given by (5.29). These results are purely classical and will not be proved. For spontaneous fission we must therefore have

$$\frac{Z^2}{A} > \frac{2a_2}{a_3} = 50 \cdot 2. \qquad (5.41)$$

It must be stressed that when this condition is satisfied, fission is not only spontaneous, but instantaneous. The fission of U^{238}, for which $Z^2/A = 36$, cannot be of this type, because of the very long life-time of the process. It must in fact be due to a tunnel effect, which can of course occur even when the energy needed for the process is not available classically. If we use (5.41), we find that instantaneous fission does not occur until $Z \simeq 140$, $A \simeq 390$.

5.5 The Alpha-particle Model

The models discussed so far have made no attempt at describing the structure of the nucleus. For that reason they could not give any information about detail within the nucleus, and in particular they could give no information about the angular momentum, and magnetic moment of the nucleus. The models discussed in this and the following section are of the structure type and the second one of these has in many ways been quite astonishingly successful. However, before describing this model, we want to dispose briefly of the α-particle model which, as we shall see, is not a very useful model.

Because α-particles are known to emerge from nuclei in natural radioactive decay, it was thought at one time that they also form more or less stable structures inside nuclei. Such α-particle structures could be either permanent or, more likely, temporary but of lifetimes long compared with the natural periods of vibration and rotation of the structures.

A second argument in favour of this model is the increased stability of He^4, C^{12} and O^{16} over neighbouring nuclides. This is explained by assuming that the binding energy of an α-particle is very much greater than the binding energy due to the forces between α-particles or between an α-particle and an individual nucleon.

Perhaps the strongest argument for the α-particle model is an extension of the foregoing one and is based on the binding energies of all the light even-even nuclides. According to the model these are made up of α-particles which are arranged in space so as to give the closest possible packing. Most of the binding energy of each nuclide is due to the binding of its constituent α-particles, the remainder being the energy of the bonds between the α-particles. In

Table 5.1 we have tabulated the configurations that probably give closest packing and the corresponding number of bonds. It should be noted that it is assumed that in the octahedron the distance between α-particles at opposite corners is too great for an interaction between them to be effective, but that in the other bipyramids the α-particles at the apices of the two pyramids are close enough together for a bond to exist. The last column gives the binding energy per bond, which is remarkably constant except in the case of Be^8.

TABLE 5.1

Nuclide	Configuration	No. of bonds	Mass M (u)	$M - \frac{1}{4}AM\alpha$ (mu)	Bond energy (mu)
He^4	—	0	4·00258	0	0
Be^8	Dumbbell	1	8·00527	− 0·11	− 0·11
C^{12}	Triangle	3	12·00000	7·81	2·60
O^{16}	Tetrahedron	6	15·99485	15·48	2·58
Ne^{20}	Square pyramid	8	19·9924	20·6	2·58
Mg^{24}	Octahedron	12	23·9849	30·6	2·47
Si^{28}	Pentagonal bipyramid	16	27·9768	41·3	2·59
S^{32}	Hexagonal bipyramid	19	31·9719	48·8	2·57
A^{36}	Heptagonal bipyramid	22	35·9673	55·9	2·54
Ca^{40}	Octagonal bipyramid	25	39·9623	63·5	2·54

None of the above arguments is very convincing. As regards the first, it is easily shown, by considering energies and life-times of decay, that α-particles are the only particles which can be emitted from naturally radioactive nuclei (see section 1.6). The second argument is not very helpful either. Almost any theory of nuclei will lead to increased stability of nuclei in which the numbers of neutrons and protons are even and equal to each other. This is because in such a nucleus it is possible to pair off nucleons with opposite spin, but in the same energy and orbital angular momentum states. This leads to a phenomenon closely allied to the " completion of shells " in atoms, which will be further discussed in the next section.

The last argument also becomes rather questionable upon closer examination. The fact that the binding energy per nucleon in even-even nuclei is hardly greater than in the α-particle may merely mean that nuclear forces are almost saturated even in the α-particle, and this explanation is supported by the observation that in nuclei other than even-even ones the binding energy per nucleon is almost the same. Further, at least one of the configuration assignments, that for Ne^{20}, is not above suspicion. A trigonal bipyramid would do equally well, it would seem, and this would yield nine bonds. Another point is that the Coulomb interaction between the α-particles has been neglected. For an inter-alpha distance of $\sim$ 3 fm this is about 2·0 mu. This raises the bond energy in Be^8, C^{12}, O^{16} to 1·9, 4·6, 4·6 mu respectively. After that Coulomb interactions beyond the nearest neighbour appear, so that for instance the bond energy in S^{32} is raised to 5·1 mu. In any case, the whole calculation is based on the equality of nearest neighbour distances, and it is clear that beyond S^{32} such an equality is not even approximately possible.

Under certain not entirely obvious assumptions the α-particle model then describes the ground state energies of even-even nuclides fairly well. It should be added that it has also had some success with the calculation of excited levels of even-even nuclides. To that extent it is a useful model, although we must be careful not to jump to the conclusion that it follows from this that α-particle clustering actually takes place in nuclei. Many of the results of the α-particle model are identical with those derived from the shell model, which we shall describe in the next section, and which is based on assumptions almost diametrically opposite. The real reason why the α-particle model is not very helpful is that it says nothing about nuclides other than even-even. A particularly glaring failure occurs with $A = 4n + 2$ nuclides. These could be described as consisting of either n α-particles and two extra nucleons or $(n + 1)$ α-particles and two holes. It is clear from Table 5.1 that the spatial configurations corresponding to these two choices are quite different from each other, and it seems likely that the true spatial configuration of such a nucleus is quite different from either of them.

5.6 The Shell Model

It has been stated in section 5.2 that because of the Pauli exclusion principle nucleons inside nuclear matter may have a very long mean-free-path. This will be so if the potential in which they move is due to all the other nucleons and so can on the average be simulated by a constant central potential. It is not at all obvious that the strong, short-range nuclear forces should average out to such a potential, and a counter example can be seen in He^3 at very low temperatures. This too is a degenerate Fermi-Dirac system with strong, short-range interactions—the Van der Waals forces between the particles. However the particles do not have long mean-free-paths, since He^3 can be solidified under pressure.

With the reservation that our assumption is not obvious, we shall now make it and the test will be the agreement with experiment. The situation is then not dissimilar to that of negatons in an atom, and it is tempting to suggest that nucleons exist in states of definite energy and angular momentum, and that the outstanding stability of some nuclides is due to the completion of a neutron or proton shell, in the same way as the stability of the rare gases is due to the completion of a negaton shell. The situation in the case of nuclei is complicated by two factors :

(*a*) The " central " potential is really an average potential, and the addition of an extra nucleon modifies this potential far more than the addition of an extra negaton modifies the central potential in the atomic case.

(*b*) Because of the Coulomb repulsion of the protons, the numbers of neutrons and protons in a nucleus are not even approximately the same in all but the lightest nuclides. It is therefore most unlikely that a nuclide with a closed shell number of neutrons can also have a closed shell number of protons and conversely. The stability characteristics of closed shells will therefore be less marked than in the atomic case.

It is found that the following numbers of neutrons or protons lead to particular stability :

$$2, 8, (14), 20, 28, 50, 82, 126.$$

The stability associated with 14 is not as pronounced as that associated with the other numbers. These numbers are called the *magic numbers* and the experimental evidence for their existence is very strong indeed [see for instance, the article by Flowers (1952)], Thus particularly stable nuclei should be and are $_2\text{He}^4$, $_8\text{O}^{16}$, $_{20}\text{Ca}^{40}$. $_{20}^{28}\text{Ca}^{48}$, $_{82}^{126}\text{Pb}^{208}$. Various attempts have been made to derive these magic numbers theoretically, by choosing a likely expression for the average potential inside the nucleus. Actually, the order of the levels is not very sensitive to the shape of the potential well. Because of the short range of nuclear forces, the average potential must be nearly constant inside the nucleus and fall off to zero rapidly near the nuclear surface (see Fig. 1.2). Any potential which satisfies these conditions will reproduce roughly the same order of levels. This order is, incidentally, quite different from the corresponding order in the atomic case. The difference arises from the fact that there the central potential far from being constant near the origin, varies rapidly and becomes infinite at the origin.

The potentials originally tried because of their mathematical simplicity were the spherical well of infinite depth, the spherical well of finite depth and the oscillator potential. These are given respectively by :

(a) Infinite spherical well
$$V = - V_0, \, r < R, \, V = + \infty, \, r > R$$

(b) Finite spherical well
$$V = - V_0, \, r < R, \, V = 0, \, r > R$$

(c) Oscillator
$$V = - V_0 + \tfrac{1}{2}Kr^2.$$

(5.42)

The last of these is parabolic and thus gives a large transition region.

The level schemes for the oscillator and for the infinite well are given in the extreme left- and right-hand columns of Fig. 5.5, and it is clear that they lead to the following magic numbers :

Oscillator :   2, 8, 20, 40, 70, 112, 168

Infinite well :   2, 8, 20, 34, 40, 58, 92, 132, 138.

(5.43)

It might be thought that a more realistic scheme would give levels lying somewhere between those given by the oscillator and the infinite well. This would change the level spacing and might even slightly change the order of levels. Such a scheme was for instance Nordheim's in which the 1g and 2d levels were exchanged and so were the 3s and 2f levels, while the 1h level was raised. The resulting scheme is as follows :

Level	1s	1p	1d	2s	1f	2p	2d	1g	2f	1h	3s
No. in level	2	6	10	2	14	6	10	18	14	22	2
No. in shell	2	6	12		30			32			
Total no.	2	8	20		50			82			

There is of course no theoretical foundation for these quite arbitrary changes. Furthermore it is difficult to see how this scheme, or indeed any scheme which relies merely on changing the order of levels in the spherical well scheme, could produce 14 and 28 as magic numbers.

A quite different suggestion was put forward independently by Mayer and by Haxel, Jensen and Suess (Mayer and Jensen, 1955). So far no account has been taken of the possible splitting of each energy level into two, according as the spin and orbital angular momenta s and l of the particle in the level are in the same or in opposite directions. Such a term could arise as a result of the two-body spin-orbit coupling introduced in section 4.5. A spin-orbit term, the so-called Thomas term, also arises from a relativistic treatment of the wave equation for a central potential $V(r)$. This is equal to

$$\frac{\hbar^2}{2M^2c^2r}\frac{dV}{dr}\mathbf{l} \cdot \mathbf{s}.$$

(5.44)

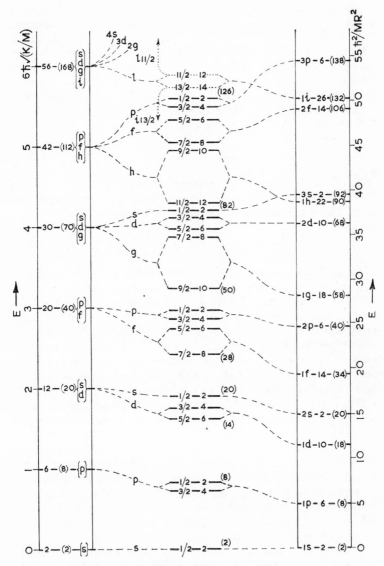

FIG. 5.5. ENERGY LEVELS OF A NUCLEON

On the left are the oscillator levels, on the right the square well levels. In between are levels that are intermediate, with spin-orbit coupling. The 1s level is taken to be the zero of energy of the system. [After Haxel, Jensen and Suess, *Z. Phys.*, **128**, p. 298 (1950), Fig. 1.]

It turns out that this is much too small, and also of the wrong sign, to give the necessary splitting. This shows that the spin-orbit term in the shell model does not arise merely from a relativistic correction, but is an integral part of the nuclear force. It is nevertheless usual to take the spin-orbit term of the form (5.44), but to change the sign and multiply it by a strength parameter λ to fit the experimental results. The radial dependence of $V(r)$ is chosen so that the potential is constant and negative in the central region of the nucleus and gradually rises to zero in the surface. The most usual functional form is that first employed by Saxon and Woods,

$$V(r) = - V_0 f(r) \text{ where } f(r) = \frac{1}{1+\mathrm{e}^{(r-c)/a}}. \tag{5.45}$$

Here c is of the order of the nuclear radius and a gives a measure of the width of the transition region in which the potential rises to zero. The complete shell model potential is then

$$V_{\mathrm{SM}}(r) = - V_0 f(r) + \frac{\lambda V_0}{2M^2c^2} \frac{1}{r} \frac{\mathrm{d}f}{\mathrm{d}r} \mathbf{l} \cdot \mathbf{s}. \tag{5.46}$$

As $f(r)$ is positive and monotonically decreasing, $\mathrm{d}f/\mathrm{d}r$ is negative everywhere. Now according to the experimental evidence, the level splitting is always such that the $j = l + \frac{1}{2}$ level is below the $j = l - \frac{1}{2}$ level.[†] Hence (see example 5.8.5) the sign in front of the spin-orbit term in (5.46) must be $+$, which is the opposite to that of the relativistic Thomas term (5.44). To obtain a splitting of the required magnitude, λ must be of the order 30. The form of the $\mathbf{l} \cdot \mathbf{s}$ operator also ensures that the splitting of the level increases linearly with l. The level scheme of $V_{\mathrm{SM}}(r)$ is in fact of the kind shown in the centre portion of Fig. 5.5. The exact level sequence depends on our choice of the parameters a, c and λ, but the scheme clearly reproduces all the magic numbers.

Direct evidence for the existence of a spin-orbit term in the interaction between a nucleon and a nucleus has been obtained from the polarization effects which are observed when unpolarized beams of protons are scattered by unpolarized targets. The mechanism is analogous to that discussed for nucleon-nuclear scattering in section 4.5, except that now the target consists of complex nuclei and not of protons (Hensinkveld and Freier, 1952).

The scheme outlined so far enables us to deduce the angular momenta of nuclides which consist entirely of closed shells, and also of nuclides which consist of closed shells plus or minus one particle.

[†] In this chapter the total angular momentum of a single particle is denoted by $\mathbf{j}$, and that of several particles by $\mathbf{J}$.

Because of the exclusion principle, the former must have zero angular momentum, and in the latter case the total angular momentum is just that of the excess particle or of the "hole", i.e. the particle which would have to be added to complete the shell. Thus the angular momenta of e.g. $_8O^{16}$, $_{20}^{20}Ca^{40}$, $_{82}^{126}Pb^{208}$ should be and are zero, and those of $_7^8N^{15}$, $_8^9O^{17}$, $_{19}^{20}K^{39}$, $_{82}^{125}Pb^{207}$ and $_{83}^{126}Bi^{209}$ should be and are $\frac{1}{2}$, $\frac{5}{2}$, $\frac{3}{2}$, $\frac{1}{2}$ and $\frac{9}{2}$ respectively. Sometimes the knowledge of the angular momentum of a certain nuclide enables us to establish the correct order of the energy levels. In this way, the fact that the angular momentum of $_{83}^{126}B^{209}$ is $\frac{9}{2}$ indicates that the $1h_{9/2}$ level is below the $2f_{7/2}$ level, at least for protons. It should be pointed out here that because of the Coulomb repulsion the order of proton levels may well be slightly different from that of neutron levels.

To proceed further we now make another assumption. It is an experimental fact that all even-even nuclei have zero angular momentum. We therefore postulate that the like nucleons in a nucleus pair off in such a way that their angular momenta cancel. The angular momentum of an odd-*A* nucleus is then due entirely to the angular momentum of the last unpaired nucleon. Apart from three exceptions, to be discussed below, this assumption is verified to be correct wherever the level order is unambiguous, and it enables us to decide the correct order of levels in places where the levels are close together. The resultant scheme is given in Fig. 5.6. It will be noticed that there are small discrepancies between the orders of neutron and proton levels.

It is apparent that a given angular momentum j of the last particle can arise from two possible orbital angular momenta, $l = j \pm \frac{1}{2}$. As these values differ by unity, they have opposite parity. To see this we note that the case of one particle moving in a central potential is quite analogous to the case of two particles moving in each other's potential, which was treated in section 4.1, where it was found that even parity corresponded to even l and odd parity to odd l. If therefore the angular momentum of the whole nucleus is due to the angular momentum of the last particle, then the parity of the whole nuclear wave function is determined by the orbital angular momentum of the last particle, which is predicted by the shell model. The nuclear state due to the last particle being in, say, a $d_{5/2}$ level would then be denoted by $\frac{5}{2}+$, while a $\frac{5}{2}-$ state would correspond to the last particle being in an $f_{5/2}$ level. The experimental verification of these predictions has come largely through the so-called d-p stripping reactions (see section 6.9). In these the target nucleus captures the neutron from an incoming deuteron into the lowest vacant shell model level. The angular distribution of

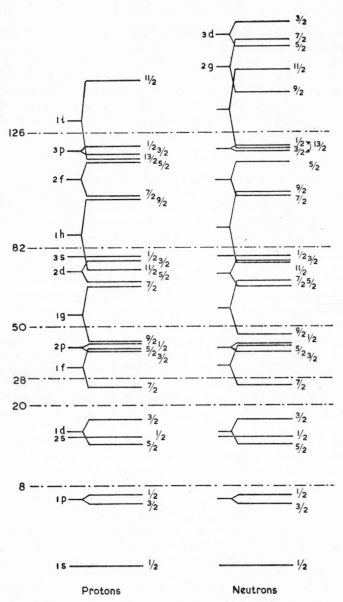

FIG. 5.6. PROTON AND NEUTRON LEVEL SCHEMES
[After Klinkenberg, P. F. A., *Revs. Mod. Phys.*, **24**, p. 63 (1952), Fig. 1.]

the scattered protons then gives information on the orbital angular momentum of the captured neutrons.

So far we have assumed that all nucleons move in a central potential and do not interact preferentially with each other. This can only be a first approximation to the truth. Nucleons outside closed shells will interact with each other as well as moving in the central field due to the closed shells, and nucleons in the same orbit will be more strongly bound to each other than to other nucleons. The effect of this so-called pairing energy is that a level will be depressed when it contains an even number of nucleons compared with its position when it contains an odd number. All this is borne out by experiment and it is further found that the effect increases with increasing orbital angular momentum. Thus if we look at the odd A nuclides with odd N above 58, these should all have angular momenta of $\frac{7}{2}$ or $\frac{11}{2}$. Instead they have angular momentum $\frac{1}{2}$, which shows that the $1g_{7/2}$ and $1h_{11/2}$ levels are depressed below the $3s_{1/2}$ level when they are filled by even numbers of nucleons.

The assumption that like nucleons outside closed shells pair off so as to cancel their angular momenta is really not at all self-evident. To prove it we should have to calculate the interaction energies of the nucleons outside closed shells and so discover which angular momentum state has the lowest energy. This has been done—at least approximately—and it has been found that the above assumption is correct except possibly when the $1d_{5/2}$, $1f_{7/2}$ and $1g_{9/2}$ levels are filled to the extent of three nucleons or three holes, and that in those cases the angular momenta might be $\frac{3}{2}$, $\frac{5}{2}$, $\frac{7}{2}$ instead of the expected $\frac{5}{2}$, $\frac{7}{2}$, $\frac{9}{2}$ (Kurath, 1953). The three exceptions to the assumption are just in those regions. They are $^{12}_{11}Na^{23}$ with angular momentum $\frac{3}{2}$ instead of $\frac{5}{2}$, $^{30}_{25}Mn^{55}$ with $\frac{5}{2}$ instead of $\frac{7}{2}$ and $^{45}_{34}Se^{79}$ with $\frac{7}{2}$ instead of $\frac{9}{2}$. In these three nuclides the total angular momentum is then due to the three nucleons outside the closed shell.

Little can be said about the odd-odd nuclides. Here the total angular momentum must be due to at least two particles, the last proton and the last neutron. The angular momenta of these can of course combine in many different ways, and exact calculations are required to decide which of these gives the most stable state. The parity of the nuclear wave function, on the other hand, can be predicted, since it is simply the product of the parities of the wave functions of the last two particles. Thus if the last two particles are in the same configuration, the nuclear parity is always even.

We next turn to the calculation of the magnetic moments of odd-A nuclides (even-even nuclides having zero angular momentum also have zero magnetic moment). If the magnetic moment of such a nucleus is due entirely to the magnetic moment of the last nucleon, then†

$$\mu = (g_l a_l + 2g_s a_s)\mathbf{j} \tag{5.47}$$

where $g_l = 1$ for a proton and 0 for a neutron ; $g_s = 2.79$ for a proton and -1.91 for a neutron. The coefficients $a_l j$ and $a_s j$ are the projections of $\mathbf{l}$ and $\mathbf{s}$ on $\mathbf{j}$, i.e.

$$\left. \begin{aligned} a_l &= \frac{\mathbf{l} \cdot \mathbf{j}}{\mathbf{j}^2} = \frac{j(j+1) + l(l+1) - s(s+1)}{2j(j+1)} \\ a_s &= \frac{\mathbf{s} \cdot \mathbf{j}}{\mathbf{j}^2} = \frac{j(j+1) + s(s+1) - l(l+1)}{2j(j+1)}. \end{aligned} \right\} \tag{5.48}$$

Now $s = \frac{1}{2}$ and, $l = j + \frac{1}{2}$ or $j - \frac{1}{2}$. If one of these is even, the other is odd and so l is a good quantum number, since the nucleus has a definite parity. Hence

$$\left. \begin{aligned} \mu &= (j - \tfrac{1}{2})g_l + g_s, & l &= j - \tfrac{1}{2} \\ \mu &= \frac{j}{j+1} \{(j + \tfrac{3}{2})g_l - g_s)\}, & l &= j + \tfrac{1}{2}. \end{aligned} \right\} \tag{5.49}$$

These values of μ are known as the Schmidt values and are plotted against J in Figs. 5.7 and 5.8. The agreement is clearly not good, although the experimental values follow the trend of the two theoretical lines, the " Schmidt lines ", and almost without exception lie between them. In general they are nearer to one line than to the other. If it is then assumed that in first approximation the experimental values would lie on the line to which they are nearer, it is possible to deduce the orbital angular momentum quantum number l of the last nucleon from the experimentally measured values of the total angular momentum j and magnetic moment μ of the nucleus.

It would be tempting to explain the fact that the experimental values of μ always lie between the two Schmidt values by saying that the nucleus is a mixture of states in which the last nucleon has $l = j - \frac{1}{2}$ and $j + \frac{1}{2}$. This, however, is impossible as these two states have opposite parity. The probably correct explanation will now be illustrated by means of an example.

The nucleus $_3^4\text{Li}^7$ consists of a closed 1s-shell and a partially filled $1p_{3/2}$ level, containing two neutrons and one proton. The total angular momentum is $J = \frac{3}{2}$. Now so far we have assumed

† The factor 2 in (5.47) arises from a comparison of equations (2.26) and (2.27).

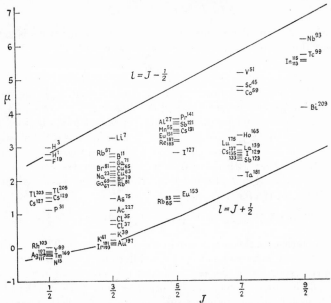

FIG. 5.7. NUCLEAR, MAGNETIC MOMENTS AND SCHMIDT LINES
FOR ODD-Z, EVEN-N NUCLIDES

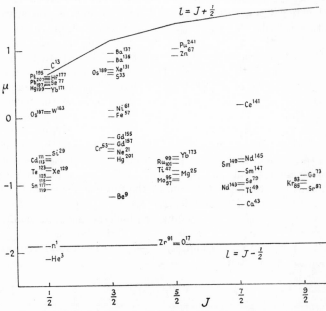

FIG. 5.8. NUCLEAR MAGNETIC MOMENTS AND SCHMIDT LINES
FOR ODD-N, EVEN-Z NUCLIDES

that the total angular momentum J_N of the two neutrons is zero, so that the wave function of the nucleus would be written

$$\Psi = \psi(1s)\psi_N(J_N = 0)\psi_P(j_P = \tfrac{3}{2}) \qquad (5.50)$$

where $\psi(1s)$ is the wave function of the closed s-shell, ψ_N is the wave function of the two p-neutrons and ψ_P that of the p-proton. However, the total angular momentum $J = \tfrac{3}{2}$ can also be obtained by vectorially adding $j_P = \tfrac{3}{2}$ and $J_N = 1$, 2 or 3 in the usual way. Actually the wave function with $J_N = 1$ or 3 has opposite symmetry properties to that with $J_N = 0$ or 2, and thus states with odd J_N and states with even J_N cannot mix. Hence the correct wave function will be of the form

$$\Psi = \psi(1s)\{\psi_N(J_N = 0) + \omega\psi_N(J_N = 2)\}\psi_P(j_P = \tfrac{3}{2}) \qquad (5.51)$$

where ω measures the admixture of the $J_N = 2$ state. The fact that for Li⁷ the magnetic moment does not differ much from the Schmidt value corresponding to $J_N = 0$ indicates that ω is small in this case.

We notice here a very important difference between the shell model predictions of angular momenta and of magnetic moments. Angular momenta are quantized, and predictions are therefore either right or wrong ; in general they are right. Now if the basic simplifying assumption of the shell model, that observable effects in odd-A nuclides are due to the last nucleon only, is not entirely correct, this will not affect the angular momentum values. It merely means that we are dealing with a mixture of states, as say in (5.51), with the same angular momentum. The situation is quite different for magnetic moments. These are not quantized, and so different mixtures of states yield different magnetic moments. That the magnetic moments as a rule do not lie on the Schmidt lines is proof that mixing of states occurs ; that on the whole they do not lie too far from them shows that the single particle state of the shell model is the most important of the states in the mixture.

The shell model also makes predictions about the electric quadrupole moment of an odd-A, odd-Z nuclide, on the assumption that this is due to the last proton in the nucleus. The quadrupole moment as measured is actually the greatest that is theoretically possible for a given j, i.e. it is the one for which the magnetic quantum number of the last proton $m_j = j$. For **l** and **s** parallel $(j = l + \tfrac{1}{2})$ this corresponds to $m_l = l$ and $m_s = +\tfrac{1}{2}$. Hence the proton wave function can be written

$$\psi = \frac{u(r)}{r} N_l P_l{}^l (\cos\theta) e^{1l\phi} \alpha \qquad (5.52)$$

where α is the spin wave function defined by (2.68) and N_l is a normalization factor, chosen so that

$$\int \mid N_l P_l{}^l (\cos\theta) e^{1l\phi} \mid^2 d\Omega = 1.$$

On substituting (5.52) into (2·42) we obtain

$$Q = \int (3z^2 - r^2) \mid \psi \mid^2 d\tau$$

$$= \int_0^\infty r^2 [u(r)]^2 dr \int N_l^2 (3\cos^2\theta - 1)[P_l{}^l(\cos\theta)]^2 d\Omega.$$

Now it is shown in books on Legendre functions that

$$(2l + 1)\cos\theta P_l{}^l(\cos\theta) = P_{l+1}^l(\cos\theta) \tag{5.53}$$

and

$$\int [P_n^m(\cos\theta)]^2 d\Omega = \frac{4\pi}{2n+1}\frac{(n+m)!}{(n-m)!} \tag{5.54}$$

i.e.

$$N_l^2 = \frac{2l+1}{4\pi(2l)!}.$$

Hence, after a little simplification,

$$Q = -\frac{2l}{2l+3}\bar{r}^2 = -\frac{2j-1}{2j+2}\bar{r}^2, \quad j = l + \tfrac{1}{2} \tag{5.55}$$

where

$$\bar{r}^2 = \int_0^\infty r^2[u(r)]^2 dr. \tag{5.56}$$

is the mean square radius of the orbit.

For **l** and **s** antiparallel, the derivation is more complicated. The proton wave function (5.52) was so simple, because in the " open " configuration $(j = l + \tfrac{1}{2})$ $m_j = j$ can only be due to $m_l = l$, $m_s = +\tfrac{1}{2}$. In the " closed " case $(j = l - \tfrac{1}{2})$ $m_j = j$ is due either to $m_l = l - 1$, $m_s = +\tfrac{1}{2}$ or to $m_l = l$, $m_s = -\tfrac{1}{2}$. The correct proton wave function is therefore a linear combination of the wave functions of these two states. We shall not develop this in detail, the result turns out to be identical with (5.55) for a given j, i.e.

$$Q = -\frac{2j-1}{2j+2}\bar{r}^2 = -\frac{2l-2}{2l+1}\bar{r}^2, \quad j = l - \tfrac{1}{2}. \tag{5.57}$$

It was pointed out after the discussion on magnetic moments that, for a given angular momentum, mixing of states led to different magnetic moments. The same is true of course of quadrupole moments, in fact these are even more sensitive to admixtures to the single particle states. Admixtures ought to be least for nuclides with one proton outside a closed shell or a proton hole in a closed shell. It follows at once from (5.55) and (5.57) that a nuclide with a proton outside a closed shell has a negative quadrupole moment and one with a proton hole a positive one. A few exceptions to this rule have been found, but in the majority of cases it is satisfied.

As regards magnitudes of quadrupole moments, we first make an estimate of $\bar{r}^2$. For a uniform charge distribution this is equal to $\frac{3}{5}R_u^2$, but for the least bound proton, which is more likely to be somewhere near the surface of the nucleus than near the centre, it will be somewhat larger. (5.55) then shows that the absolute value of the quadrupole moment should be of the order of, but rather less than R_u^2. This is found to be so for small A, but for $A > 150$ values as large as 10 R_u^2 occur. These deviations from the single particle model may well be due to mixing of states, but in general there are so many possible states that any detailed calculations become quite prohibitive.

A further puzzling feature is that the quadrupole moments of odd-A, odd-N nuclides are not significantly smaller than those of odd-A, odd-Z nuclides, as might be expected if the quadrupole moment is largely due to the odd nucleon. The rotation of the rest of the nucleus about the common centre of mass of it and the last neutron is certainly not sufficient to account for these comparatively large quadrupole moments, and we shall return to this point in the next section.

So far we have considered only the ground states of nuclei. Our next use of the shell model will be concerned with isomeric transitions, i.e. it will involve the lowest excited states. An isomer is a nucleus in an excited state which has a long lifetime against decay to the ground state with emission of a γ-ray. Isomeric transitions always involve large changes of angular momentum ($\triangle I \geqslant 3$), and it is this large change which leads to the long lifetime. Now it is found that with two exceptions all isomers are found in four distinct groups, the so-called " islands of isomerism," given by

(1) $19 \leqslant N$ or $Z \leqslant 27$

(2) $39 \leqslant N$ or $Z \leqslant 49$

(3) $63 \leqslant N$ or $Z \leqslant 81$

(4) $91 \leqslant N$ or Z.

The level scheme indicates that in these regions the following levels lie close together :

(1) the $1f_{7/2}$ and $2s_{1/2}$ levels

(2) the $1g_{9/2}$ and $2p_{1/2}$ levels

(3) the $1g_{7/2}$, $1h_{11/2}$ and $3s_{1/2}$, $2d_{3/2}$ levels

(4) the $1i_{13/2}$ and $3p_{1/2}$ levels.

Further there is no other region where two levels differing in angular momentum by 3 or more are close together. The explanation of the shell model of these islands of isomerism is, therefore, that in these regions and in these regions only does the lowest excited state have an angular momentum very different from that of the ground state.

All the predictions of the shell model we have discussed so far have been concerned with spins and moments. We lastly consider the question of energies of excited states. If we consider Fig. 5.5, then we would expect excited states to have configurations in which one or more nucleons had been raised to levels higher than those which they occupied in the ground state. However, because of the considerable degeneracies that occur in the level scheme, this mechanism is quite incapable of producing the very large number of excited states observed in the first few MeV of excitation in most nuclides. Also, the energies involved in single particle excitations are generally much larger than the excitation energies of the low-lying levels. There must therefore be other mechanisms involved in the excitation of nuclear systems.

If we neglect many-body forces, then the Hamiltonian of a system of A nucleons is given by

$$H = \sum_{i=1}^{A} T_i + \tfrac{1}{2} \sum_{i \neq j}^{A} V_{ij} \qquad (5.58)$$

where T_i is the kinetic energy of the ith particle and V_{ij} the potential energy between the ith and jth particles. Now the mutual two-body interaction will in part produce an average central potential V_i for each particle. Hence

$$H = \sum_i (T_i + V_i) + \tfrac{1}{2} \sum_{ij} v_{ij}, \qquad (5.59)$$

where v_{ij} denotes the residual two-body interaction. Note that the central potential need not be the same for all the particles, although it is generally taken to be so.

In the simple shell model, we assume that the whole of the interaction can be represented by a central potential, i.e. we take $v_{ij} = 0$ for all i,j. The success of the shell model indicates that the v_{ij} certainly ought to be small and that it may be possible to treat them as a perturbation. It should be clear from this discussion that this residual two-body potential is in no way the same as the free two-body potential, discussed in chapter 4, although it will have many of its characteristics.

Let us now consider a nuclide which has two nucleons outside closed proton and neutron shells, e.g. $^{50}_{22}\mathrm{Ti}^{50}$. It is reasonable to consider the residual interaction to be negligible in the closed shell configuration, corresponding to $^{28}_{20}\text{Ca}^{48}$, but the two protons outside this core will move not only in the central potential due to the core, but also in the potential due to a residual interaction between the two protons themselves. According to Fig. 5.5, these protons are both in $f_{7/2}$ levels, so that different angular momentum couplings of the two protons will give values $J = 0$ to $J = 7$ for the angular momentum of the nucleus as a whole. The odd values are not actually permitted, since they lead to totally symmetric wave functions for the two proton system. This is most easily seen for the " stretched " configuration $J = 7$, for which the magnetic quantum numbers would have to be be the same for both particles, which conflicts with the exclusion principle. There remain $J = 0^+$, 2^+, 4^+, 6^+. The positive parity is a consequence of having two like particles in the same orbital angular momentum state.

In the simple shell model picture all these states have exactly the same energy. However, if there is a residual interaction between the last two protons, then it may well remove this degeneracy, in which case we would expect to find low-lying excited states with even angular momentum and parity. This is indeed the case, in that the first three excited states of Ti^{50} are $2^+(1\cdot56 \text{ MeV})$ 4^+ $(2\cdot75 \text{ MeV})$ and 6^+ $(3\cdot2 \text{ MeV})$. The actual J-values and excitation energies of these levels will of course give information on the residual two-body interaction. It should be added that few nuclei have such pure spectra, and that, for instance, in Ca^{42} there is a 0^+ level at $1\cdot836$ MeV which cannot be accounted for by the above mechanism.

5.7 The Collective Model

We have seen that the shell model cannot account for the observed large quadrupole moments of certain nuclei, and a likely explanation of this fact is that these nuclei have permanent non-spherical shapes. The quadrupole moment would then be a co-operative phenomenon, i.e. it would be due to an aspherical distribution of the whole nuclear charge, instead of being due merely to the last proton. The development of this idea is due to Rainwater (1950) and to A. Bohr and Mottelson (1953).

The equilibrium shape of a nucleus is due to two opposing tendencies. On the one hand, the individual nucleons outside the closed shell core try to deform the latter and so move in a deformed field. (A similar effect can arise in another way. If there are two nucleons outside a closed shell core, then the second correlates its orbit to the shape of the field due to the core plus the first nucleon, which leads to an aligned coupling between the two nucleons.) On the other hand, the pairing forces couple two equivalent nucleons to a state of zero angular momentum, i.e. to a state of spherical symmetry. Thus, as we go away from closed shells, the tendency to deformation increases. At first this will not affect the spherical equilibrium shape in the ground state, but the core will tend to become more easily deformable, so that excited vibrational modes of the core become possible. If the frequency of such a mode is ω, then the corresponding energy is quantized in units of $\hbar\omega$. The energy quanta are called *phonons* in analogy with the quanta that arise in the mechanical vibrations of atoms in crystals. The more easily the core is deformed, the smaller the frequency of the vibration and hence the lower the corresponding energy levels of the excited states. Further, as the levels have energies that are multiples of $\hbar\omega$, they are evenly spaced. For nuclei, whose ground states are 0^+, the first excited state will then be 2^+ and the second 0^+, 2^+ or 4^+, since $l = 2$ deformations are the first to arise (see equation 5.38).

Eventually, with sufficient particles outside the closed shell, the spherical shape may become unstable even in the ground state. The nucleus then becomes ellipsoidal, and we have the additional possibility of rotational modes, in which the nucleus as a whole rotates about an axis which is not an axis of symmetry of the system. The energies of these modes tend to be lower than the corresponding vibrational ones. We shall show below that the lowest rotational states are 2^+, 4^+, 6^+, 8^+ with excitation energies in the ratio $3 : 10 : 21 : 42$. A set of such states is referred to as a *rotational band*.

We thus see that nuclear deformations should be reflected in the energy level schemes, as we move away from closed shells. At first, single particle excitations in a spherical well will be lowest, then the vibrational levels arise which are lower, and finally, half-way between shells, the rotational levels appear, which again are below the vibrational ones. All this is seen in Fig. 5.9.

As we move away on either side from the doubly-magic nucleus Pb^{208}, the level schemes are first due to single particle excitations (Pb^{206}, Po^{212}), then to vibrations ($Hg^{200}(?)$, Pt^{192}, Rn^{218}, Rn^{220}), then to rotations ($Os^{186} \rightarrow Sm^{152}$, $Ra^{224} \rightarrow Fm^{254}$) and finally again to vibrations (Sm^{150}). The transition from single particle excitations to vibrations is not clear-cut and it is quite probable that no level structure is either exclusively the one or the other. On the other hand, the point at which rotational excitations begin is astonishingly definite and the structure of spectra beyond this point really is purely rotational. Particularly good examples of rotational bands occur for Hf^{178}, U^{234}, Pu^{238}, Cm^{244}. The reason for only considering even-even nuclei is that their ground states are invariably 0^+. In other nuclei,

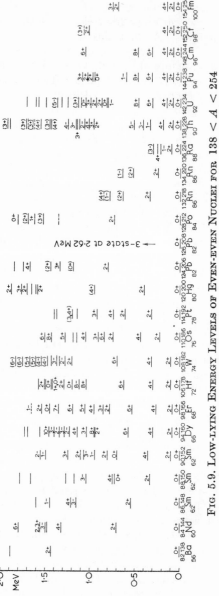

FIG. 5.9. LOW-LYING ENERGY LEVELS OF EVEN-EVEN NUCLEI FOR 138 < A < 254

[By kind permission of Professor A. Bohr]

the level schemes are more complicated, because of the angular momentum of the ground state.

It will be noticed that the nuclei $Os^{186} \to Sm^{152}$, $Ra^{224} \to Fm^{254}$ are just exactly in that region where odd-A nuclei have large quadrupole moments, i.e. in the region $150 < A < 190$, $224 < A$, although they themselves have of course zero quadrupole moment, since they have zero angular momentum. This is additional evidence that nuclei in this region are likely to be permanently deformed. The classical Hamiltonian for the rotation of such a system is

$$H = \tfrac{1}{2} \sum_{k=1}^{3} I_k \omega_k^2 \qquad (5.60)$$

where ω_1, ω_2, ω_3 are the angular velocity components along principal axes and I_1, I_2, I_3, are the principal moments of inertia. To translate this into quantum mechanics, we write it in terms of angular momenta,

$$H = \tfrac{1}{2}\hbar^2 \sum_k \frac{J_k^2}{I_k} \qquad (5.61)$$

where the $\hbar J_k$ are the components of the angular momentum operator. However, these are for axes fixed in the body, not in space, and so we do not as yet know how far they are constants of motion. We first investigate their commutation properties.

Using axes fixed in space, we can show that for any two position vectors $\mathbf{a}$, $\mathbf{b}$ (see example 5.8.9),

$$(\mathbf{J} \cdot \mathbf{a})(\mathbf{J} \cdot \mathbf{b}) - (\mathbf{J} \cdot \mathbf{b})(\mathbf{J} \cdot \mathbf{a}) = -i\mathbf{J} \cdot \mathbf{a} \times \mathbf{b}. \qquad (5.62)$$

Now put $\mathbf{a}$, $\mathbf{b}$ as unit vectors along body axes 1, 2. Then

$$J_1 J_2 - J_2 J_1 = -iJ_3, \text{ (cyclic)} \qquad (5.63)$$

i.e. the commutation relations for components in the body system are obtained from those in the space systems by taking complex conjugates. This does not affect eigenvalues. In particular, for the symmetric top ($I_1 = I_2 \neq I_3$), for which we have a preferred axis, J_3 is a constant of motion. Naturally, $\mathbf{J}^2$ and J_z are also constants of motion, so that we put

$$\mathbf{J}^2 = J(J+1), \quad J_z = M, \quad J_3 = K. \qquad (5.64)$$

(see Fig. 5.10.) Putting $I_1 = I_2 = I$ and substituting eigenvalues for operators in (5.61) to obtain the rotational energy, we have

$$H = \tfrac{1}{2}\hbar^2 \left\{ \frac{\mathbf{J}^2 - J_3^2}{I} + \frac{J_3^2}{I_3} \right\} \qquad (5.65)$$

and

$$E_{J,K} = \tfrac{1}{2}\hbar^2 \left\{ \frac{J(J+1) - K^2}{I} + \frac{K^2}{I_3} \right\}. \qquad (5.66)$$

Now even-even spherical nuclei, such as Pb²⁰⁸, do not show a rotational spectrum. Thus nuclear matter does not appear to rotate about a symmetry axis. If this is generally true for even-even nuclei, then we can put $K = 0$ in (5.66) and have

$$E_J = \frac{\hbar^2}{2I} J(J + 1). \tag{5.67}$$

This gives the experimental level scheme, provided only even

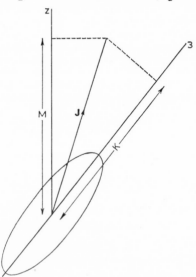

FIG. 5.10. CONSTANTS OF MOTION FOR DEFORMED NUCLEI

values of J are admissible, for we then have for the first three levels

$$E_2 : E_4 : E_6 = 3 : 10 : 21.$$

The absence of odd J-values can be shown to imply that the nuclear wave function has inversion symmetry about the (1, 2) plane.

It is finally possible to combine the shell and collective models by considering the nucleus as an assembly of nucleons in an aspherical central well, which itself rotates in space. This *unified model* (Nilsson, 1955; Gottfried, 1956) accounts for a remarkable range of nuclear properties.

5.8. EXAMPLES

5.8.1. Show that the lowest energy levels for a particle of mass M in a cubical and a spherical box of the same volume $\frac{4}{3}\pi R^3$ are $1 \cdot 9\hbar^2/MR^2$ and $5 \cdot 0\hbar^2/MR^2$ respectively. What is the reason for this very large difference?

5.8.2. Particles of spin $\frac{1}{2}$ move independently in a spherical box

$$V = 0, \quad r < R ; \quad V = + \infty, \quad r > R.$$

Show that the wave function inside the box of a particle of energy E and angular momentum l is

$$\psi_l = r^{-\frac{1}{2}} J_{l+\frac{1}{2}}(kr) P_l^m (\cos \theta) e^{im\phi} \tag{5.68}$$

where $k^2 = 2ME/\hbar^2$. By considering the zeros of $J_{l+\frac{1}{2}}(kR)$ for $kR < 9.5$, show that there are 92 particles in the box with energy less than

$$E_{\max} = 45\hbar^2/MR^2.$$

Show also that according to the approximation (5.5) there are 120 particles with energy less than $E_{\max}$, and that the maximum energy for 92 particles is $37.5 \, \hbar^2/MR^2$.

5.8.3. Use the semi-empirical mass formula to investigate the stability of U^{235} against emission of (a) a proton, (b) a neutron, (c) an α-particle. (The experimental result is that U^{235} emits α-particles of energy 4.56 MeV.)

5.8.4. Use the semi-empirical mass formula to investigate the stability against β-decay of the isobars $A = 64$. Compare your results with experiment

5.8.5. Show that

$$2\mathbf{l} \cdot \mathbf{s} = \begin{cases} l, & \text{if } j = l + \frac{1}{2}, \\ -(l+1), & \text{if } j = l - \frac{1}{2}. \end{cases} \tag{5.69}$$

[Hint : Use the fact that $2\mathbf{l} \cdot \mathbf{s} = \mathbf{j}^2 - \mathbf{l}^2 - \mathbf{s}^2$.]

5.8.6. Show that the nth energy level of angular momentum l in the infinite spherical well (5.43) is given by

$$E_{nl} = -V_0 + \frac{\hbar^2 w_{nl}^2}{2MR^2} \tag{5.70}$$

where w_{nl} is the nth zero of the equation $J_{l+\frac{1}{2}}(w) = 0$. In particular, show that for S-states

$$E_{n0} = -V_0 + \frac{n^2 \hbar^2 \pi^2}{2MR^2}. \tag{5.71}$$

5.8.7. Show that the nth energy level of an S-state in the finite spherical well (5.42) is given by

$$E_n = -V_0 + \frac{\hbar^2 x_n^2}{2MR^2} \tag{5.72}$$

where x_n is the nth root of the equation

$$x \cot x = -\left(\frac{2MR^2}{\hbar^2} V_0 - x^2\right)^{1/2}. \tag{5.73}$$

Evaluate the energies of the first three S-levels, when $V_0 = 42$ MeV, $R = 7$f, and compare this with the corresponding energies for the infinite well. (See example 5.8.6.)

5.8.8. Calculate the magnetic moments of H^3, He^3, N^{15}, O^{17}, K^{39}, Pb^{207}, Bi^{209}, using (5.49), and compare with experiment. Why would one expect agreement to be close in these cases?

5.8.9. If $\mathbf{j} = \mathbf{l} + \mathbf{s}$, show that

$$[\mathbf{j}_x, y] = iz \text{ (cyclic)}$$

and hence that for any position vectors $\mathbf{a}(a_x, a_y, a_z)$, $\mathbf{b}(b_x, b_y, b_z)$

$$(\mathbf{j} \cdot \mathbf{a})(\mathbf{j} \cdot \mathbf{b}) - (\mathbf{j} \cdot \mathbf{b})(\mathbf{j} \cdot \mathbf{a}) = -i \, \mathbf{j} \cdot \mathbf{a} \times \mathbf{b}$$

[Hint : Use $\mathbf{l} = -i\hbar \mathbf{r} \times \nabla$ and the fact that $\mathbf{r}$ and $\mathbf{s}$ commute.]

CHAPTER 6

Nuclear Reactions

6.1 Introduction

THE idea of a nuclear reaction was outlined briefly in section 1.5. It is the purpose of the present chapter to attempt to build up a theoretical foundation of this subject. As a nuclear reaction is a many-body problem, it will of course be necessary to make some simplifying assumptions, and the experimental verification of these assumptions will in itself give interesting information about the properties of nuclei.

It was stated in section 1.5 that a nuclear reaction $X(x, y)Y$ is not determined by the nature of the bombarding particle x and the target nucleus X ; but that on the other hand to a given X and x there correspond a whole series of residual nuclei Y and emitted particles y. As we shall have to distinguish not only between different residual nuclei, but also between different quantum states of the same residual nuclei, it will be convenient to denote each quantum state of each residual nucleus by a different letter. Thus for instance if the process is one of inelastic scattering, then Y is the same nucleus as X, but in an excited state, and y the same particle as x, but of lower energy. Any such possible pair, denoted by (B, b), (C, c) . . ., will be called a reaction channel and as such be denoted by the corresponding Greek letter $\beta, \gamma, \ldots$ The channel α is called the entrance channel. From this it is clear that to each channel there corresponds a definite total energy $E = E_\alpha$. The idea of channels has been taken over from waveguide junctions. In the same way as a wave entering a junction through one channel will leave through all the channels of the junction in a way determined by the channels, so a nucleus X bombarded by a particle x forms the residual nuclei and emitted particles (B, b), (C, c), . . . in definite proportions depending on their probabilities of creation. A special case which in many ways is different from all others is that of elastic scattering, in which the reaction channel coincides with the entrance channel, corresponding to that part of the wave in the waveguide which is reflected back by the junction into the entrance channel.

Before discussing particular nuclear reactions, we shall in the next two sections derive some general results about scattering and reaction cross-sections. Here " scattering " will refer to elastic scattering only. Inelastic scattering is included among the nuclear reactions proper. The nuclear reactions treated in the following sections will in general be reactions which are initiated by neutrons of orbital angular momentum $l = 0$. This will enable us to show all the important features of the theory without encumbering ourselves with rather heavy mathematics. The form in which the theory is presented is due largely to Feshbach and Weisskopf (1947) and (1949).

6.2 Maximum Cross-sections

We consider in a way similar to section 3.3 the scattering of a stream of particles by a centre of force, but now include the possibility that part of the incident beam reacts with the centre of force instead of being scattered elastically. The proof leading up to (3.43), which shows that the total cross-section is equal to the sum of the partial cross-sections of given angular momentum l, is just as valid in the present case, as it depends only on the properties of the Legendre polynomials. We therefore need consider only partial cross-sections with given l.

The incident wave is given by (3.29) and (3.31), i.e.

$$\psi_{\text{inc}}^l \sim (kr)^{-1} i^l (2l + 1) \sin (kr - \tfrac{1}{2} l\pi) P_l (\cos \theta) \qquad (6.1)$$

where $k = Mv/\hbar$. Here M is the reduced mass of the particle in the entrance channel, $M = M_x M_X / (M_x + M_X)$, and v is the relative velocity of the incident particles. The scattered wave is of the form (3.37)

$$\psi_{\text{sc}}^l \sim r^{-1} C_l \, \mathrm{e}^{\mathrm{i}kr} P_l (\cos \theta). \qquad (6.2)$$

Hence the elastic scattering cross-section is

$$\sigma_{\text{sc}}^l = 2\pi \int_0^\pi | \, C_l \, |^2 [P_l (\cos \theta)]^2 \sin \theta \mathrm{d}\theta = \frac{4\pi}{2l + 1} | \, C_l \, |^2. \qquad (6.3)$$

The reaction cross-section, which includes the inelastic scattering cross-section, is equal to the number of particles taken out of the beam per unit incident particle, i.e.

$$\sigma_{\text{re}}^l = \frac{\text{Number of particles taken out of beam per second}}{\text{Number of incident particles per square centimetre per second.}} \qquad (6.4)$$

The denominator of this expression is just the incident velocity v. The numerator is the net inward radial flux $\mathcal{N}$ over a large sphere of radius R_0. This is equal to the integral of the probability current density $(\hbar/2im)[\psi^* \, \text{grad} \, \psi - (\text{grad} \, \psi^*)\psi]$ over the surface of the sphere, i.e.

$$\mathcal{N} = -\frac{\mathrm{i}\hbar}{2M} \int \left(\psi^* \frac{\partial \psi}{\partial r} - \frac{\partial \psi^*}{\partial r} \psi \right) \mathrm{d}S. \qquad (6.5)$$

Substituting $\psi = \psi_{\text{inc}}^l + \psi_{\text{sc}}^l$, we obtain after a little simplification

$$\sigma_{\text{re}}^l = \frac{4\pi}{2l+1}\left\{\frac{\text{i}}{2k}(2l+1)(C_l^* - C_l) - |C_l|^2\right\}. \qquad (6.6)$$

It is easily verified that this vanishes when C_l is given by (3.39) with η_l real. The combined scattering and reaction cross-section is obtained from (6.3) and (6.6) and is

$$\sigma^l = \sigma_{\text{sc}}^l + \sigma_{\text{re}}^l = \frac{2\pi i}{k}(C_l^* - C_l). \qquad (6.7)$$

We can now establish certain inequalities. Since

$$|C_l|^2 > \tfrac{1}{4}|C_l^* - C_l|^2$$

it follows that

$$\sigma_{\text{sc}}^l > \frac{\pi}{2l+1}|C_l^* - C_l|^2 = \frac{(\sigma^l)^2}{\sigma_{\text{sc,max}}^l} \qquad (6.8)$$

where

$$\sigma_{\text{sc,max}}^l = \frac{4\pi}{k^2}(2l+1) \qquad (6.9)$$

is the maximum possible scattering cross-section [see (3.43)]. Also

$$\sigma_{\text{re}}^l = \sigma^l - \sigma_{\text{sc}}^l$$
$$< \sigma^l - \frac{(\sigma^l)^2}{\sigma_{\text{sc,max}}^l}$$
$$< \tfrac{1}{4}\sigma_{\text{sc,max}}^l \qquad (6.10)$$

since the right-hand side is largest for $\sigma^l = \tfrac{1}{2}\sigma_{\text{sc,max}}^l$. Hence

$$\sigma_{\text{re}}^l < \frac{\pi}{k^2}(2l+1) \qquad (6.11)$$

and when σ_{re}^l has its maximum value, then $\sigma_{\text{re}}^l = \sigma_{\text{sc}}^l$. Lastly, although it is possible to have a finite scattering cross-section and zero reaction cross-section, it follows from (6.8) that it is not possible to have a finite reaction cross-section and zero scattering cross-section. In other words, all nuclear reactions are accompanied by some elastic scattering.

Another way of looking at this problem is to consider the scattering phase η_l. For elastic scattering we know that η_l is real, but if there is a finite reaction cross-section then the elastically scattered wave is attenuated and such an attenuation is achieved by making η_l complex. If we put $\eta_l = \lambda_l + i\mu_l$ we obtain from (3.39)

$$C_l = \frac{1}{2ik}(2l+1)(e^{2i\lambda_l}e^{-2\mu_l} - 1), \qquad (6.12)$$

with a corresponding modification in the elastic scattering amplitude $f(\theta)$. [See (3.41).]

Hence from (6.3), (6.6) and (6.7),

$$\sigma_{\text{sc}}^l = \frac{2\pi}{k^2}(2l+1)e^{-2\mu_l}(\cosh 2\mu_l - \cos 2\lambda_l) \qquad (6.13)$$

$$\sigma_{\text{re}}^l = \frac{2\pi}{k^2}(2l+1)e^{-2\mu_l}\sinh 2\mu_l \qquad (6.14)$$

$$\sigma^l = \frac{2\pi}{k^2}(2l+1)(1-e^{-2\mu_l}\cos 2\lambda_l). \qquad (6.15)$$

The inequalities proved above follow at once. Thus σ_{sc}^l is greatest when $\lambda_l = \tfrac{1}{2}\pi$, $\mu_l = 0$ and σ_{re}^l is greatest when $\mu_l = \infty$. As cross-sections are always positive, (6.14) shows that $\mu_l \geqslant 0$.

An important application of the above is the scattering of very high energy particles by a perfectly absorbing sphere of radius R. In this case we need only consider the first l partial cross-sections, where $l < kR$; i.e. $\lambda_l = 0$ for $l > kR$ [see (3.44)]. This result which in general is only approximately true becomes exact as $k \to \infty$. Now for a perfectly absorbing sphere we clearly have in the same way $\mu_l = \infty$ for $l < kR$ and $\mu_l = 0$ for $l > kR$. Hence

$$\left.\begin{aligned}
\sigma_{\text{sc}} &= \sum_{l=0}^{kR}\sigma_{\text{sc}}^l = \frac{\pi}{k^2}\sum_{l=0}^{kR}(2l+1) = \pi R^2 \\
\sigma_{\text{re}} &= \sum_{l=0}^{kR}\sigma_{\text{re}}^l = \frac{\pi}{k^2}\sum_{l=0}^{kR}(2l+1) = \pi R^2 \\
\sigma &= \sigma_{\text{sc}} + \sigma_{\text{re}} = 2\pi R^2 = 2 \times \text{geometrical cross-section.}
\end{aligned}\right\} \qquad (6.17)$$

But for particles of very high energy we would expect the cross-section to be geometrical, since their wavelength is much less than the radius of the scattering sphere, i.e. we would expect $\sigma_{\text{re}} = \pi R^2$, $\sigma_{\text{sc}} = 0$. The above paradoxical result is due to the fact that even at very high energies the scattering is still not purely classical. There is always a wave mechanical diffraction scattering, which is elastic, into the shadow behind the obstacle and at high energies the cross-section σ_{sc} for this is just πR^2.

6.3 Inverse Processes

An interesting problem of a very general nature concerns the relationship between the total cross-section $\sigma(\alpha \to \beta)$ of the reaction with entrance channel α and reaction channel β, and the total cross-section $\sigma(\beta \to \alpha)$ of the inverse reaction.

We imagine the particles X, B, x and b to occur in arbitrary numbers in a large box of volume Ω. The reactions $X + x \rightleftarrows B + b$ both take place. Then it is a fundamental theorem of statistical mechanics known as the principle of overall balance, that when the system is in dynamical equilibrium all energetically permissible states are occupied with equal probability. We are interested in two particular states, the reaction channels α and β. The theorem is then equivalent to stating that the number of channels in the box is proportional to the number of possible channels in the box in a given energy range. Now this latter is [see (5.6)]

$$N_\alpha = \frac{p_\alpha^2 \Omega \mathrm{d}p_\alpha}{2\pi^2\hbar^3} = \frac{p_\alpha^2 \Omega \mathrm{d}E}{2\pi^2\hbar^3 v_\alpha} \tag{6.18}$$

since $v\mathrm{d}p = \mathrm{d}E$. Similarly for N_β.† The energy range for the two channels must of course be the same. Hence

$$\frac{\text{No. of channels } \alpha \text{ in the box}}{\text{No. of channels } \beta \text{ in the box}} = \frac{N_\alpha}{N_\beta} = \frac{p_\alpha^2 v_\beta}{p_\beta^2 v_\alpha}. \tag{6.19}$$

If the number of transitions $\alpha \to \beta$ per sec is equal to the number of transitions $\beta \to \alpha$ per sec, then the system is certainly in dynamical equilibrium. Though this condition is not necessary, it usually holds.‡ It is known as the principle of detailed balance. Further,

No. of transitions $\alpha \to \beta$ per sec

$$= \text{no. of channels } \alpha \text{ in box} \times w(\alpha \to \beta) \quad (6.20)$$

where $w(\alpha \to \beta)$ is the transition probability for the reaction $\alpha \to \beta$. Hence

$$p_\alpha^2 v_\beta w(\alpha \to \beta) = p_\beta^2 v_\alpha w(\beta \to \alpha). \tag{6.21}$$

Lastly we have to find a relationship between the transition probability $w(\alpha \to \beta)$ and the cross-section $\sigma(\alpha \to \beta)$. The transition probability measures the chance that one particle moving with velocity v in volume Ω is scattered per second. In other words the flux of the incident beam is v/Ω per unit area and time. But the cross-section σ corresponds to unit incident flux. Hence

$$\sigma = \frac{\Omega w}{v}. \tag{6.22}$$

Combining (6.21) and (6.22) and putting $k = p/\hbar$, we have finally

$$k_\alpha^2 \sigma(\alpha \to \beta) = k_\beta^2 \sigma(\beta \to \alpha). \tag{6.23}$$

This is the required relationship.

---

† At present we assume the particles to have zero intrinsic angular momenta. Hence the expression (6.18) is only half of (5.6), where we had to take account of two possible spin directions. The general case of arbitrary intrinsic angular momenta is treated below.

‡ If for instance there are just three different channels in the box, α, β and γ, then dynamical equilibrium could be maintained by a cycle $\alpha \to \beta \to \gamma \to \alpha$, without any reactions in the opposite direction taking place at all. The principle of detailed balance is thus a hypothesis to be tested against experiment, and it is not by any means an obvious hypothesis.

So far we have assumed zero intrinsic angular momenta for the particles. If the intrinsic angular momentum of any one of the particles is I, then the corresponding density of states (6.18) must be multiplied by $2I + 1$. This leads to the more general formula

$$(2I_x + 1)(2I_x + 1)k_\alpha^2\sigma(\alpha \to \beta) = (2I_B + 1)(2I_b + 1)k_\beta^2\sigma(\beta \to \alpha).$$
(6.24)

In this formula the cross-sections have been averaged over initial and summed over final intrinsic angular momentum states. This is what is usually done experimentally, since incident beams are generally unpolarized and scattered beams cannot be analysed for different intrinsic angular momenta. If, however, the initial and final states have definite angular momenta, then (6.23) must be employed.

6.4 The Compound Nucleus

It was pointed out by N. Bohr (1936) that it is possible to divide a nuclear reaction into two stages, the capture of the incident particle by the target nucleus to form a compound nucleus, and the subsequent decay of the compound nucleus. Thus a nuclear reaction is described schematically by

$$x + X \to C \to B + b.$$
(6.25)

The reason for the formation of an intermediate state C lies in the strong interaction between the incident particle and the nucleons of the target. In consequence of this Bohr postulated that the energy of the incident particle is rapidly shared between all the nucleons of the system and it is not until sufficient energy is again concentrated on one nucleon that the compound nucleus can decay with the emission of that nucleon. This is likely to take a considerable time on a nuclear time-scale, the characteristic time of a nucleus being the time which it takes for a nucleon to travel across the nucleus, and this is of the order of 10^{-12} cm$/10^9$ cm sec$^{-1} = 10^{-21}$ sec. Thus the compound nucleus will have "forgotten" how it was formed by the time it decays. This then is Bohr's assumption—that the decay of the compound nucleus depends only on its energy, angular momentum and parity, but not on its particular mode of formation. We shall therefore treat the formation and the disintegration of the compound nucleus as completely independent processes.

The independence of the processes of formation and decay can be demonstrated experimentally in suitable situations. Ghoshal (1950) investigated the compound nucleus Zn^{64}, which can be formed in two ways

$$Ni^{60} + \alpha \to Zn^{64}, \quad Cu^{63} + p \to Zn^{64}.$$

Because of the energy difference between the Ni^{60} and Cu^{63} nuclei, it is necessary that the energy of the α-particle should exceed that of the proton by 7 MeV. When this is done the compound nucleus is formed in the same state of excitation in each case. It is then found to decay through the following three channels

$$Zn^{64} \rightarrow Zn^{63} + n$$
$$Zn^{62} + 2n$$
$$Cu^{62} + p + n$$

and according to the independence hypothesis the ratios of the cross-sections for these decays should be independent of the mode of formation. This was verified for proton energies from 3 to 33 MeV.

The picture of a nucleus outlined here is very different from that described by the shell model theory. On a crude individual particle picture we would expect the incident particle to occupy one of the free orbits of energy higher than those occupied by the nucleons of the target nucleus and not to interact with them at all because of the exclusion principle. This is of course too simple a picture, but the idea that an incident nucleon at once strongly interacts with all the target nucleons and thus shares its energy with them is at the opposite extreme to the shell model theory in its assumptions. We shall return to this difficulty later.

It is now possible to write the cross-section for a nuclear reaction as

$$\sigma(\alpha \rightarrow \beta) = \sigma_c(\alpha)G_c(\beta) \qquad (6.26)$$

where $\sigma_c(\alpha)$ is the cross-section for formation of C through channel α and $G_c(\beta)$ is the probability that C will decay through channel β. For the sake of simplicity we shall neglect the dependence of $G_c(\beta)$ on angular momentum and parity. It can be shown that this does not lead to any important errors (Blatt and Weisskopf, *Theoretical Nuclear Physics*, Chapter VIII, section 10). $G_c(\beta)$ then only depends on the excitation energy of the compound nucleus E_c. This energy cannot be a sharply defined quantity, as, because of the Heisenberg uncertainty principle, only stationary states can have sharp energies. The uncertainty in E_c is measured by a quantity $\Gamma_\beta(E_c)$ which, because of the uncertainty principle, must be inversely proportional to the decay time of the compound nucleus through channel β, $\tau_\beta(E_c)$. It is therefore defined by the equation

$$\Gamma_\beta(E_c)\tau_\beta(E_c) = \hbar. \qquad (6.27)$$

The quantity $\Gamma/\hbar$ is thus a decay probability. If the total decay probability of the compound nucleus is $\Gamma(E_c)/\hbar$, then clearly

$$\Gamma(E_c) = \sum_\beta \Gamma_\beta(E_c). \qquad (6.28)$$

Further, as $G_c(\beta)$ is the probability that the compound nucleus decays through channel β,

$$G_c(\beta) = \frac{\Gamma_\beta(E_c)}{\Gamma(E_c)}. \tag{6.29}$$

If now (6.26) and (6.29) are substituted into (6.23), we obtain

$$\frac{k_\alpha^2 \sigma_c(\alpha) \Gamma_\beta(E_c)}{\Gamma(E_c)} = \frac{k_\beta^2 \sigma_c(\beta) \Gamma_\alpha(E_c)}{\Gamma(E_c)}$$

or, on rearranging,

$$\frac{k_\alpha^2 \sigma_c(\alpha)}{\Gamma_\alpha(E_c)} = \frac{k_\beta^2 \sigma_c(\beta)}{\Gamma_\beta(E_c)} = U(E_c) \tag{6.30}$$

where $U(E_c)$ is a function depending only on the energy of the compound nucleus, but not on the particular channel used. On combining (6.29) and (6.30) we can write the probability of decay through channel β,

$$G_c(\beta) = \frac{k_\beta^2 \sigma_c(\beta)}{\displaystyle\sum_\gamma k_\gamma^2 \sigma_c(\gamma)}. \tag{6.31}$$

It is therefore possible to derive the decay probability through a given channel of the compound nucleus C, once the formation cross-section for formation of C through all possible channels is known.

6.5 Nucleus with a Well-defined Surface

To obtain a more quantitative formulation of the problem of nuclear reactions, we now make the further assumption that the target nucleus has a well-defined surface of radius R_X. This is quite a fair assumption when the wavelength of the incident particle is long compared with nuclear dimensions, as is the case at low energies. Then no interaction takes place between the incident particle, which we shall take to be a $l = 0$ neutron, and the target nucleus, if their distance apart is greater than R_X. To avoid complications that arise from the fact that the incident nucleon has an intrinsic spin $\frac{1}{2}$, we shall assume that the target nucleus has zero total angular momentum.

We can now see why it is such a simplification to consider only $l = 0$ neutrons as incident particles. As they are uncharged, they are not subject to the Coulomb potential $Z_x Z_X e^2/r_{xX}$, and as they have no orbital angular momentum, they are not subject to the "centrifugal" potential $l(l + 1)\hbar^2/2M r_{xX}^2$. In consequence their radial wave function $u(r)$ satisfies, for $r > R_X$, the very simple equation [see (3.46)]

$$\frac{\mathrm{d}^2 u}{\mathrm{d}r^2} + k^2 u = 0, \, r > R_\mathrm{X} \tag{6.32}$$

so that

$$u(r) = C \sin(kr + \eta_0), \, r > R_\mathrm{X}. \tag{6.33}$$

The function is completely determined by the boundary conditions on the surface, and these are therefore sufficient to determine the phase shift η_0. Now the boundary condition consists of the continuity of the logarithmic derivative of $u(r)$ across the boundary, i.e.

$$f(r) = \frac{R_\mathrm{X}}{u} \frac{\mathrm{d}u}{\mathrm{d}r} \tag{6.34}$$

must be continuous near $r = R_\mathrm{X}$. Substituting (6.33) into (6.34) we have

$$f(R_\mathrm{X}) = kR_\mathrm{X} \cot(kR_\mathrm{X} + \eta_0) \tag{6.35}$$

where in future we shall write f for $f(R_\mathrm{X})$. Clearly η_0 is real if f is real and conversely, so that a real f corresponds to pure scattering. Now (6.35) can be rearranged to read

$$e^{2i\eta_0} = \frac{f + ikR_\mathrm{X}}{f - ikR_\mathrm{X}} e^{-2ikR_\mathrm{X}} \tag{6.36}$$

which, using (3.39), leads to a scattering amplitude

$$\begin{aligned} C_0 &= \frac{1}{2ik}\left(\frac{f + ikR_\mathrm{X}}{f - ikR_\mathrm{X}} e^{-2ikR_\mathrm{X}} - 1\right) \\ &= -\frac{1}{2ik} e^{-2ikR_\mathrm{X}}\left(\frac{-2ikR_\mathrm{X}}{f - ikR_\mathrm{X}} + e^{2ikR_\mathrm{X}} - 1\right) \end{aligned} \tag{6.37}$$

Hence

$$\sigma_\mathrm{sc}^0 = \frac{\pi}{k^2} | C_\mathrm{0I} + C_\mathrm{0S} |^2 \tag{6.38}$$

where

$$C_\mathrm{0I} = \frac{-2ikR_\mathrm{X}}{f - ikR_\mathrm{X}}, \quad C_\mathrm{0S} = e^{2ikR_\mathrm{X}} - 1. \tag{6.39}$$

The reason for splitting up the scattering amplitude is that for hard sphere scattering, the wave function $u(r)$ must vanish on the nuclear surface, so that $f = \infty$ in that case. For hard sphere scattering the cross-section is therefore given entirely by C_0S. The additional amplitude C_0I, which depends on the internal structure of the nucleus, measures the departure from hard sphere scattering.

The reaction cross-section is obtained from (6.6). This yields

$$\sigma_\mathrm{re}^0 = \frac{\pi}{k^2} \frac{-4kR_\mathrm{X}\mathrm{Im}f}{(\mathrm{Re}f)^2 + (\mathrm{Im}f - kR_\mathrm{X})^2}. \tag{6.40}$$

As $\sigma_{r_0}^0 \geqslant 0$, we must have

$$\mathrm{Im} f \leqslant 0.$$

6.6 Resonance Scattering

We now proceed to investigate the interaction of neutrons with nuclei at various energies, starting with the lowest. At energies below the lowest excitation energy of the compound nucleus the only decay channel that can be open is the entrance channel. There can then be no energy loss and the only reaction possible is elastic scattering. Further, since the incident energy is very low, only $l = 0$ neutrons will be affected by the nucleus [see (3.44)]. In this section therefore, the restriction to $l = 0$ neutrons is a real one, imposed by the physical conditions.

We require the wave function of the neutron when inside channel α, i.e. for $r < R_{\mathrm{X}}$. Inside the nucleus the neutron interacts of course with all the nucleons of the nucleus, and so its behaviour cannot be described by means of a one-particle wave function. However, we can consider the wave function roughly to consist of an ingoing and an outgoing wave of equal intensity and wave number, the two being out of phase with each other. The wave number K is connected with the kinetic energy T^α of the neutron in channel α through

$$T_\alpha = \frac{\hbar^2 K^2}{2M}. \tag{6.41}$$

Now as the neutron enters the nucleus, it will occupy the lowest available energy level. According to section 5.2 its kinetic energy there is about 33 MeV. Compared with this energy the incident energy of the neutron—that is, the kinetic energy outside the nucleus—is quite negligible, so that we can put $T_\alpha \simeq 33$ MeV. This gives $K \simeq 1 \cdot 3 \, \mathrm{fm}^{-1}$.

The wave function in channel α is then

$$u(r) = \mathrm{e}^{-\mathrm{i}Kr} + \mathrm{e}^{\mathrm{i}(Kr + 2\zeta)}, \; r < R_{\mathrm{X}} \tag{6.42}$$

where ζ is real. The boundary condition at $r = R_{\mathrm{X}}$ gives

$$f = -KR_{\mathrm{X}} \tan (KR_{\mathrm{X}} + \zeta). \tag{6.43}$$

We shall show in section 7.3 that $\mathrm{d}f/\mathrm{d}E \leqslant 0$ always, where E is the incident energy. Then it follows at once that the quantity $z(E) = KR_{\mathrm{X}} + \zeta$ is a monotonically increasing function of the incident energy E. Hence f as a function of E passes through successive zeros and infinities for increasing E. We define the so-called resonance energies E_n by

$$f(E_n) = 0, \quad n = 0, 1, \ldots \tag{6.44}$$

corresponding to $z = n\pi$.

In the neighbourhood of any particular resonance we can expand $f(E)$ and obtain

$$f(E) = (E - E_n)\left(\frac{\mathrm{d}f}{\mathrm{d}E}\right)_{E=E_n} + \ldots, \quad E \simeq E_n. \tag{6.45}$$

We now introduce the quantity

$$\Gamma_n = -\frac{2kR_\mathrm{X}}{(\mathrm{d}f/\mathrm{d}E)_{E=E_n}} \tag{6.46}$$

which is positive, since $\mathrm{d}f/\mathrm{d}E \leqslant 0$, and substitute (6.45) into (6.39). This gives the resonance amplitude

$$C_{0\mathrm{I}} = \frac{i\Gamma_n}{(E - E_n) + \frac{1}{2}i\Gamma_n}, \quad E \simeq E_n. \tag{6.47}$$

This expression has the form typical of a resonance in a damped forced oscillation. Near resonance, when $E \simeq E_n$,

$$C_{0\mathrm{I}} = 2. \tag{6.48}$$

On the other hand

$$C_{0\mathrm{S}} = e^{2ikR_\mathrm{X}} - 1 \simeq 2ikR_\mathrm{X} \tag{6.49}$$

since $kR_\mathrm{X} \ll 1$, i.e. near resonance $|C_{0\mathrm{I}}| \gg |C_{0\mathrm{S}}|$. Thus near resonance the hard sphere scattering is negligible compared with the internal structure scattering, which in this connection is termed resonance scattering. The reason why we termed the energies E_n resonance energies is now quite clear. The width of the resonance is measured by Γ_n. This is identical with the uncertainty in the energy level, which was denoted by Γ_β in (6.27).

At a distance from a resonance, $f(E)$ increases until at some point between two resonances it becomes infinite. At that point the scattering is then purely hard sphere scattering. On substituting the values of $C_{0\mathrm{I}}$ and $C_{0\mathrm{S}}$ into (6.38), we thus have

$$\sigma_\mathrm{sc}^0 = \begin{cases} 4\pi/k^2 & \text{near resonance} \\ 4\pi R_\mathrm{X}^2 & \text{far from resonance.} \end{cases} \tag{6.50}$$

Further, between these extremes $C_{0\mathrm{I}}$ and $C_{0\mathrm{S}}$ are purely imaginary and have the same sign (if Γ_n is neglected compared to $E - E_n$ and $kR_\mathrm{X} \ll 1$) when $E_n < E$ and the opposite sign when $E_n > E$. Hence the amplitudes interfere constructively for $E_n < E$ and destructively for $E_n > E$. The general picture is shown in Fig. 6.1. Thus the elastic scattering cross-section at low energies shows pronounced resonances.

The assumption made in the derivation of the resonance picture can now be seen. It is that the resonance widths Γ_n are very much smaller than the distances between the resonance levels. At higher energies, when the level spacing decreases, the resonances overlap and become less and less distinct.

We shall now try to describe these resonances in more physical terms. The incident neutron wave outside the nucleus is of the form

$$A \cos (kr + \delta)$$

where k is the wave number outside the nucleus. This wave must be joined to the wave function (6.42) inside the nucleus which can be written

$$B \cos (Kr + \zeta). \tag{6.51}$$

As we have assumed the nuclear boundary to be sharp this means that the magnitudes of the two waves and their gradients must be

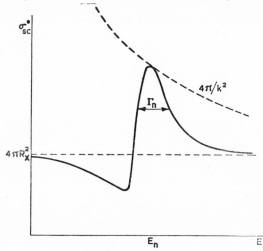

FIG. 6.1. TYPICAL ELASTIC SCATTERING CROSS-SECTION FOR $l = 0$ NEUTRONS NEAR RESONANCE

the same on the nuclear boundary. In general this means that if $k \ll K$, as is the case here, then $A \gg B$. This is easily seen from the matching conditions

$$A \cos (kR_X + \delta) = B \cos (KR_X + \zeta)$$
$$Ak \sin (kR_X + \delta) = BK \sin (KR_X + \zeta) \tag{6.52}$$

which lead to

$$A^2k^2 = B^2\{K^2 \sin^2(KR_X + \zeta) + k^2 \cos^2(KR_X + \zeta)\}. \tag{6.53}$$

Unless $\sin (KR_X + \zeta) = 0$, the second term in the bracket is much smaller than the first, and so if $k \ll K$, then $A \gg B$. The exception occurs when $\sin (KR_X + \zeta) = 0$, in which case clearly $A \simeq B$.

Physically this means that the incident wave has in general a much larger amplitude than the transmitted wave, and that in fact the nuclear boundary acts as an almost perfect reflector. The exception occurs when the matching takes place near maximum amplitude, when nearly the whole of the incident energy is transmitted into the nucleus. Only then is it at all probable for the compound nucleus to be formed. It is then that resonance scattering occurs.

The converse occurs when the compound nucleus decays. A barrier which is a good reflector from one side is a good transmitter from the other and vice versa. Once the compound nucleus has been formed at a resonance energy therefore, the sudden potential jump at the nuclear boundary tends to prevent its decay. As the compound nucleus has therefore a much greater degree of stability at the resonance energies than at energies between the resonance energies, we can speak of almost stable energy levels embedded in the continuum of free states. These levels are also called virtual levels. They are not completely stable, as the compound nucleus will of course decay eventually. As was shown in section 6.4, this leads to an uncertainty $\Gamma(E_c)$ in the energy of the compound nucleus. The quantity $\Gamma(E_c)$ therefore gives the width of the almost stable energy level.

So far we have assumed that all channels except the entrance channel are closed. At slightly higher incident energies there will be a small probability that the system decays through a second channel, β, i.e. there will be a small reaction cross-section. Usually this will take the form of radiative capture, in which the target nucleus captures the incident neutron and is left in an excited state from which it decays to the ground state with the emission of a photon. The wave function (6.42) in the entrance channel must then be of the form

$$u(r) = e^{-iKr} + e^{i(Kr + 2\zeta + 2iq)} \tag{6.54}$$

where we shall assume that q is small. Hence

$$f = -KR_X \tan(KR_X + \zeta + iq). \tag{6.55}$$

We again expand $f(E, q)$ which is now a function of E and q, this time about the value $f(E_n, 0)$,

$$f(E, q) = (E - E_n)\left(\frac{\partial f}{\partial E}\right)_{E = E_n, q = 0} + q\left(\frac{\partial f}{\partial q}\right)_{E = E_n, q = 0} + \cdots$$

$$= (E - E_n)\left(\frac{\partial f}{\partial E}\right)_{E = E_n, q = 0} - iqKR_X. \tag{6.56}$$

Further we again define widths Γ through

$$\Gamma_n^\alpha = - \frac{2kR_X}{(\partial f/\partial E)_{E\,=\,E_n,\,q\,=\,0}}$$

$$\Gamma_n^\beta = - \frac{2qKR_X}{(\partial f/\partial E)_{E\,=\,E_n,\,q\,=\,0}} \qquad (6.57)$$

$$\Gamma_n = \Gamma_n^\alpha + \Gamma_n^\beta.$$

Then we obtain from (6.38) and (6.40) near resonance that

$$\sigma_{\text{sc}}^0 = \frac{\pi}{k^2} \left| \frac{\Gamma_n^\alpha}{(E - E_n) + \frac{1}{2}i\Gamma_n} + 2kR_X \right|^2, \, E \simeq E_n \qquad (6.58)$$

and

$$\sigma_{\text{re}}^0 = \frac{\pi}{k^2} \frac{\Gamma_n^\alpha \Gamma_n^\beta}{(E - E_n)^2 + \frac{1}{4}\Gamma_n^2}, \, E \simeq E_n. \qquad (6.59)$$

These are the famous Breit-Wigner formulae for the special case of only one reaction channel.

We have still to justify our notation, in which Γ_n^α was the channel width for α as ingoing channel, and Γ_n^β the channel width for β as reaction channel. We shall now use subscripts i and r to distinguish these. Then

$$\sigma(\alpha \to \beta) = \frac{\pi}{k_\alpha^2} \frac{\Gamma_{ni}^\alpha \Gamma_{nr}^\beta}{(E_\alpha - E_{n\alpha})^2 + \frac{1}{4}(\Gamma_{ni}^\alpha + \Gamma_{nr}^\beta)^2} \qquad (6.60)$$

$$\sigma(\beta \to \alpha) = \frac{\pi}{k_\beta^2} \frac{\Gamma_{ni}^\beta \Gamma_{nr}^\alpha}{(E_\beta - E_{n\beta})^2 + \frac{1}{4}(\Gamma_m^\beta + \Gamma_{nr}^\alpha)^2}. \qquad (6.61)$$

When this is substituted into the reciprocity relation (6.23), it follows that

$$\frac{\Gamma_{ni}^\alpha \Gamma_{nr}^\beta}{(E_\alpha - E_{n\alpha})^2 + \frac{1}{4}(\Gamma_{ni}^\alpha + \Gamma_{nr}^\beta)^2} = \frac{\Gamma_{ni}^\beta \Gamma_{nr}^\alpha}{(E_\beta - E_{n\beta})^2 + \frac{1}{4}(\Gamma_{ni}^\beta + \Gamma_{nr}^\alpha)^2}. \qquad (6.62)$$

Now if an amount of energy Q is released in the $\alpha \to \beta$ reaction, then

$$E_\beta = E_\alpha + Q. \qquad (6.63)$$

Hence (6.62) can be satisfied for all E_α only if

$$E_{n\beta} = E_{n\alpha} + Q \qquad (6.64)$$

and

$$\Gamma_{ni}^\alpha = \Gamma_{nr}^\alpha, \quad \Gamma_{ni}^\beta = \Gamma_{nr}^\beta. \qquad (6.65)$$

Thus the resonances in the $\alpha \to \beta$ and $\beta \to \alpha$ reactions occur at the same total energies and the channel widths are the same whether they are entrance or reaction widths. Furthermore it follows from

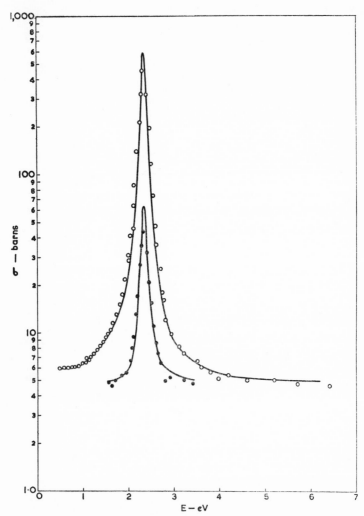

FIG. 6.2. RESONANCE OF THE TE^{123} $(I = \frac{1}{2})$ ISOTOPE

The experimental cross-sections were obtained for natural tellurium, in which the isotope Te^{123} occurs with 0·85 per cent abundance, and fitted with theoretical curves according to (6.67) and (6.68), where resonance energy $E_n = 2·33$ eV, elastic scattering width $\Gamma^\alpha_n = 0·0104$ eV, radiative capture width $\Gamma^\beta_n = 0·104$ eV, channel angular momentum $S = 1$. A shape elastic cross-section of 5 barns due to other isotopes of tellurium is assumed. (After Hughes, D. J. and Harvey, J. A., *Neutron Cross-Sections*, McGraw-Hill.)

(6.58) and (6.59) that the resonances of σ_{sc} and σ_{re} occur at the same energy E_n and with the same reaction width Γ_n. This is a very stringent test of the theory.

So far we have only considered the case in which the angular momentum of the target nucleus $I = 0$. If I is not zero, then the total angular momentum S in the entrance channel is either $I + \frac{1}{2}$ or $I - \frac{1}{2}$. Because of the quantization of direction of angular momentum the multiplicities of these states are $2(I + \frac{1}{2}) + 1$ and $2(I - \frac{1}{2}) + 1$ respectively. If the incident beam is unpolarized, the statistical weights of the channels corresponding to these two cases are then

$$g(S) = \frac{2S + 1}{2(2I + 1)}, \, S = I + \tfrac{1}{2} \text{ or } I - \tfrac{1}{2}. \qquad (6.66)$$

In our derivation of the resonance formulae we have assumed that channels other than the resonating one can be neglected. This is valid for the resonance part of the cross-sections, but not for the part of σ_{sc} which is due to potential scattering. In the latter all channels of a given energy contribute, so that (6.58) and (6.59) must be amended for a channel angular momentum S to read

$$\sigma_{sc}^0 = g(S) \frac{\pi}{k^2} \left| \frac{\Gamma_n^\alpha}{(E - E_n) + \tfrac{1}{2}i\Gamma_n} + 2kR_X \right|^2 + \{1 - g(S)\} \cdot 4\pi R_X^2 \qquad (6.67)$$

$$\sigma_{re}^0 = g(S) \cdot \frac{\pi}{k^2} \frac{\Gamma_n^\alpha \Gamma_n^\beta}{(E - E_n)^2 + \tfrac{1}{4}\Gamma_n^2}. \qquad (6.68)$$

The Breit-Wigner formulae have been verified experimentally with a very high degree of accuracy, particularly for low incident energies where the only nuclear reaction possible is radiative capture. A good example of the fitting of (6.67) and (6.68) to experimental results is the $2 \cdot 33$ eV resonance in $_{52}\text{Te}^{123}$, which is shown in Fig. 6.2. The dip in the elastic cross-section to the left of the resonance, due to interference between resonance and potential scattering, is too small to be observed. To be able to fit both resonance curves with just two parameters is really very satisfying.

We can now see more clearly the justification of the so-called independence hypothesis, that the decay of the compound nucleus, that has the energy of a given resonance, is independent of its formation. If the almost stable state corresponding to this resonance were a definite quantum state with a sharp energy, then it would decay in a definite manner, irrespective of its mode of formation. The width of a resonance level is therefore a measure of the breakdown of the independence hypothesis—the narrower the level, that is the longer-lived the state, the more nearly is the independence hypothesis true.

The resonance width, as defined by (6.46), depends not only on the target nucleus, but also on the bombarding energy. It is therefore useful to define a *reduced width* for the decay channel β. This is traditionally denoted by $\gamma_{n\beta}^2$ and defined by

$$\gamma_{n\beta}^2 = \frac{\Gamma_n^\beta}{2k} = -\frac{R_X}{(\mathrm{d}f/\mathrm{d}E)_{E=E_n}} . \tag{6.69}$$

Clearly, it depends only on the wave function of the target nucleus. Now, from (6.43),

$$-\left(\frac{\mathrm{d}f}{\mathrm{d}E}\right)_{E=E_n} = K R_X \left(\frac{\mathrm{d}z}{\mathrm{d}E}\right)_{E=E_n} . \tag{6.70}$$

We shall assume that $z(E)$ is a smoothly varying function of energy, in which case

$$\frac{\mathrm{d}z}{\mathrm{d}E} \simeq \frac{\pi}{D} \tag{6.71}$$

where D is the distance between levels near the level with energy E_n. This follows from the fact that $z(E)$ increases by π, as E increases by D. Hence

$$\gamma_{n\beta}^2 \simeq \frac{D}{\pi K} . \tag{6.72}$$

According to this result, the reduced width is the same for all channels. This is certainly not so and the above formula can only give an order of magnitude estimate.

We now return to the difficulty, mentioned before, that the concept of the compound nucleus is in direct conflict with the concepts underlying the shell model. This model requires that the mean-free-paths of nucleons bound in nuclei be several nuclear diameters long, these very long mean-free-paths being due to the working of the exclusion principle. Nucleons that are incident upon the nucleus from the outside, even at very low incident energies, have of course much larger kinetic energies, once they are inside the nucleus, than nucleons bound in nuclei, and the exclusion principle is then less important. Nevertheless, the mean-free-paths are still very long even then and the reason why the nucleons stay in the nucleus, once they have entered it, is that the transmission coefficient across the nuclear surface is very small. The nucleon is thus reflected several times by the inside of the nuclear surface until it is eventually captured into the compound nucleus. At higher incident energies the transmission coefficient rapidly increases, so that then, even though the mean-free-path is shorter, nucleons are more likely to escape. This we shall discuss in section 6.8.

We calculate the transmission coefficient for a square well of the form (3.45) by sending in a wave from the outside and allowing part of it to be reflected and part transmitted at the boundary. (The transmission coefficient is the same in both directions.) The wave is given by

$$u(r) = \begin{cases} e^{-ikr} + a\, e^{ikr}, & r < R_X, \\ b\, e^{-iKr}, & r > R_X. \end{cases} \tag{6.73}$$

From the usual continuity condition at the boundary it then follows that

$$a = -\frac{K-k}{K+k} e^{-2ikR_X}, \quad b = \frac{2k}{K+k} e^{-i(k+K)R_X}. \tag{6.74}$$

The transmission coefficient is given by subtracting the reflection coefficient $|a|^2$ from unity

$$T = 1 - |a|^2 = \frac{4kK}{(K+k)^2} \simeq \frac{4k}{K} \text{ for } k \ll K. \tag{6.75}$$

Alternatively it could be obtained from the amplitude b of the transmitted wave, but it would then be necessary to take into account the change in wave flux, due to the change in wave velocity.

The oscillations of the neutron in the well are similar to the collective vibrational modes discussed in section 5.7. These led to equispaced levels with separation $\hbar\omega = 2\pi\hbar\nu$, where we now interpret ν as the number of times that the neutron reaches the surface. We also put $D = \hbar\omega$, where we are therefore assuming that the levels in the compound nucleus are equally spaced. This is approximately true at high energies. The partial width for decay of the compound nucleus is then, using (6.27) and (6.75),

$$\Gamma_n^\beta = \hbar\nu T \simeq \frac{DT}{2\pi} \simeq \frac{2Dk}{\pi K}, \tag{6.76}$$

i.e.

$$\gamma_{n\beta}^2 \simeq \frac{D}{\pi K}. \tag{6.77}$$

We have thus obtained the same result as before, which shows that we can reconcile the apparently very different ideas of the shell model and of the compound nucleus.

If the captured neutron can really be taken as moving in a shell model potential $V(r)$ of the type (5.46), then we can obtain another expression for the reduced width. The wave functions of the neutron at energies E and E' will satisfy the equations

$$\left. \begin{aligned} \frac{d^2u}{dr^2} + \frac{2M}{\hbar^2}(E - V)u &= 0, \\ \frac{d^2u'}{dr^2} + \frac{2M}{\hbar^2}(E' - V)u' &= 0. \end{aligned} \right\} \qquad (6.78)$$

We multiply these equations by u' and u respectively, subtract and integrate to the nuclear radius—

$$\int_0^{R_X} \frac{2M}{\hbar^2}(E - E')uu'\,dr = \left[u\frac{du'}{dr} - u'\frac{du}{dr} \right]_{r=R_X}. \qquad (6.79)$$

We now let $E' \to E$. Then, since $u' = u + (\partial u/\partial E)(E' - E)$,

$$\begin{aligned} \frac{2M}{\hbar^2}\int_0^{R_X} u^2\,dr &= -\left[u\frac{\partial^2 u}{\partial E \partial r} - \frac{\partial u}{\partial E}\frac{\partial u}{\partial r} \right]_{r=R_X} \\ &= -\left[\frac{u^2}{R_X}\frac{\partial}{\partial E}\left(\frac{R_X}{u}\frac{\partial u}{\partial r} \right) \right]_{r=R_X} \end{aligned} \qquad (6.80)$$

Using (6.34) and (6.69) we have, for the *single particle width*,

$$\gamma_{SP}^2 = \frac{\hbar^2 u^2}{2M} \Big/ \int_0^{R_X} u^2 dr. \qquad (6.81)$$

This expression is independent of the normalization of the wave function, and it is usual to normalize the radial function to unity in the nuclear volume. Further for $l = 0$ neutrons in a square well, $u(r)$ is given by (3.66) with $KR_X = (n + \tfrac{1}{2})\pi$ at resonance, and (6.81) then reduces to

$$\gamma_0^2 = \frac{\hbar^2}{MR_X}. \qquad (6.82)$$

Reduced widths are frequently given in terms of this width as a unit, so that

$$\gamma_{SP}^2 = \tfrac{1}{2}R_X u^2(R_X)\,\gamma_0^2. \qquad (6.83)$$

Departures of experimental reduced widths from the single particle widths indicate how far the single particle picture of the nucleus is an adequate one.

6.7 Continuum Theory

As the energy of the incident neutrons increases, the number of available channels increases too. We now go to the opposite limit, in which the number of available channels is very large. For medium and heavy nuclei this will be the case when the energy of the incident neutrons is of the order of several MeV. At such energies neutrons with non-zero orbital angular momenta certainly contribute to the cross-section. However, we shall evaluate only the $l = 0$ partial cross-section, and quote results for the other partial cross-sections.

To see why the postulate of a very large number of open channels simplifies the problem let us consider elastic scattering under this condition.

This can take place in two ways—

(a) Without formation of a compound nucleus. The incident wave is reflected at the entrance to channel α.

(b) With formation of a compound nucleus. The incident wave enters the channel junction and leaves subsequently through the channel through which it had entered. It should be noted that this process cannot be described simply by putting $\beta = \alpha$ in (6.26), since the outgoing wave now interferes with the incoming one. The Bohr assumption that the decay of the compound nucleus is independent of its formation then breaks down.

Now if the number of exit channels is very large, then the chance that the incident particle will leave through the entrance channel after formation of the compound nucleus is negligible. The elastic scattering is then due entirely to process (a) above and the cross-section for formation of the compound nucleus, $\sigma_c(\alpha)$, is equal to the reaction cross-section σ_{re} for the process. There will then be no resonances and thus no almost-stable levels in the continuum. For that reason this theory is referred to as the continuum theory.

The justification of the independence hypothesis of the compound nucleus must now be quite different from before. To say that there are no almost-stable levels is only another way of saying that the resonances are broad and overlapping. In this energy region a compound nucleus of given energy consists therefore of a mixture of a large number of excited states, and it is by no means obvious, or indeed necessary, that different ways of exciting the nucleus to the same energy form the excited state always in the same mixture. Different mixtures would lead to different decays, and hence to a breakdown of the independence hypothesis. Our assumption then is that so many states are involved that the mixture is effectively a random one, so that on a probability basis the decay is independent of the formation.

When a nuclear reaction has definite parity, then the scattering amplitude is either symmetric or anti-symmetric about the scattering angle $\theta = 90°$ in the centre-of-mass system, depending on whether the parity is even or odd. Hence the scattering cross-section is always symmetric under these circumstances. However, a reaction can only have definite parity, if only a single resonance is excited by a single incident partial wave. When several resonances are excited together and several incident partial waves are involved, then the reaction does not have definite parity and interference terms occur in the scattering amplitude which destroy the symmetry about 90°. The randomness assumption of the continuum theory implies that these interference terms average to zero, so that the symmetry about 90° is re-established. Hence the existence of fore-and-aft symmetry of the angular distribution of the reaction products in the c.m. system is an indication that the randomness hypothesis is applicable for a particular reaction.

It must be stressed that it is not at all certain that the energy region described above really exists. The higher the energy, the shorter lived is the compound nucelus, and it may well be that in the region in which the excited states form a random mixture the life-time of the compound nucleus is not long enough to make statistical considerations applicable. The presently accepted theory is that at high energies compound nucleus formation can occur, but does not do so invariably, and that it is in competition with direct reaction processes (see section 6.9) in which the incident nucleon does not interact with the nucleus as a whole. For different nuclear reactions it will thus be necessary to postulate different mechanisms, and in fact the same reaction may occur partly with and partly without compound nucleus formation.

While therefore the pure compound nucleus continuum theory does not account for the experimental facts, it will nevertheless be instructive to formulate it for the simplest case, i.e. for $l = 0$ neutrons. As regards the kinetic energy of the neutron once it is inside the target nucleus, the considerations leading up to (6.42) are still valid, but equation (6.42) is not. According to our postulate, the chance of the incident neutron leaving through channel α is negligible, and so the wave function in channel α is now

$$u(r) = e^{-iKr}, \quad r < R_X. \tag{6.84}$$

Hence

$$f = -iKR_X \tag{6.85}$$

and, from (6.38) and (6.40),

$$\sigma_{re}^0 = \sigma_c^0(\alpha) = \frac{\pi}{k^2} \frac{4kK}{(k+K)^2} \tag{6.86}$$

and

$$\sigma_{sc}^0 = \frac{\pi}{k^2} \left| \frac{2k}{k+K} + e^{2ikR_X} - 1 \right|^2. \tag{6.87}$$

It is easily verified that these cross-sections satisfy the inequalities (6.8) and (6.11). The complete cross-section $\sigma = \sigma_{re} + \sigma_{sc}$, which is obtained by summing σ_{re}^l and σ_{sc}^l over all l, has been plotted in Fig. 6.3 for two particular values of $K_0 R_X$, where $K_0^2 = K^2 - k^2$, as a function of energy. As a comparison the cross-section for scattering from a perfectly reflecting sphere ($K_0 = \infty$) is also drawn.

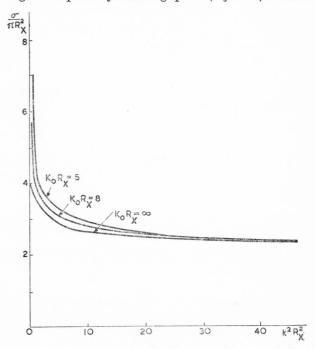

FIG. 6.3. TOTAL CROSS-SECTIONS FOR NEUTRONS, ACCORDING TO THE CONTINUUM THEORY

$K_0 R_X = 5$ and $K_0 R_X = 8$ correspond to a light and a medium nucleus respectively, $K_0 R_X = \infty$ to a perfectly reflecting sphere. The energy, in MeV, of the incident neutron is given by $E = 1.4 k^2 R_X^2$ for $K_0 R_X = 5$ and $E = 0.57 k^2 R_X^2$ for $K_0 R_X = 8$, if $K_0 = 1.3$ fm^{-1}.

It will be seen that for fairly high energies the scattering is almost independent of K_0 and equal to the scattering from a perfectly reflecting sphere. This makes it possible to determine the nuclear radius, even though at that energy the cross-section is still very far from its asymptotic value $2\pi R_X^2$. This is the method referred to in section 2.2.1. Its results are not altogether reliable as they stand, as will be shown in the next section.

We can relate the average capture cross-section into channel α to the reduced width for this channel. While the relation (6.71) is only an order of magnitude estimate for any particular resonance, it should be exact as an average over many resonances. Hence we may substitute from (6.75), (6.76) and (6.69) into (6.86) and obtain

$$\langle \sigma_{\text{re}}^0 \rangle = \langle \sigma_{\text{c}}^0(\alpha) \rangle = \frac{\pi T}{k^2} = \frac{2\pi^2}{k^2} \frac{\Gamma_n^\alpha}{D} = \frac{4\pi^2}{k} \frac{\gamma_{n\alpha}^2}{D}. \tag{6.88}$$

The quantity $\gamma_{n\alpha}^2/D$ is called the *strength function*. Its significance is that we expect it to vary considerably less from nucleus to nucleus than either $\gamma_{n\alpha}^2$ or D separately. In fact, if (6.71) were strictly correct, we would expect the strength function to be constant.

Finally we relate the strength function to the average total cross-section for s-waves. It can be shown in exactly the same manner as we did in chapter 3, that at low energies the phase shift is proportional to k [see (3.129)], so that we have from (6.13) and (6.14), on expanding for small λ_0 and μ_0,

$$\sigma_{\text{sc}}^0 = \frac{4\pi}{k^2}(\lambda_0^2 + \mu_0^2), \quad \sigma_{\text{re}} = \frac{4\pi}{k^2}\mu_0.$$

Thus the scattering cross-section is constant and equal to $4\pi a^2$, where we define a scattering length a in the same way as in chapter 3. The average total cross-section is then obtained with the help of (6.88) and is

$$\langle \sigma_{\text{tot}}^2 \rangle = 4\pi a^2 + \frac{4\pi^2}{k} \frac{\gamma_{n\alpha}^2}{D}. \tag{6.89}$$

The second term is inversely proportional to the incident neutron velocity. This dependence has been verified experimentally in suitable energy regions. We have here therefore a method for determining the strength function.

The above formula is of great importance in the analysis of nuclear reactions, and it may be noted that it is valid at energies which are considerably lower than those at which the continuum theory can be expected to be valid. The reason for this is that the averaging process over many separated resonances that led to it yields the same kind of randomness that we presupposed in the continuum theory. The formula is in fact applicable at energies where the restriction to $l = 0$ partial waves is perfectly correct.

6.8 The Optical Model

Although the experimental results follow the general trend of the curves in Fig. 6.3 at energies of a few MeV, more detailed investigation shows (Barschall, 1952) that when the total cross-section is plotted against energy, the experimental curves have pronounced maxima and minima, reminiscent of wave interference, so that the

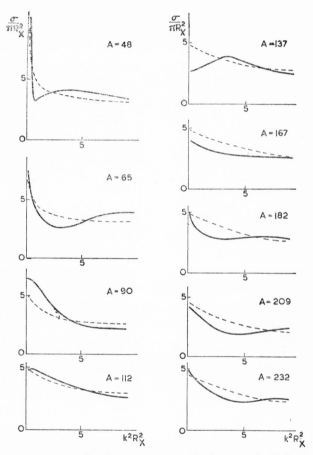

Fig. 6.4. Total Cross-sections for Neutrons Incident on Nuclei of Various Mass Numbers A

The full lines give the experimental results and the broken lines the predictions of the continuum theory. For the experimental results the old value of $R_X = 1.45A^{1/3}$ fm was used.

cross-sections do not decrease smoothly with increasing energy, as is predicted by the continuum theory (see Fig. 6.4). Furthermore, the trend of these maxima and minima with energy is a smooth function of the mass number A. This shows that the disagreement between experiment and theory is not due to unexpected resonances in individual nuclides, but to a general flaw in our theory which shows up systematically in all nuclides. Such widely spaced shallow maxima and minima, quite different from the closely packed narrow ones at lower energies, are in fact what would be expected from scattering by a potential well, where resonances occur whenever an extra half wavelength can be fitted into the well.

A further disagreement concerns the strength function. When this is plotted as a function of the mass number A, it is seen that, far from being constant, it has pronounced maxima in the region $A \simeq 55$ and $A \simeq 160$ with a minimum near $A \simeq 105$, for which the strength function is only about 5 per cent of its value at maximum. Thus the capture cross-section for compound nucleus formation averaged over individual resonances [see (6.83)] has broad maxima, which are easily interpreted as resonances in a potential well. In fact, the maxima correspond to fitting $2\frac{1}{2}$ and $3\frac{1}{2}$ half-waves into the well (see ex. 6.11.3).

So far we have assumed that elastic scattering can take place in two ways, (*a*) through compound elastic scattering, and (*b*) through hard sphere scattering, i.e. scattering by the potential $V = + \infty$, $r < R$; $V = 0$, $r > R$. If we now replace (*b*) by a more general potential

$$V(r) = \begin{cases} - V_0, & r < R \\ 0, & r > R \end{cases}. \qquad (6.90)$$

Then the potential-scattered wave will penetrate into the nucleus and produce just the kind of interference phenomenon that is observed.

Is such a replacement permissible? We have already pointed out that at low energies the shell model concepts lead with certainty to compound nucleus formation, but that at higher energies some neutrons may escape from the nucleus before being captured into the compound nucleus. We clearly have now reached the region where this is so. There will then be some nucleons that pass through the nucleus scattered but unabsorbed, and others that are absorbed into the compound nucleus and may eventually be re-scattered or else take part in nuclear reactions. This is just exactly equivalent to the replacement of hard sphere scattering by the more general potential (6.90).

There remains the task of putting our theory on a mathematical basis (Feshbach, 1953). We first show that the partial absorption of the wave into the compound nucleus can be obtained with the help of a complex scattering potential. If the potential is

$$V(r) + iW(r), \qquad (6.91)$$

then the wave equation of the neutron is

$$\nabla^2\psi + \frac{2M}{\hbar^2}(E - V - iW)\psi = 0. \tag{6.92}$$

Now if the rate of removal of neutrons per unit volume from the incident beam is P, then the usual equation of continuity is

$$\frac{\partial\rho}{\partial t} + \text{div } \mathbf{j} = -P \tag{6.93}$$

where $\rho = \psi^*\psi$ and $\mathbf{j} = (\hbar/2iM)(\psi^* \text{ grad } \psi - \psi \text{ grad } \psi^*)$. In words this equation expresses the fact that the rate of increase of the neutron density in unit volume, $-P$, is equal to the sum of the rate of increase of the probability density ρ and the flux into the volume of the probability current density $\mathbf{j}$. Now for a steady state ρ is constant and hence (6.93) reduces to

$$P = \frac{\hbar}{2iM}(\psi\nabla^2\psi^* - \psi^*\nabla^2\psi)$$

i.e.

$$P = -\frac{2\rho}{\hbar}W, \tag{6.94}$$

using (6.92). Thus the attenuation of the incident beam is proportional to $-W$, and we must have $W(r) < 0$ everywhere.

We now solve (6.92) for the special case of $l = 0$ neutrons and a square well, for which the potential is

$$V(r) = \begin{cases} -V_0, & r < R \\ 0, & r > R \end{cases}, \qquad W(r) = \begin{cases} -W_0, & r < R \\ 0, & r > R \end{cases}. \tag{6.95}$$

The radial equation is then

$$\left. \begin{aligned} \frac{d^2u}{dr^2} + k'^2 u = 0, & \quad r < R \\ \frac{d^2u}{dr^2} + k^2 u = 0, & \quad r > R \end{aligned} \right\} \tag{6.96}$$

where $k'^2 = k^2 + (2M/\hbar^2)(V_0 + iW_0)$. The solution with the correct boundary conditions is

$$u = \begin{cases} A \sin k'r & , r < R \\ B \sin(kr + \lambda_0 + i\mu_0) & , r > R \end{cases} \tag{6.97}$$

where the continuity condition

$$k' \cot k'R = k \cot(kR + \lambda_0 + i\mu_0) \tag{6.98}$$

7

determines the complex phase shift. The corresponding absorption
cross-section for any l is then given by (6.14),

$$\sigma_{\text{abs}}^{l} = \frac{\pi}{k^2}(2l + 1)(1 - e^{-4\mu'_l}).$$ (6.99)

The experimental data between 0·5 and 3 MeV have been fitted
with $V_0 = 42$ MeV, $W_0 = 1·3$ MeV and $R = r_0 A^{\frac{1}{3}}$ with $r_0 = 1·45$ fm,
but the fit is insensitive to quite large variations of V_0 and r_0,
provided that $V_0 r_0^2 = C^2$ is kept constant (see example 6.11.3). Now
we shall show (see end of section 7.3) that the mean-free path of a
nucleon in nuclear matter is given by

$$L = \frac{\hbar}{2W_0}\left[\frac{2(E + V_0)}{M}\right]^{1/2}$$ (6.100)

and since $E \ll V_0$, we can put

$$\frac{L}{R} = \frac{\hbar}{\xi}\left[\frac{1}{2MR^2 V_0}\right]^{1/2} = \frac{1}{\sqrt{(2M)}}\frac{\hbar}{\xi C},$$ (6.101)

where $\xi = W_0/V_0$. For the figures quoted this gives

$$\frac{L}{R} = 16\ A^{-1/3}.$$ (6.102)

As the mean distance across a sphere of radius R is $\frac{3}{2}R$, the probability of a nucleon traversing a nucleus uncaptured [see (7.57)] is

$$p = \exp(-3R/2L) = \exp(-\tfrac{3}{32}A^{1/3})$$ (6.103)

for a heavy nucleus. There is thus a 40 per cent probability of
compound nucleus formation and a 60 per cent probability of
potential scattering. The conjecture that what was required
was a compromise between the two processes has been fully justified.

The complex potential that we have used here has the same
effect of partial absorption and transmission on the incident neutron
wave as has a complex refractive index on an electromagnetic wave.
For that reason this potential is now known as the *optical potential*.
It used to be known as the cloudy crystal ball model, but this
appellation mercifully did not survive. The justification for the
potential is of course the same as for the shell model potential, and
it is usual to take the real part of the same form as $V_{\text{SM}}(r)$ in equation (5.46). However, the strength of the potential must be taken as
a function of the incident energy in order to fit experimental results.
This is not surprising since the optical potential is of course the
outcome of an average over two-body interactions, which themselves
are strongly energy dependent.

There is little to guide us regarding the imaginary part. Absorption inside nuclear matter is due to a collision between the incident neutron and a target nucleon. This collision is inhibited by the exclusion principle, which is most effective at low energies, but on the other hand the collision cross-section decreases with increasing energy. Absorption is thus expected to reach a maximum in some intermediate region. This gives information on the strength W_0,

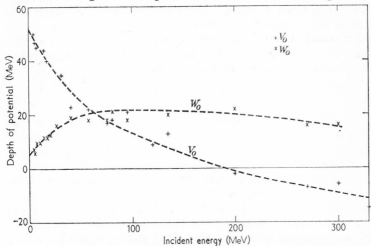

FIG. 6.5. DEPTHS OF REAL AND IMAGINARY PARTS OF
OPTICAL POTENTIAL FOR NUCLEONS

The points are fits to experimental data ; the curves indicate the general
trend of the results and have no theoretical significance.
[From Elton, L. R. B., *Nuclear Sizes* (Oxford, 1961)]

and for the shape it is usual to take the same shape $f(r)$ [see (5.45)] as for the real part. The experimentally determined energy dependence of V_0 and W_0 is shown in Fig. 6.5. At low incident energies, where the exclusion principle prevents collisions particularly in the inside of the nucleus, where the nuclear density is greatest, most of the absorption is likely to take place in the nuclear surface. It may then be more realistic to take for the imaginary part of the potential a shape which has a sharp maximum in the nuclear surface.

As has already been stated, beams of unpolarized nucleons are polarized when scattered by a nucleus, and it is therefore necessary to include a spin-orbit term in the optical potential. The strength constant λ of its real part can be taken to be approximately the same as for the shell model potential, but there is at present no evidence for any imaginary part to the spin-orbit term.

A consequence of the results of this section is that it is now much more difficult to measure nuclear radii. As long as we assumed that the potential scattering was merely hard sphere scattering, i.e. scattering by an infinite potential, the total cross-section depended only on the nuclear radius. But if the potential is finite, then the scattering depends both on its depth and its extent, and as has already been mentioned, at low energies it is largely insensitive to changes in these, provided $V_0 R^2$ is kept constant. An analysis of proton scattering at $10 - 40$ MeV has shown that this is true even at such comparatively high energies, though it is essential at such energies to take into account the tapering off of the nuclear potential. At present it is possible to fit the results with a value for the half-way radius of

$$c = c_0 A^{\frac{1}{3}}, \quad c_0 = 1 \cdot 2 - 1 \cdot 3 \text{ fm}, \quad (6.104)$$

where the higher value applies to small A and the lower to large A. This radius cannot of course be directly compared with the radius of the proton distribution, as obtained from electromagnetic measurements. It does not even necessarily measure the extent of the nucleon distribution, since the finite range of nuclear forces enters into the picture. It is in fact the radius of the nuclear potential which influences the incident nucleon and as such may well extend outwards further by a constant amount, related to the range of nuclear forces, than the radius of the nucleon distribution. It is actually possible (Elton, 1961) to fit the half-way radius of the optical potential with the formula

$$c_{pot} = c_{elec} + 0 \cdot 8 \text{ fm} \quad (6.105)$$

where c_{elec} is the half-way radius (2.17) of the proton distribution, which we assume to be the same as that of the nucleon distribution. That such a fit is possible is evidence in favour of this assumption.

6.9 Direct Reactions

It appears that under certain circumstances a nuclear reaction can take place in which the incident particle reacts only with a part of the nucleus, while the rest remains undisturbed. Put more precisely, this means that the interaction takes place between the incident particle and only some of the degrees of freedom of the nucleus. The particular degrees of freedom may be the co-ordinates of a target nucleon which is localized in a definite spatial region of the nucleus, or they may be those which describe a target nucleon of a definite angular momentum, or again they may be collective co-ordinates of the type discussed in section 5.7. Correspondingly, there is a bewildering choice of mechanisms through which a direct reaction can proceed. One property that is expected to distinguish all direct reaction processes from compound nuclear processes is that they should proceed much more rapidly, in times of the order of transit times of nucleons across nuclei, which typically are 10^{-22} sec. We shall distinguish in what follows between reactions in which discrete levels of the final nucleus can be resolved experimentally, and those in which they cannot.

6.9.1 DISCRETE LEVELS NOT RESOLVED. In medium and heavy nuclei the density of levels is so large that it is quite impossible to resolve individual ones. The experiment then consists of measuring differential cross-sections as functions of both scattering angle and energy of the emitted particle. One of the first experiments that gave a clear indication that nuclear reactions were not always of the compound nucleus type was that of Eisberg and Igo (1954) who investigated inelastic proton scattering by various nuclei at 32 MeV bombarding energy. The compound nucleus theory here makes the following predictions—

(*a*) The incident proton is captured into a compound nucleus. Emission of a proton from the compound nucleus is strongly inhibited by the Coulomb barrier (the process is similar to α-disintegration discussed in section 7.4), so that the nucleus will decay almost entirely by neutron emission. The cross-section for inelastic proton scattering will therefore be very small.

(*b*) Those protons that are emitted will tend to have energies just above the Coulomb barrier and protons emitted with energies near the incident energy will be very rare indeed. This is a consequence of the fact that in the compound nucleus picture the energy of the incident particle is shared among the target particles and then partially re-concentrated on one nucleon at a later stage.

(*c*) The angular distribution will be symmetric about 90° in the centre-of-mass system. This, as we have seen, is a general result of the continuum theory.

The experimental results disagreed on every point. They showed that—

(*a*) The cross-section is large (about 15 per cent of the total reaction cross-section).

(*b*) The energy spectrum of the emitted protons has a maximum at 20-30 MeV.

(*c*) The differential cross-section is strongly peaked in the forward direction.

These facts can be accounted for, if it is assumed that some of the incident protons interact with nucleons in the equatorial rim of the nucleus. In the process they lose some energy and are deflected through a small angle, but they are not captured into the compound nucleus. Because of the diffuseness of the nuclear surface, the rim region is actually quite large and it is therefore possible to account for the large cross-sections, which have been observed, in this way. Those protons that interact with nucleons in the interior of the nucleus will thereafter be reflected by total internal reflection from the inside of the Coulomb barrier until they are captured into the compound nucleus (Elton and Gomes, 1957).

The interpretation of this experiment is thus that at this bombarding energy the interior of a medium-size nucleus is extremely opaque to incident protons, so that protons can emerge from the reaction only if they are scattered in the equatorial rim of the nuclear surface. In other reactions, where the opacity of the interior region is less, it will be necessary to take into account scattering taking place in the whole of the surface region, or even throughout the nuclear volume.

All this is not to say that the compound nucleus theory is wrong; in fact, those protons that enter the opaque core are expected to form a compound nucleus. However, because of the Coulomb barrier, which prevents protons from escaping from the inside of the nucleus, the compound nucleus will decay predominantly through the emission of a neutron, so that the compound process is dominant in the (p, n) reaction, but does not contribute significantly to the (p, p') inelastic scattering. Our conclusion is therefore that, at energies in the MeV region, compound nucleus formation is merely one of several competing processes, and that direct reactions may be able to yield information about comparatively localized regions of the nucleus, such as the nuclear surface.

6.9.2 DISCRETE LEVELS RESOLVED. The most spectacular successes of the direct reaction theory have been achieved in the region of comparatively light nuclei, where it is possible to resolve a definite energy level of the final state of the target nucleus. If the orbital angular momentum of the target nucleus before and after the reaction is L_i and L_f respectively, then the orbital angular momentum l transferred by the bombarding particle in an inelastic scattering is given by

$$L_i + L_f \geqslant l \geqslant | L_i - L_f |. \tag{6.106}$$

cacording to the usual rules of addition of angular momenta. (We restrict our discussion to the case in which the direction of the intrinsic spin of the incident particle is unchanged.) In a direct interaction, in which only one target nucleon takes part, this reduces to

$$l_i + l_t \geqslant l \geqslant |l_i - l_t|, \qquad (6.107)$$

where l_i and l_t refer to the target nucleon.

We begin by describing such a direct interaction by means of a semi-classical approach due to Butler, Austern and Pearson (1958). While this cannot be expected to give quantitatively correct results,

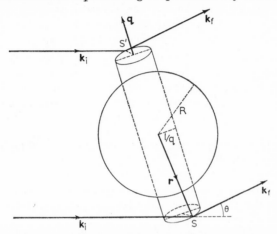

FIG. 6.6. INTERFERENCE IN DIRECT INTERACTIONS IN THE
SURFACE OF THE NUCLEUS

it will help us to visualize what is going on. Such visualizations must be treated cautiously, but in fact physicists find them indispensable.

We assume that the core of the nucleus is moderately absorptive, so that direct reactions take place throughout the nuclear surface. Let the wave vectors of the incident and scattered particles be $\mathbf{k}_i$ and $\mathbf{k}_f$. Then the angular momentum transfer is given by

$$\mathbf{l} = (\mathbf{k}_i - \mathbf{k}_f) \times \mathbf{r} = \mathbf{q} \times \mathbf{r}, \qquad (6.108)$$

where $\mathbf{r}$ is the position vector at the point of interaction of the incident and target nucleons, and $\mathbf{q}$ is the linear momentum transfer (in units of $\hbar$). We ignore refractive effects due to the nuclear potential, so that the wave vectors are the same at infinity and at the point of interaction.† This is a reasonable simplification, as long as the interaction takes place in the nuclear surface only.

It follows from (6.108) that the locus of the points of interaction for a given $\mathbf{l}$ and $\mathbf{q}$ is the surface of a cylinder of radius l/q with its

† It may be noted that the angular momentum is unchanged by refraction. This follows at once from Snell's law.

axis in the direction of $\mathbf{q}$. (See Fig. 6.6). Now in terms of the scattering angle θ,

$$q = [k_i^2 + k_f^2 - 2k_ik_f \cos \theta]^{\frac{1}{2}}, \qquad (6.109)$$

and k_f is determined by conservation of energy. Thus q determines the scattering angle. If we ignore the contribution to the scattering from the interior of the nucleus, then the scattering into angle θ, due to a given partial incident wave, is the result of an interference from the two ends of the cylinder, where they enter the surface region of the nucleus. Two such interfering rays are shown in Fig. 6.6. We can now draw the following conclusions—

(a) Because of the interference from opposite sides of the nucleus, the differential cross-section will exhibit a diffraction pattern.

(b) For the excitation of low-lying states in a direct reaction, the struck nucleon must receive little energy, and hence little momentum, i.e. $\mathbf{k_i} \simeq \mathbf{k_f}$, so that q is small. Hence scattering will be largely in the forward direction.

(c) On the other hand, if R is the radius of the absorbing region of the nucleus, then for $l/q > R$ there will be little interaction, since the cylinder then only intersects a narrow rim of the nuclear surface. Thus, except for $l = 0$, scattering into very small angles is inhibited, and the larger l, the larger the angle at which the first scattering maximum occurs.

The actual position of the scattering maximum can now be found. To find the total amplitude for the reaction, we have to add coherently all the outgoing rays with a given $\mathbf{q}$, and to do this we must allow for the different total path lengths of rays scattered at different points of the cylindrical surface. These path length differences lead to phase factors $\exp(i\mathbf{q} \cdot \mathbf{r})$ for each ray, and these must be summed over the cylindrical surface, weighting each point S by the probability $p(r)$ that the reaction occurs at this point. This probability depends both on the density of nuclear matter at the point and on the chance of the incident particle reaching it.

The reaction amplitude is thus given by

$$T = \int p(r)e^{i\mathbf{q} \cdot \mathbf{r}}d^2r, \qquad (6.110)$$

where the integration is over the part of the cylinder for which $r \geqslant R$. If we put $\mathbf{q} \cdot \mathbf{r} = qr \cos \beta$, then

$$T = 2\int_{R'}^{\infty} p(r)e^{iqr \cos \beta}\frac{l}{q}\,d\phi\,\frac{dr}{\cos \beta}$$

$$= 4\pi l\int_{R'}^{\infty} \frac{\cos \sqrt{(q^2r^2 - l^2)}}{\sqrt{(q^2r^2 - l^2)}}\,rp(r)dr, \qquad (6.111)$$

where $R' = R$ if $R > q/l$ and $R' = q/l$ if $R < q/l$. As $p(r)$ rapidly decreases for $r > R$, we can put for the case $R > q/l$, i.e. when the cylinder intersects the nuclear core,

$$T = 4\pi l P(R) \cos \sqrt{(q^2 R^2 - l^2)}/\sqrt{(q^2 R^2 - l^2)}, \qquad (6.112)$$

where $P(R)$ is an average probability. When $R < q/l$, $p(r)$ is small over the whole integration range and T tends to zero. Hence the scattering cross-section is of the form

$$\sigma(\theta) \propto \begin{cases} \cos^2 \sqrt{(q^2 R^2 - l^2)}/(q^2 R^2 - l^2), & R > q/l \\ \to 0, & R < q/l \end{cases}. \qquad (6.113)$$

When $l \neq 0$, the scattering cross-section therefore has a maximum at

$$qR = l. \qquad (6.114)$$

For angles of scattering beyond this, $\sigma(\theta)$ displays the typical form of a diffraction pattern with successively decreasing maxima. The apparent infinity at $qR = l$ is of course due to the approximation made in going from (6.111) to (6.112).

So far we have ignored the absorption effect of the core. Now, except when S and S' are in the equatorial rim of the nucleus, incident particles reaching them will have travelled through unequal regions of nuclear matter. Thus the probability $p(r)$ will not be the same at the two points and interference between the corresponding rays will be incomplete. This will tend to smooth out the diffraction pattern. The matter is made more complicated by a strange phenomenon discovered by McCarthy (1959), who showed by means of a wave mechanical treatment that the nucleus focuses part of the incident wave onto a point on the far side of the nucleus, so that a direct reaction can occur in a region of the surface which, on a simple absorption picture, would be almost inaccessible to an incident particle. This is shown in Fig. 6.7 (frontispiece).

Another point on which caution is indicated concerns conclusion (c) above. When refraction at the nuclear surface is included, this conclusion does not necessarily hold, for, as can be seen from Fig. 6.8, it is then possible to have a zero scattering angle, even though the linear and angular momentum transfer in the direct interaction is far from zero. This may account for the experimentally observed large cross-section at $\theta = 0$ in the excitation of C^{12} to the first excited state by inelastic proton scattering. This is a $0^+ \to 2^+$ transition, so that we must have $l = 2$.

A quantum mechanical approach to inelastic scattering is given in the appendix. There we derive the cross-section formula [see (A.39), (A.50), (A.51)] in *plane wave Born approximation*,

$$\sigma(\theta) = \left(\frac{\mu}{2\pi\hbar^2}\right)^2 \frac{k_f}{k_i} \left| \int e^{i\mathbf{q}\cdot\mathbf{r}_0} V_{fi}(\mathbf{r}_0) \mathrm{d}^3 r_0 \right|^2, \qquad (6.115)$$

where

$$V_{fi}(\mathbf{r}_0) = \int \psi_f^*(\mathbf{r}_1, \ldots, \mathbf{r}_A) \sum_{n=1}^{A} V(\mathbf{r}_0 - \mathbf{r}_n) \, \psi_i(\mathbf{r}_1, \ldots, \mathbf{r}_A) \mathrm{d}^3 r_1 \ldots \mathrm{d}^3 r_A.$$

$$(6.116)$$

Here μ is the reduced mass of the incident particle, ψ_i and ψ_f are the initial and final nuclear wave functions, and $V(\mathbf{r}_0 - \mathbf{r}_n)$ is the

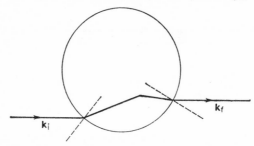

FIG. 6.8. EFFECT OF REFRACTION ON SCATTERING ANGLE

Note that although $\theta = 0$, the initial and final angular momenta differ because of the difference in impact parameters.

interaction potential between the incident particle and the target nucleon

We can write (6.116) as

$$V_{fi}(\mathbf{r}_0) = \int f(\mathbf{r}) V(\mathbf{r}_0 - \mathbf{r}) \mathrm{d}\mathbf{r} \qquad (6.116')$$

where

$$f(\mathbf{r}) = \sum_{n=1}^{A} \int \psi_f^*(\mathbf{r}_1, \ldots \mathbf{r}_{n-1}, \mathbf{r}, \mathbf{r}_{n+1} \ldots \mathbf{r}_A)$$
$$\times \ \psi_i(\mathbf{r}_1, \ldots \mathbf{r}_{n-1}, \mathbf{r}, \mathbf{r}_{n+1} \ldots \mathbf{r}_A)$$
$$\mathrm{d}^3 r_1 \ldots \mathrm{d}^3 r_{n-1} \mathrm{d}^3 r_{n+1} \ldots \mathrm{d}^3 r_A \qquad (6.116'')$$

is known as the *transition density*. The reason for this name is that for the special case in which i = f, i.e. the initial and final states are the same, the expression reduces to the nuclear density. [See (2.39), where we calculated the proton density.] To obtain the transition density, we must make an assumption about the choice of nuclear wave functions, i.e. we must choose the model which best represents the transition. As an example we might take a *single-particle excitation*, for which the target wave function for the initial and final states is the same in all but one of the co-ordinates, while the wave function of the last co-ordinate changes from, say, $\phi_i(\mathbf{r}_A)$ to $\phi_f(\mathbf{r}_A)$. If then we further simplify our calculation by assuming a point interaction of the form†

$$V(\mathbf{r}_0 - \mathbf{r}_A) = V_0\delta(\mathbf{r}_0 - \mathbf{r}_A) \tag{6.117}$$

the integration in (6.116″) can be carried out at once. Using the orthonormality property of the nuclear wave functions, we have

$$f(\mathbf{r}) = \phi_f^*(\mathbf{r})\phi_i(\mathbf{r})$$

and

$$V_{fi}(\mathbf{r}_0) = V_0\phi_f^*(\mathbf{r}_0)\phi_i(\mathbf{r}_0). \tag{6.119}$$

For excitations involving more than one particle, e.g. for those involving collective transitions, it is not possible to write down such a simple expression for the transition density.

We now return to (6.116) and evaluate (6.115) in general, without making any assumptions about nuclear models. We expand $\exp(i\mathbf{q} \cdot \mathbf{r}_0)$ in partial waves [see (3.31)],

$$e^{i\mathbf{q}\cdot\mathbf{r}_0} = \sum_{l=0}^{\infty} (2l + 1)i^l\left(\frac{\pi}{2qr_0}\right)^{\frac{1}{2}} J_{l+\frac{1}{2}}(qr_0)P_l(\cos\theta), \tag{6.120}$$

where $\mathbf{q} \cdot \mathbf{r}_0 = qr_0\cos\theta$. Now ψ_i and ψ_f carry definite orbital angular momenta L_i, L_f, and it can then be shown quite generally that the integral in (6.115) vanishes unless (6.107) is satisfied. Thus

$$\sigma(\theta) \propto \left| \sum_{l=|L_i-L_f|}^{L_i+L_f} \int r_0^{-\frac{1}{2}}J_{l+\frac{1}{2}}(qr_0)P_l(\cos\theta)V_{fi}(\mathbf{r}_0)\mathrm{d}^3r_0 \right|^2. \tag{6.121}$$

If the interaction takes place only in the surface region, i.e. if we make the same assumption as before, then we can take the Bessel function, which is only slowly varying, outside the integral. In cases where only one value of l contributes significantly to $\sigma(\theta)$ we have then finally

$$\sigma(\theta) \propto |J_{l+\frac{1}{2}}(qR)|^2, \tag{6.122}$$

where R is a radius that describes the surface. In practice it is left as a free parameter, in order to fit experimental scattering data. The fact that it is generally found to be much larger than would be expected from electron scattering shows that its physical interpretation is not straightforward. A good example of the kind of fit obtained with (6.116) is shown in Fig. 6.9. Of course, the result (6.122) does not depend on the particular model used; what is different for different models is the constant of proportionality. The

† The three-dimensional δ-function is an obvious generalization of the ordinary Dirac δ-function and obeys the integral

$$\int f(\mathbf{r})\,\delta(\mathbf{r} - \mathbf{a})\,\mathrm{d}^3r = f(\mathbf{a}). \tag{6.118}$$

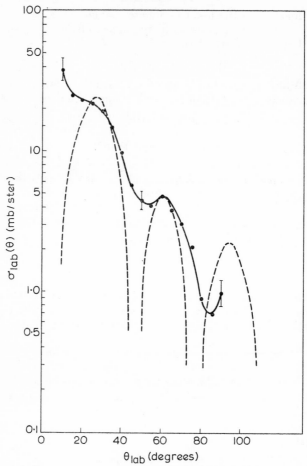

FIG. 6.9. INELASTIC SCATTERING OF 40 MeV PROTONS FROM Mg²⁴

——— Experiment
- - - - Theory

The transition is from the ground state (0+) to the first excited state (2+),
so that the only possible l-value is $l = 2$. The theoretical curve is proportional
to $|J_{5/2}(qR)|^2$ with $R = 5\cdot30$ fm.

[Hintz, N. and Stovall, T., *Phys. Rev.*, **135**, B330 (1964)]

fit in Fig. 6.9 is actually only a relative fit, i.e. the theoretical cross-
section has been adjusted in magnitude to match the experimental
one, and no conclusion regarding the nature of the excitation can be
drawn from it. In fact it is a collective excitation, as the first
excited state in Mg²⁴ is a member of a 0+, 2+, 4+ rotational band,
based on the ground state (see section 5.7).

Another matter that can be seen in Fig. 6.9 is the way in which omission of absorption effects enhances the diffraction pattern, compared with the experimental results. We explained this above in terms of the semi-classical picture. It should be noted that $\sigma(\theta)$ as obtained from (6.122) has a very similar functional dependence on θ to the semi-classical value (6.113), and that the result (6.114) is approximately valid also for the Bessel function.

We next consider the inelastic scattering of heavier particles, such as α-particles. For these the nucleus is almost completely opaque, so that it is no longer correct to assume that the incident wave will reach the far side of the nucleus, even in attenuated form. The argument that an increased absorption will tend to smooth out the diffraction pattern cannot be applied then, and in fact it was found (see Fig. 6.10) that the diffraction pattern was very pronounced indeed. This too can be understood semi-classically

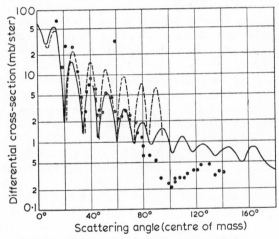

FIG. 6.10. INELASTIC SCATTERING OF 43 MeV α-PARTICLES BY Mg^{24}

- - - - - Adiabatic Fraunhofer calculation
———— Distorted wave Born approximation
The transition is the same as in Fig. 6.9.
[Blair, J. S., *Int. Conf. Nuclear Structure, Kingston* 1960, p. 831]

(Blair, 1959). When the nucleus is completely opaque, then particles scattered in the front surface are subsequently absorbed, and it is essentially impossible for particles ever to reach the back surface. In consequence, scattering can only take place in a narrow equatorial rim, and there is strong interference between particles scattered at diametrically opposite points of the rim. In essence this is similar to Young's double-slit interference.

In his quantum mechanical treatment, Blair points out that a particular simplification is possible for collective excitations. The co-ordinates describing the collective motion vary slowly, compared with those of the incident particle. It is then permissible to " freeze " the motion of the nucleus during the time of the collision. This is known as the *adiabatic approximation* and it enables one to divide the problem into two parts. We first calculate the elastic scattering amplitude $f(\theta, \epsilon)$, which is a function of both the scattering angle and the collective co-ordinates ϵ. The inelastic scattering amplitude is then obtained as the matrix element of $f(\theta, \epsilon)$ between the initial and final nuclear wave functions of the collective motion, i.e.

$$f_{fi}(\theta) \propto \langle \psi_f(\epsilon) \mid f(\theta, \epsilon) \mid \psi_i(\epsilon) \rangle. \qquad (6.123)$$

Because for α-scattering the nucleus is essentially opaque, Blair is able to use Fraunhofer diffraction theory to fit the elastic scattering and the inelastic scattering is then obtained from (6.123). Very good agreement is obtained at small angles, as is seen in Fig. 6.10.

The adiabatic approximation is superior to the plane wave Born approximation, in that it allows for the absorptive distortion of the incident wave and relates the inelastic to the elastic scattering, thereby reducing the number of free parameters in the theory. Another way of achieving these ends is the *distorted wave Born approximation*, referred to in the appendix, which certainly much improves agreement with experiment, when compared with the plane wave approximation. It can also obtain as good and better agreement as the adiabatic approximation (see Fig. 6.10) in cases where the plane wave approximation fails completely (Rost and Austern, 1960). It thus appears to unify the two apparently so different simpler approximations.

A different type of reaction which has been explained through the direct interaction process is the (d,p) reaction. (Butler, 1951.) Here too we have the typical forward peak of the cross-section, together with a diffraction pattern at larger angles. When a deuteron passes close to a nucleus, then because of its very small binding energy and comparatively large size, the neutron may be captured into the nuclear surface, while the proton is repelled by the Coulomb interaction and passes on. Because the neutron is stripped off the deuteron, this process is referred to as a *stripping reaction*. Similar considerations apply to the inverse (p, d) process, the so-called *pick-up reaction*.

If in a stripping reaction the target nucleus has orbital angular momentum L_i and L_f before and after capture of the neutron, then the angular momentum transfer l is given by

$$L_i + L_f + \tfrac{1}{2} \geqslant l \geqslant \mid L_i \pm L_f \pm \tfrac{1}{2} \mid \text{ min} \qquad (6.124)$$

and the scattered protons will have a differential cross-section with a maximum at $qR \simeq l$, where $\mathbf{q} = \mathbf{k}_d - \mathbf{k}_p$ is the momentum transfer. The reaction can therefore give information about the angular momentum of the neutron after capture, which can be correlated with information obtained from the shell model. Further, since the addition of the neutron to the nucleus leads to a definite level of the final nucleus with definite parity, l is restricted to be either even or odd. The position of the maximum of the angular distribution thus by itself determines the parity change between the initial and final states of the nucleus. The absolute value of the cross-section depends on the two-nucleon interaction and the deuteron wave function, both of which are tolerably well though by no means completely known, and also on the probability of the neutron being captured. This is related to the reduced width of the final state for decay into a neutron and the initial state.

Another reaction of considerable interest is the (p, 2p) reaction. At very high incident energies this can be considered as an almost free proton-proton scattering in which the incident proton interacts with a target proton and knocks it out of the nucleus. Energy balance then immediately yields the binding energy of the proton in the target nucleus, through the equation

$$E_0 = E_1 + E_2 + E_B + E_R, \qquad (6.125)$$

where 0, 1 and 2 refer to the incoming and the two outgoing protons, E_B is the binding energy of the knocked-out proton and E_R is the recoil energy of the remaining target nucleus. This can easily be calculated from a knowledge of the proton momenta,

$$\mathbf{p}_0 = \mathbf{p}_1 + \mathbf{p}_2 + \mathbf{p}_R. \qquad (6.126)$$

The experiment is set up symmetrically, i.e. proton co-incidences are observed at equal angles θ with the incident beam and in a plane with it. The differential cross-section of the scattered protons as a function of the angle 2θ between them then gives information on the angular momentum of the target proton before it is knocked out. For free proton-proton scattering, the angle between their final directions of motion in the lab. system is always 90°. (See ex. 3.10.2.) Now, in general, the proton in the target nucleus, which is about to be knocked out, is not at rest in the target lab. system, but moves either towards or away from the incident proton, so that the angle 2θ is either somewhat larger or somewhat smaller than 90°, and the differential cross-section has a mimimum at $\theta \simeq 45°$. The exception to this rule occurs when the target proton is in an s-state for it then has a high probability of being at rest relative to the target nucleus. With the experimental set-up described, the (p, 2p) cross-section thus has a maximum at $\theta = 45°$ when the target proton is in an s-state, while it has a minimum with maxima on either side for target protons in states of higher orbital angular momenta. (Actually the central angle is shifted slightly from 45° owing to target recoil and the fact that the target proton is not free originally.)

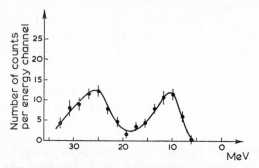

FIG. 6.11. SUMMED ENERGY SPECTRUM FOR THE TWO SCATTERED PROTONS IN THE Li⁷(p, 2p)He⁶ REACTION

Scattering angle is 30°. The spectrum shows that protons were ejected from levels at 11·3 MeV and 25·8 MeV.

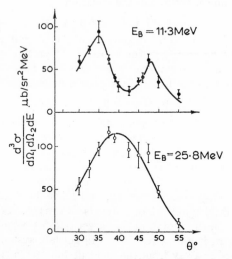

FIG. 6.12. ANGULAR CORRELATION DISTRIBUTIONS FOR THE TWO PEAKS OBSERVED IN THE Li⁷(p, 2p)He⁶ SPECTRA

They show that the more firmly bound proton was ejected from an s-state and the other from a state with $l > 0$.

[Both figures from Tibell, G., Sundberg, O. and Renberg, P. U., *Ark. Fys.*, **25**, 433 (1963).]

Experiments have been performed for a large number of light nuclei, and results for Li[7] are shown in Figs. 6.11 and 6.12. These strikingly confirm the conclusions of the shell model. The protons inside the nucleus clearly occupy definite energy levels with just the correct spacing, and the angular momentum assignments are also in agreement with the shell model.

6.10 Absorption Cross-sections at Very High Energies

At very high energies inelastic processes such as (n, n′) take place via a direct interaction between the incident particle and one target nucleon throughout the whole nucleus, the rest of the nucleus remaining instantaneously unaffected. Such a process can never be elastic, since the target nucleon is bound in the nucleus and its recoil leaves the latter in an excited state. Scattering can in fact only be elastic if it is scattering from the nucleus as a whole. This is what was described by means of the optical potential of section 6.8, so that elastic scattering can give direct information only about the potential and never about the density distribution. It is different with inelastic processes and nuclear reactions. The higher the incident energy, the more nearly do these become two-particle inter-actions, so that an incident particle of very high energy that is absorbed by the nucleus (and this includes being inelastically scat-tered) measures the nuclear density distribution.

When the energy of the incident particle is in the GeV region, the de Broglie wavelength is so short that the particle can be treated classically. Furthermore, it is most unlikely at these energies for the incident particle to react with more than one of the tar-get nucleons on its way through the nucleus. It is therefore possible to pic-ture it as proceeding in a straight line into the nu-cleus, being scattered once by a target nucleon and then proceeding in a straight line out of the nucleus (see Fig. 6.13). The scattering is essentially a two-body process, the cross-section for which we shall denote by $\bar{\sigma}$. This is

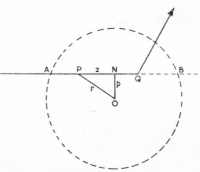

FIG. 6.13. PATH OF A HIGH-ENERGY PARTICLE THROUGH A NUCLEUS

The impact parameter of the path is p, and the co-ordinates of the particle are (p, z). The boundary of the nucleus, which is not of course sharp, has been indicated by the broken line.

not necessarily the same as the free cross-section which can be obtained experimentally from the scattering of the incident particle by a free nucleon similar to the target nucleon, since the target nucleon is not free, but the effect of the nuclear binding must be small at these energies and will be neglected. The picture then is of an incident beam which enters the nucleus and is attenuated exponentially with an absorption coefficient $K(r) = \rho(r)\bar{\sigma}$. The total attenuation is obtained by integrating over the length of the possible

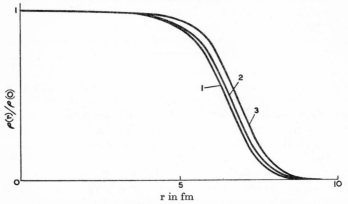

FIG. 6.14. NUCLEAR DENSITY DISTRIBUTION FOR Pb,
as obtained from (1) elastic negaton scattering, (2) neutron absorption,
(3) pion absorption.
[From L. R. B. Elton, *Revs. Mod. Phys.*, **30**, p. 557 (1958).]

path AB in Fig. 6.13, so that the probability of interaction along the path is

$$1 - e^{-S(p)}, \text{ where } S(p) = \int_A^B \rho[\sqrt{(p^2 + z^2)}]\bar{\sigma}dz. \qquad (6.127)$$

As the nucleus does not really have a sharp boundary, we replace the limits of integration by $-\infty$ and $+\infty$, and assume $\rho(r)$ to be given by a functional form similar to that of example 2.9.2. Actually, a form which is both more realistic physically and in this case simpler mathematically, is

$$\rho(r) = \rho(0)\frac{1 + \exp[-c^2/a^2]}{1 + \exp[(r^2 - c^2)/a^2]}. \qquad (6.128)$$

The total absorption cross-section is obtained by integrating the probability (6.127) over the whole nuclear volume, i.e.

$$\sigma_{\text{abs}} = \int_0^\infty \left[1 - \exp\left\{-\int_\infty^\infty \rho[\sqrt{(p^2 + z^2)}]\bar{\sigma}dz\right\}\right]2\pi p dp. \qquad (6.129)$$

At first sight this is not a very hopeful method of attack. As we are only measuring one quantity, σ_{abs}, we can only obtain one nuclear parameter, say the equivalent uniform radius. If however we assume that the nuclear parameters are functions of A in the way we found from negaton scattering, then measurement of σ_{abs} for a range of nuclides gives much more information. The experiments have been performed for neutrons and pions of 1·4 GeV incident energy, and the most important result is (Elton, 1958) that the half-way radius and the $90 - 10$ per cent transition region are almost identical with those for negaton scattering. The results for Pb are shown in Fig. 6.14. This is probably the strongest evidence for our belief that the neutron and proton distributions in nuclei are essentially the same, although the small difference between the negaton scattering and the absorption cross-section results may indicate that the neutrons occupy a slightly larger volume.

6.11. EXAMPLES

6.11.1. Obtain explicit expressions for λ_0 and μ_0 in (6.97) on the assumption that $W_0/V_0 \ll 1$. Show that in the limit of zero incident energy, σ_{sc}^0 remains finite, but σ_{re}^0 becomes infinite, $O(k^{-1})$. Is this in conflict with the rules established in section 6.2 for maximum cross-sections?

6.11.2. By comparing (6.35) with (3.130), show that the scattering length for the elastic scattering of zero energy nucleons by nuclei is given by

$$\frac{1}{R_X - a} = \frac{1}{R_X} \lim_{k \to 0} f(R_X). \tag{6.130}$$

(The theory of resonance scattering is developed in terms of the scattering length in Bethe and Morrison, *Elementary Nuclear Theory*, Chapter 20.)

6.11.3. Show that optical potential scattering at low energies leads to S-wave resonances of the total cross-section when

$$K_0 \cot kR = - k \tan K_0 R,$$

where $K_0^2 = 2MV_0/\hbar^2$, and that the mass numbers of the nuclides for which such resonances occur depend only on the product $V_0 r_0^2$. For the values of the optical potential given in section 6.8, show that such resonances occur in the neighbourhood of $A = 11, 55, 150$. (This is actually the way in which the constant C is determined from the experimental results.)

[Hint : S-wave resonances occur when λ_0 passes through $(n + \frac{1}{2})\pi$.]

6.11.4. On the same graph plot the cross-section for elastic S-wave scattering of neutrons of energy below 1 MeV by a nucleus of radius $R = 5·0$, $5·4$, $5·5$ fm, (a) according to the continuum theory, (b) according to the optical model. Take the depth of the nuclear potential to be $V_0 = 42$ MeV in both cases. Explain the differences in the results in the three cases.

6.11.5. With the density distribution (6.128) show that the $90 - 10$ per cent transition region is

$$s = \sqrt{(c^2 + 2a^2 \ln 3)} - \sqrt{(c^2 - 2a^2 \ln 3)} \tag{6.131}$$

and that

$$S(p) = a\rho(0)\bar{\sigma}(1 + e^{-c^2/a^2}) \int_0^\infty \frac{x^{-1/2}}{1 + \exp{(x - k)}} \, dx \tag{6.132}$$

where $k = (c^2 - p^2)/a^2$.

[This last integral has been tabulated by J. McDougall and E. C. Stoner, *Phil. Trans. Roy. Soc. A*, **237**, 67 (1939).]

6.11.6. Use the results of examples 2.9.12 and 6.11.5 to evaluate σ_{abs} for the absorption of $1\cdot4$ GeV neutrons by Pb, taking s and c as given by (2.17) and (2.18). Repeat, increasing c by $0\cdot2$ fm. The experimental two-body cross-section is $\bar{\sigma} = 43$ mb.

[Experimentally it is found that σ_{abs} for Pb and $1\cdot4$ GeV neutrons is 1,730 mb.]

6.11.7. Use (6.15) and (6.12) to show that the total cross-section σ and the forward scattering amplitude for elastic scattering, $f(0)$, are related by

$$\sigma = \frac{4\pi}{k} \operatorname{Im} f(0). \tag{6.133}$$

This is called the *optical theorem*.

CHAPTER 7

Nuclear Disintegration

7.1 Nuclear Instability

As was explained in section 1.4, a nucleus is stable if its binding energy is greater than the total binding energy of any fragments into which it can be imagined to disintegrate. Such a nucleus can of course be disintegrated if energy is supplied to it. Conversely an unstable nucleus will disintegrate spontaneously with liberation of energy, which appears as the kinetic energy of the disintegration fragments. We shall now investigate these statements more closely, using the semi-empirical formula (5.34) for the binding energy of a nucleus.

Although a nucleus can disintegrate instantaneously into several fragments, this becomes progressively less likely as the number of fragments increases and we shall restrict ourselves to disintegrations into two fragments. Let us take the case then of a nucleus of mass number A which disintegrates into two fragments with mass numbers αA and $(1-\alpha)A$, and charge numbers βZ and $(1-\beta)Z$ respectively. We then apply (5.34) to the nucleus (A, Z). Here we can neglect the term $\delta(A, Z)$, since this is so small that it is significant only in β-decays, where the energy differences involved are very much smaller than in nuclear disintegrations. Hence the difference in the binding energy between two daughter nuclei and the parent nucleus is

$$\triangle B = 17 \cdot 8 A^{2/3}[1 - \alpha^{2/3} - (1 - \alpha)^{2/3}]$$
$$+ 0 \cdot 71\ Z^2 A^{-1/3}[1 - \beta^2 \alpha^{-1/3} - (1 - \beta)^2 (1 - \alpha)^{-1/3}]$$
$$+ 95 Z^2 A^{-1}[1 - \beta^2 \alpha^{-1} - (1 - \beta)^2 (1 - \alpha)^{-1}]. \quad (7.1)$$

It is easily seen (see example 7.6.1) that this is a maximum when $\alpha = \beta = \frac{1}{2}$, so that

$$\triangle B_{\max} = - 4 \cdot 6 A^{2/3} + 0 \cdot 26 Z^2 A^{-1/3}. \quad (7.2)$$

Disintegration is possible if $\triangle B > 0$. Hence from (7.2) nuclei can disintegrate provided

$$Z^2 > 17 \cdot 7 A. \quad (7.3)$$

According to these simple energy considerations, spontaneous fission should occur for all nuclei with Z greater than approximately

40. Further with increasing Z fission into fragments that are more and more asymmetric becomes possible, although for any particular Z the probability of fission will always be greatest for symmetric fragments and decrease with increasing asymmetry.

The fallacy in the above argument is immediately obvious. For disintegration to take place it is not sufficient that the energy of the initial state be greater than the sum of the energies of the fragments when separated by infinite distances. This is the criterion that has been used so far. What is required is that the energy of the initial state be greater than the sum of the energies of the fragments when separated by any finite distance. Now because of the Coulomb repulsion between the fragments the energy at a finite distance of separation is certainly greater than that at an infinite distance. The correct condition for spontaneous fission was in fact deduced in section 5.4 from the liquid drop model. The considerations there are essentially equivalent to energy considerations and they lead to the criterion

$$Z^2 > 52A. \qquad (7.4)$$

In induced fission a neutron coalesces with a nucleus forming a compound nucleus in an excited state. Such a nucleus will of course be fissile for much lower values of Z than those given by (7.4), since the excitation energy is available to overcome the Coulomb barrier. In this way for instance the nucleus U^{236} (formed by bombarding U^{235} with neutrons) is fissile. However, instead of breaking up largely into fragments of mass number $A = 118$ the preferred mass numbers are approximately 96 and 140. It may be that this is the result of a shell structure effect, due to the magic neutron numbers 50 and 82.

The type of disintegration discussed so far is not only spontaneous, but instantaneous, since the arguments employed have been essentially classical. It is well known however that the quantum mechanical tunnel effect, to be discussed more fully in following sections, makes it possible for transitions to occur with a finite lifetime, provided they are energetically possible, by leakage through the intervening barrier. Thus while (7.4) is the condition for instantaneous fission, (7.3) is the condition for fission with a finite lifetime. The reason why, except in the case of U^{238}, it is not observed experimentally, is of course that the lifetimes involved are far too long.

Since leakage through a barrier by a particle becomes progressively more likely the lighter the particle, this process may become observable if a nucleus splits up into two fragments, one of which is very much lighter than the other. An investigation of (7.1) for the emission of light particles (see example 7.6.2) shows that such an emission is possible only for values of Z greatly in excess of those occurring in nature, except for α-particles where the threshold is $Z = 75$. Experimentally the lightest natural α-radioactive nuclides have $Z = 83$ and it can be shown (example 7.6.3) that for lighter nuclides the lifetimes are too long for observation.

7.2 Jeffreys' Approximation

Before discussing the tunnel effect in detail, we must deal with an approximate method for solving the wave equation, which is very useful in many cases. It was originally derived by Jeffreys and applied to problems in quantum mechanics independently by Wentzel, Kramers and Brillouin. For that reason it is often referred to as the WKB method. (Other permutations of W, K and B are also employed.) It is essentially an expansion of the solution of the wave equation in powers of $\hbar$. As according to the correspondence principle classical mechanics is the limit of quantum mechanics as $\hbar \to 0$, the first term in the expansion gives the classical solution. For that reason Jeffreys' approximation, which we shall take as far as terms of order $\hbar$, is most useful for problems which are almost classical.

We start with the radial wave equation in the form (3.57),†

$$\frac{\mathrm{d}^2 u}{\mathrm{d}r^2} + \left[\frac{2\mu}{\hbar^2} \{E - V(r)\} - \frac{l(l+1)}{r^2} \right] u = 0 \tag{7.5}$$

and put

$$u(r) = A \exp\left\{ \frac{\mathrm{i}}{\hbar} s(r) \right\} \tag{7.6}$$

and

$$\frac{2\mu}{\hbar^2} \{E - V(r)\} - \frac{l(l+1)}{r^2} = k^2(r). \tag{7.7}$$

Then (7.5) reduces to

$$\mathrm{i}\hbar \frac{\mathrm{d}^2 s}{\mathrm{d}r^2} - \left(\frac{\mathrm{d}s}{\mathrm{d}r} \right)^2 + \hbar^2 k^2 = 0 \tag{7.8}$$

On expanding $s(r)$ in powers of $\hbar$,

$$s(r) = s_0(r) + \hbar s_1(r) + \dots \tag{7.9}$$

and comparing coefficients of like powers of $\hbar$, we obtain

$$- s_0'^2 + \hbar^2 k^2 = 0 \tag{7.10}$$

$$\mathrm{i}s_0'' - 2s_0' s_1' = 0, \text{ etc.} \tag{7.11}$$

† In the notation of this chapter the reduced mass of the system is μ, not $\frac{1}{2}M$ as was the case in Chapter 3.

[Note that it follows from (7.7) that k is of order $\hbar^{-1}$.] Integration of these equations leads to

$$s_0(r) = \pm \, \hbar \int^r k(x)\mathrm{d}x, \quad s_1(r) = \tfrac{1}{2}\mathrm{i} \ln k(r) \tag{7.12}$$

where arbitrary constants have been omitted as they can be absorbed in A in (7.6). Hence to $O(\hbar)$,

$$u(r) = A[k(r)]^{-\frac{1}{2}} \exp\{\pm\, \mathrm{i}\textstyle\int^r k(x)\mathrm{d}x\}, \quad [k(r)]^2 > 0. \tag{7.13}$$

If $[k(r)]^2 < 0$, we put $\mathrm{i}k(r) = \kappa(r)$ and obtain similarly

$$u(r) = B[\kappa(r)]^{-\frac{1}{2}} \exp\{\pm\, \textstyle\int^r \kappa(x)\mathrm{d}x\}, \quad [k(r)]^2 > 0. \tag{7.14}$$

When is this a good approximation? On comparing (7.12) with (7.8) we see that the zeroth approximation, $s(r) = s_0(r)$ is obtained by omitting the first term from (7.8). The first approximation will thus be good provided

$$\left| \, \mathrm{i}\hbar\frac{\mathrm{d}^2 s}{\mathrm{d}r^2} \, \right| \ll \left| \left(\frac{\mathrm{d}s}{\mathrm{d}r}\right)^2 \right|. \tag{7.15}$$

To order $\hbar$ this yields

$$|\, \hbar s_0'' \,| \ll |\, s_0' \,|^2$$

i.e.

$$\left| \frac{k'}{k^2} \right| \ll 1. \tag{7.16}$$

Now

$$-\frac{k'}{k^2} = \frac{\mathrm{d}}{\mathrm{d}r}\!\left(\frac{1}{k}\right) = \frac{\mathrm{d}\lambdabar}{\mathrm{d}r}, \tag{7.17}$$

where $\lambdabar$ is the reduced local de Broglie wavelength, $\lambdabar = \lambda/2\pi$. It is called local, because it clearly varies from point to point. The condition for the validity of Jeffreys' approximation in a given region is therefore that the change of the reduced wavelength within the region should be very much smaller than the dimensions of the region. Similarly, when $k^2 < 0$, the criterion for validity is

$$-\left| \frac{\kappa'}{\kappa^2} \right| \ll 1 \tag{7.18}$$

although it is not of course possible to interpret this condition in terms of a wavelength.

It often happens that the expression in square brackets in (7.5) changes sign for some value of r, say r_0. Let us assume for the sake of definiteness that it is positive for $r > r_0$ and negative for $r < r_0$. Then the solution is of the form

$$\left.\begin{aligned} u(r) &= A[k(r)]^{-\frac{1}{2}} \exp\{\pm\, \mathrm{i}\textstyle\int^r k(x)\mathrm{d}x\} && r \gg r_0 \\ u(r) &= B[\kappa(r)]^{-\frac{1}{2}} \exp\{\pm\, \textstyle\int^r \kappa(x)\mathrm{d}x\} && r \ll r_0. \end{aligned}\right\} \tag{7.19}$$

In the neighbourhood of $r = r_0$ the approximation is invalid since at $r = r_0$ the local wavelength becomes infinite and so changes very rapidly. It is however possible (see for example Schiff, *Quantum Mechanics*, Chapter VII) to find connexion formulae which join the value of the function for $r \ll r_0$ to the correct value for $r \gg r_0$ and vice versa. These formulae are

$$[\kappa(r)]^{-\frac{1}{2}} \exp\left\{ - \int_r^{r_0} \kappa(x)\mathrm{d}x \right\} \to 2[k(r)]^{-\frac{1}{2}} \cos\left\{ \int_{r_0}^r k(x)\mathrm{d}x - \frac{\pi}{4} \right\} \quad (7.20)$$

$$[\kappa(r)]^{-\frac{1}{2}} \exp\left\{ + \int_r^{r_0} \kappa(x)\mathrm{d}x \right\} \leftarrow [k(r)]^{-\frac{1}{2}} \cos\left\{ \int_{r_0}^r k(x)\mathrm{d}x + \frac{\pi}{4} \right\}. \quad (7.21)$$

It is important to use the arrows only in the directions indicated. Thus if in (7.21) we used the arrow in the opposite direction, then a small admixture of the negative exponential term, which would be quite negligible on the left-hand side, would result in a small, but unknown, phase shift on the right-hand side; i.e

$$[\kappa(r)]^{-\frac{1}{2}} \exp\left\{ + \int_r^{r_0} \kappa(x)\mathrm{d}x \right\} \to [k(r)]^{-\frac{1}{2}} \cos\left\{ \int_{r_0}^r k(x)\mathrm{d}x + \frac{\pi}{4} + \delta \right\} \quad (7.21)$$

where $|\delta|$ is small.

7.3 Penetration through a Square Barrier

Although the problem of barrier penetration can be solved by means of Jeffreys' approximation for a physically realistic potential,

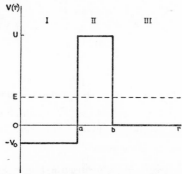

FIG. 7.1. SQUARE POTENTIAL TO ILLUSTRATE BARRIER PENETRATION

we shall first of all solve it for a potential which makes it possible to obtain an exact solution. This will enable us to investigate the quantum mechanics of the problem without being troubled with mathematical difficulties. The method is adapted from one originally devised by Gamow.

We take as our potential (see Fig. 7.1)

$$V = \begin{cases} -V_0, & 0 < r < a, \text{ region I,} \\ U, & a < r < b, \text{ region II,} \\ 0, & b < r, \quad \text{region III,} \end{cases} \tag{7.22}$$

and try to evaluate the probability that a particle which is initially inside the barrier will leak through it. We restrict ourselves to S-waves, for which $l = 0$. The wave equation

$$\frac{d^2u}{dr^2} + \frac{2\mu}{\hbar^2}(E - V)u = 0 \tag{7.23}$$

in the three regions reduces to

$$\left. \begin{array}{l} u_I'' + p^2 u_I = 0 \\ u_{II}'' - q^2 u_{II} = 0 \\ u_{III}'' + k^2 u_{III} = 0 \end{array} \right\} \tag{7.24}$$

where

$$k^2 = 2\mu E/\hbar^2, \quad p^2 = 2\mu(E + V_0)/\hbar^2, \quad q^2 = 2\mu(U - E)/\hbar^2. \tag{7.25}$$

We require a solution which vanishes at the origin and corresponds to an outgoing wave at infinity. Hence

$$\left. \begin{array}{l} u_I = A \sin pr, \\ u_{II} = B_+ e^{q(r-a)} + B_- e^{-q(r-a)}, \\ u_{III} = C e^{ik(r-b)}. \end{array} \right\} \tag{7.26}$$

The continuity conditions at $r = a$ and $r = b$ yield

$$\left. \begin{array}{l} A \sin pa = B_+ + B_- \\ Ap \cos pa = q(B_+ - B_-) \\ B_+ e^s + B_- e^{-s} = C \\ q(B_+ e^s - B_- e^{-s}) = ikC \end{array} \right\} \tag{7.27}$$

where we have put $s = q(b - a)$. Eliminating B_+ and B_-, we have

$$2qC = A[(q \sin pa + p \cos pa)e^s + (q \sin pa - p \cos pa)e^{-s}]. \tag{7.28}$$

Now the condition that the equations (7.27), which are homogeneous in A, B_+, B_- and C, should have a non-zero solution leads to

$$(k + iq)(q \sin pa + p \cos pa)e^s$$
$$+ (k - iq)(q \sin pa - p \cos pa)e^{-s} = 0. \tag{7.29}$$

Hence $\quad\quad \dfrac{C}{A} = \dfrac{i}{k + iq}(q \sin pa - p \cos pa)e^{-s}. \tag{7.30}$

Equation (7.29) gives the energy levels in which the particle can exist inside the barrier. For those energies (7.30) shows, since

$s \gg 1$, that $C \ll A$, so that there is a small but finite probability for the particle to be outside the barrier. For all other energies we should find that $C \gg A$. For such energies the particle can exist outside the barrier, but cannot have come from inside.

Let us now investigate (7.29) further. Since $s \gg 1$, the energy levels are to a first approximation given by the roots of the equation

$$q \sin pa + p \cos pa = 0. \tag{7.31}$$

We take the root corresponding to a level to be given by q_0, p_0, k_0 and obtain a better approximation by putting

$$q = q_0 + \triangle q,\ p = p_0 + \triangle p,\ k = k_0 + \triangle k \tag{7.32}$$

in (7.29). It follows from (7.25) that

$$- q_0 \triangle q = p_0 \triangle p = k_0 \triangle k = \frac{\mu}{\hbar^2} \triangle E. \tag{7.33}$$

On substituting (7.33) and (7.32) into (7.29), and evaluating to first order in $\triangle E$ we have

$$\left(\frac{1 - ap_0}{q_0^2} + \frac{1 + aq_0}{p_0^2} \right) \triangle E = \frac{2\hbar^2}{\mu} \frac{k_0 - iq_0}{k_0 + iq_0} e^{-2s_0}. \tag{7.34}$$

Thus the energy levels correspond to complex values of the energy.

The existence of complex energy levels requires some explanation. The wave equation (7.23) from which we started is the time-independent Schrödinger equation, which is suitable for the solution of stationary problems. A radioactive decay is certainly not a stationary problem and so we should have used the time dependent equation (Schiff, *Quantum Mechanics*, Chapter II)

$$i\hbar \frac{\partial \Psi}{\partial t} = - \frac{\hbar^2}{2\mu} \nabla^2 \Psi + V \Psi. \tag{7.35}$$

If E is the energy of the system, we can write

$$\Psi(\mathbf{r},\, t) = \psi(\mathbf{r}) \exp\left(- \frac{i}{\hbar} Et \right) \tag{7.36}$$

and (7.35) then reduces to

$$\nabla^2 \psi + \frac{2\mu}{\hbar^2} (E - V) \psi = 0. \tag{7.37}$$

For S-waves $\psi(\mathbf{r}) = u(r)/r$, and (7.37) specializes to (7.23).

If, as is usual, E is real, then (7.36) shows that

$$|\, \Psi(\mathbf{r},\, t)\, | = |\, \psi(\mathbf{r})\, |,$$

so that the total probability of finding the particle anywhere remains constant in time. If E is complex, this is no longer the case.

Let us write

$$E = \alpha - i\beta \tag{7.38}$$

where α and β are real and positive. Then

$$\int_{\Omega} \Psi^* \Psi d\tau = e^{-2\beta t/\hbar} \int_{\Omega} \psi^* \psi d\tau \tag{7.39}$$

so that the probability of finding the particle in any given volume Ω decreases exponentially, with time, as it should do for a radio-active decay. [Clearly in (7.38) we must have $\beta > 0$, as otherwise the probability will increase with time.] The radio-active decay constant λ (see section 1.6) is given by

$$\lambda = \frac{2\beta}{\hbar}. \tag{7.40}$$

It should be pointed out that the fact that E is complex leads to another complication. At large distances we have from (7.26)

$$u = C \exp \left\{ \frac{i}{\hbar} (r - b) \sqrt{[2\mu(\alpha - i\beta)]} \right\}$$

$$\simeq C \exp \left\{ \frac{i}{\hbar} (r - b) \sqrt{(2\mu\alpha)} \right\} \exp \left\{ (r - b) \frac{\lambda}{2} \sqrt{\left(\frac{\mu}{2\alpha} \right)} \right\} \tag{7.41}$$

so that the amplitude of the wave increases exponentially with distance. However, this is merely the consequence of the fact that the probability of finding the particle at a distance r from the source of radioactivity depends on the strength of the source at a time r/v earlier, where $v = \sqrt{(2\alpha/\mu)}$ is the velocity of the particle. At that time the source was stronger by a factor $\exp \{ \lambda r \sqrt{(\mu/2\alpha)} \}$, which is just exactly the exponentially increasing factor in $|u|^2$ in (7.41).

We return to a discussion of the energy levels of the system. As will be clear from our treatment of the compound nucleus in the last chapter, these energy levels cannot be completely sharp, since there is a finite probability of the system decaying. They are in fact of exactly the same type as the almost stable levels introduced in the discussion of resonances of the compound nucleus in section 6.6. The uncertainty in such an energy level was given by (6.27), which in our case leads to a level width

$$\Gamma(\alpha) = \hbar\lambda. \tag{7.42}$$

Substituting (7.42) into (7.38), we obtain, for the complex energy level, the value

$$E = \alpha - \tfrac{1}{2} i\Gamma(\alpha). \tag{7.43}$$

The same considerations can now be applied to the energy levels of the compound nucleus. In section 6.6 we discussed a compound nucleus that decays either through the entrance channel α (compound elastic scattering) or through another channel β (nuclear reaction proper). The corresponding widths were Γ_n^α and Γ_n^β [see (6.57)]. The nth energy level of this compound nucleus is therefore given by

$$E = E_n - \tfrac{1}{2}i\Gamma_n^\alpha - \tfrac{1}{2}i\Gamma_n^\beta. \tag{7.44}$$

So far we have obtained such complex energy levels by using non-conserving boundary conditions for our wave function, e.g. in (7.26). We now describe the possible decay through the reaction channel β by adding an imaginary term $H^{(1)}$ with eigenvalues $-\tfrac{1}{2}i\Gamma_n^\beta$ to the Hamiltonian H of the system. Then instead of the equation

$$H\psi = E\psi \tag{7.45}$$

we have to solve the equation

$$(H + H^{(1)})\psi^{(1)} = E\psi^{(1)}. \tag{7.46}$$

This can be rewritten as

$$H\psi^{(1)} = (E - H^{(1)})\psi^{(1)} = (E + \tfrac{1}{2}i\Gamma_n^\beta)\psi^{(1)}. \tag{7.47}$$

Comparing (7.45) and (7.47), we see that

$$\psi(E) = \psi^{(1)}(E + \tfrac{1}{2}i\Gamma_n^\beta) \tag{7.48}$$

so that the logarithmic derivative on the boundary (6.34) is

$$f(E) = f^{(1)}(E + \tfrac{1}{2}i\Gamma_n^\beta) \simeq f^{(1)}(E) + \tfrac{1}{2}i\Gamma_n^\beta \frac{df^{(1)}}{dE} \tag{7.49}$$

if Γ_n^β is small, as is the case at low energies. But $f^{(1)}(E)$ is what we called $f(E)$ in (6.43), since there we assumed that $\Gamma_n^\beta = 0$, and so $f^{(1)}(E)$ is real. Further we showed quite generally [see (6.40)] that for any f

$$\text{Im} f < 0. \tag{7.50}$$

Hence

$$\frac{df^{(1)}}{dE} < 0 \tag{7.51}$$

and

$$\frac{d}{dE}(kR_X + \zeta) = -\frac{1}{KR_X}\cos^2(KR_X + \zeta)\frac{df}{dE} > 0. \tag{7.52}$$

Therefore $kR_X + \zeta$ in (6.43) is a monotonically increasing function of E. This is the result that we assumed true in section 6.6.

Similar considerations will now give us the length of the mean-free-path of nucleons in nuclear matter. If the optical potential inside nuclear matter is given by (6.91) and (6.95) then the velocity of a nucleon in nuclear matter is given by

$$v = \frac{\hbar}{M} \operatorname{Re} k' = \left(\frac{2}{M}\right)^{1/2} \operatorname{Re}[E + V_0 + iW_0]^{1/2} \qquad (7.53)$$

where k' is the complex wave number of the nucleon inside nuclear matter. The lifetime of the nucleon is given by (7.40)

$$\tau = \frac{1}{\lambda} = \frac{\hbar}{2W_0} \qquad (7.54)$$

and since ξ is small, the velocity of the nucleon is approximately, from (7.53),

$$v = \left[\frac{2(E + V_0)}{M}\right]^{1/2} . \qquad (7.55)$$

Hence the mean-free-path in nuclear matter is

$$L = v\tau = \frac{\hbar}{2W_0} \left[\frac{2(E + V_0)}{M}\right]^{1/2} . \qquad (7.56)$$

From the definition of the lifetime τ it follows at once that the probability of the nucleon not having coalesced into the compound nucleus after travelling a distance x through nuclear matter is

$$p = e^{-x/L}. \qquad (7.57)$$

7.4 Alpha-disintegration

To obtain a more realistic model of α-decay we now postulate that the α-particle moves in the field of the daughter nucleus. The corresponding potential will be Coulomb right up to the nuclear boundary, will then drop sharply and remain constant throughout the nucleus in the manner of the optical potential for nucleons. To a good approximation we can represent it by

$$V = \begin{cases} -V_0, & r < R \\ \dfrac{2Ze^2}{r}, & r > R \end{cases} \qquad (7.58)$$

where Z is the atomic number of the daughter nucleus. Here V_0 must be much less than it was in the case of the optical potential for nucleons, since even the lowest state of the α-particle in the well is unbound. Fortunately none of the results to be derived depend in any way critically on the magnitude of V_0, and we shall probably not be far wrong if we take $V_0 \simeq 10$ MeV. For a given energy E of the α-particle, space will again be divided into three regions (see Fig. 7.2)

$$\text{region I,} \qquad r < R$$
$$\text{region II,} \qquad R < r < b = 2Ze^2/E \qquad (7.59)$$
$$\text{region III,} \qquad b < r.$$

We shall again restrict ourselves to S-waves since it turns out that higher angular momenta do not lead to significantly different results.

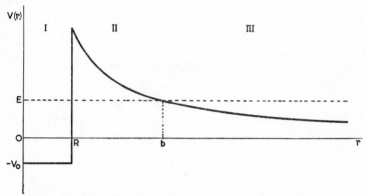

FIG. 7.2. ONE-PARTICLE POTENTIAL FOR ALPHA-DECAY

If we put

$$\left. \begin{aligned} p^2 &= \frac{2\mu}{\hbar^2}\,(E + V_0) \\[4pt] [\kappa(r)]^2 &= \frac{2\mu}{\hbar^2}\!\left(\frac{2Ze^2}{r} - E\right), \quad r < b \\[4pt] [k(r)]^2 &= \frac{2\mu}{\hbar^2}\!\left(E - \frac{2Ze^2}{r}\right), \quad r > b \end{aligned} \right\} \qquad (7.60)$$

where, as before, μ is the reduced mass of the system α-*particle* + *residual nucleus*, then the radial equation (7.23) can be written

$$\left. \begin{aligned} u_{\mathrm{I}}'' + p^2 u_{\mathrm{I}} &= 0 \\ u_{\mathrm{II}}'' - [\kappa(r)]^2 u_{\mathrm{II}} &= 0 \\ u_{\mathrm{III}}'' + [k(r)]^2 u_{\mathrm{III}} &= 0. \end{aligned} \right\} \qquad (7.61)$$

In all practical cases

$$\kappa(R) \gg \kappa'(R)/[\kappa(R)]^2, \quad p, \quad R^{-1} \qquad (7.62)$$

and we shall very much simplify the algebra by neglecting small quantities accordingly.

The boundary conditions are the same as in the previous section, but we have now to use Jeffreys' method to solve the radial equation in regions II and III. Hence

$$u_I = A \sin pr,$$

and, using (7.14),

$$u_{II} = B_+[\kappa(r)]^{-\frac{1}{2}} \exp\left[\int_R^r \kappa(x) dx\right] + B_-[\kappa(r)]^{-\frac{1}{2}} \exp\left[-\int_R^r \kappa(x) dx\right]. \tag{7.64}$$

Because of the sudden change in potential at $r = R$, $\kappa(R) \neq 0$ and so Jeffreys' approximation is valid right up to $r = R$. Applying the usual boundary condition we have

$$\left.\begin{array}{l} A \sin pR = (B_+ + B_-)[\kappa(R)]^{-\frac{1}{2}} \\ Ap \cos pR = (B_+ - B_-)[\kappa(R)]^{\frac{1}{2}}. \end{array}\right\} \tag{7.65}$$

Across $r = b$ we bridge the wave function by means of the connexion formulae (7.20) and (7.21), the latter having to be used against the arrow. Therefore

$$\left.\begin{array}{l} [\kappa(r)]^{-\frac{1}{2}} \exp\left[\int_R^r \kappa(x) dx\right] \\ \qquad \to 2\exp\left[\int_R^b \kappa(x) dx\right][k(r)]^{-\frac{1}{2}} \cos\left[\int_b^r k(x) dx - \frac{\pi}{4}\right] \\ [\kappa(r)]^{-\frac{1}{2}} \exp\left[-\int_R^r \kappa(x) dx\right] \\ \qquad \to \exp\left[-\int_R^b \kappa(x) dx\right][k(r)]^{-\frac{1}{2}} \cos\left[\int_b^r k(x) dx + \frac{\pi}{4} + \delta\right] \end{array}\right\} \tag{7.66}$$

where δ is small. Hence

$$u_{III} = 2B_+[k(r)]^{-\frac{1}{2}} \cos\left[\int_b^r k(x) dx - \frac{\pi}{4}\right] e^s$$

$$\qquad + B_-[k(r)]^{-\frac{1}{2}} \cos\left[\int_b^r k(x) dx + \frac{\pi}{4} + \delta\right] e^{-s} \tag{7.67}$$

where

$$s = \int_R^b \kappa(x) dx. \tag{7.68}$$

This represents an outgoing wave if

$$2B_+ e^{\frac{i\pi}{4}+s} + B_- e^{-\frac{i\pi}{4}-i\delta-s} = 0,$$

i.e.

$$B_+ = \tfrac{1}{2} i e^{-i\delta} e^{-2s} B_-. \tag{7.69}$$

As before the possible energy levels are given by the condition for a non-zero solution of the set of homogeneous equations (7.65) and (7.69),

$$[\kappa(R) \sin pR - p \cos pR] \mathrm{i} \mathrm{e}^{-\mathrm{i}\delta} \, \mathrm{e}^{-s} - 2[\kappa(R) \sin pR + p \cos pR] \mathrm{e}^s = 0.$$

To a first approximation an energy level E is again given by

$$\kappa(R) \sin pR + p \cos pR = 0 \qquad (7.70)$$

and the next approximation yields for the correction $\triangle E$ to E,

$$2R[\kappa(R) \cos pR - p \sin pR] \frac{\mu}{\hbar^2} \triangle E = \mathrm{i} p \mathrm{e}^{-\mathrm{i}\delta} [\kappa(R) \sin pR - p \cos pR] \mathrm{e}^{-2s}$$

which with the help of (7.70) and (7.62) reduces to

$$\frac{\mu}{\hbar^2} \triangle E = -\frac{\mathrm{i} p^2}{R \kappa(R)} \mathrm{e}^{-\mathrm{i}\delta} \, \mathrm{e}^{-2s}. \qquad (7.71)$$

As δ is small, the imaginary part of $\triangle E$ is given very nearly by

$$-\beta = -\frac{\hbar^2 p^2}{\mu R \kappa(R)} \mathrm{e}^{-2s} \qquad (7.72)$$

which again turns out to be negative, indicating that the process described is a decay. The corresponding decay constant in full is

$$\lambda = \frac{4(E + V_0)}{\sqrt{[2\mu R(2Ze^2 - ER)]}} \exp\left\{-2 \int_R^b \sqrt{\left[\frac{2\mu}{\hbar^2}\left(\frac{2Ze^2}{r} - E\right)\right]} \mathrm{d}r\right\}. \quad (7.73)$$

Let us take a closer look at the structure of this formula, and in particular at the integral in the exponential factor. It is clear from Fig. 7.2 that a small increase in the energy E will have the effect of reducing both the integrand and the range of integration. Furthermore this integral is the power of an exponential. Because of this λ is an extremely sensitive function of E, and actual calculations show (see example 7.6.4) that doubling E may change λ by as much as 10^{15}. Variations of the other factors of λ are quite negligible compared with this huge variation due to the exponential factor. This is fortunate, since slightly different formulations of the problem lead to some variation in the other factors, but do not change the exponential factor. For different treatments the reader should consult different books on quantum mechanics and nuclear physics. Hardly any two give the same treatment.

As is well known, the successful explanation by Gamow of the enormous variation of α-decay lifetimes for quite small variations of the energies of the α-particles was one of the first great triumphs

8

of wave mechanics. Gamow showed that if the known values of λ and E for different radioactive decays were substituted in (7.73), almost exactly the same value of R was obtained each time (see example 7.6.5). This method of obtaining a value of the nuclear radius was referred to in section 2.2.1.

Although the theory as presented gives such good agreement with experiment, it can hardly be more than a first approximation to the truth, and the good agreement must be due to the insensitivity of the results to detailed assumptions about the mechanism of the

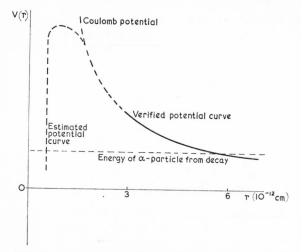

FIG. 7.3. ILLUSTRATION OF RUTHERFORD'S EXPERIMENTS ON URANIUM

The fully drawn part of the potential curve has been verified by α-particle scattering experiments.

decay. The essential part of the theory is its requirement that the decay takes place through barrier penetration. This requirement is based firmly on fact. In a famous experiment Rutherford showed that, while the spontaneous decay of uranium produced α-particles of 4 MeV energy, the scattering of 8·8 MeV α-particles by uranium was in accordance with a pure Coulomb interaction. The outer slope of the potential barrier therefore reaches a height of at least 8·8 MeV corresponding to a distance from the centre of the nucleus of 3×10^{-12} cm. The α-particles from the decay of uranium then do not overcome this barrier, but, tunnelling through it appear with an energy of 4 MeV at a distance of 6×10^{-12} cm from the centre of the nucleus (see Fig. 7.3).

The portion of the potential curve on Fig. 7.3 which is drawn as a broken line is not only estimated, it is very considerably over-simplified. Once the α-particle is inside the nucleus, it is no longer possible to describe the wave function of the system by means of a single co-ordinate. The problem here is exactly the same as in the treatment of the compound nucleus in the last chapter. There it was found that if it is assumed that a nucleus has a well-defined surface, then observable effects were determined by the value of the wave function and its derivative on the nuclear surface and a knowledge of the behaviour of the wave function inside the nucleus was not required. For that reason our simple theory is bound to give very similar results to a theory based on the compound nucleus. This is in fact so (see Blatt and Weisskopf, *Theoretical Nuclear Physics*, Chapter 11).

7.5 Fission

So far we have only investigated (7.73) for the variation of λ with E for a given μ. We now conclude further that, as μ increases, λ decreases rapidly. This is important because radioactive emission by a heavy nucleus of particles as heavy as O^{16} is energetically possible. The lifetimes of such decays are however unobservably long. There is no contradiction between this conclusion and the observed fact that most nuclides beyond $A = 230$ are spontaneously fissile into roughly equal fragments. For although spontaneous fission is the result of a barrier penetration, the detailed theory out-lined in sections 7.3 and 7.4 is not applicable, since it depends essentially on the fact that the emitted particle is much lighter than the remaining nucleus.

The great interest that exists in the problem of fission is due to the immense practical importance of the process rather than to any intrinsic fundamental importance of it to an understanding of nuclear physics. At present no satisfactory quantum mechanical treatment of it exists, which is not surprising in view of the great complexity of the phenomenon. The simple liquid drop theory, which was briefly discussed in section 5.4, is certainly inadequate, in that it predicts fission into two equal fragments as the most likely process. Experi-mentally this is found to be so only for fission induced by highly energetic particles. For spontaneous fission and for fission induced by slow neutrons asymmetric fission is a great deal more probable. Thus the most common fragments from the spontaneous fission of U^{238} have mass numbers $A = 98$ and 140, and this decay mode is about a hundred times more probable than symmetric fission. It has been suggested that the prevalence of asymmetric fission is due to the increased stability of fragments in the neighbourhood of the closed shell of 82 neutrons, but again there is no detailed argument to support this statement. That fission tends to become symmetric at high energies is however supporting evidence, since shell model effects decrease in importance with increasing energy. (A full account of the properties of fission is given in an excellent appendix to W. E. Burcham, *Nuclear Physics*.)

7.6. EXAMPLES

7.6.1. Show that ΔB in (7.1) is a maximum for $\alpha = \frac{1}{2}$, $\beta = \frac{1}{2}$. If $\alpha = \beta$, plot Z as a function of α for $\Delta B = 0$, and show that the fission

$$Cd^{108} \rightarrow Kr^{81} + Mg^{27}$$

is energetically possible.

7.6.2. Use the semi-empirical formula for the binding energy (5.34) to show that the emission of an α-particle by a nucleus is possible for A greater than about 180, but that the emission of a proton or a neutron is not possible for even the heaviest nuclides known.

[Note that the semi-empirical formula must not be used for the α-particle, and that $Z \simeq 0.4A$ for $A > 120$.]

7.6.3. Calculate the energy released in the reaction

$$Pb^{209} \rightarrow Hg^{205} + \alpha$$

using the experimental masses of the nuclides. Show that the decay has an unobservably long lifetime.

7.6.4. The α-particles emitted in the decays of Ra^{226} and Th^{226} have energies 4·9 and 6·5 MeV respectively. If it is assumed that the nuclear radius is the same for both nuclides, show that the ratio of the lifetimes is approximately 2.5×10^{7}.

7.6.5. The experimental half-lives of the decays in example 7.6.4 are 1600 years and 31 min respectively. Show that the α-decay radii of the two nuclides differ by at most a few per cent from each other.

CHAPTER 8

Interaction of Nuclei with the Electromagnetic Field

In Chapter 2 we discussed the interaction of a nucleus with an electrostatic and a magnetostatic field and found that a nucleus was charged and that it possessed an electric quadrupole and a magnetic dipole moment. In the present chapter we are going to discuss the interaction of a nucleus with an electromagnetic field. This results in the absorption by and emission from the nucleus of quanta of electromagnetic radiation. We shall first treat the problem in a fairly general way to indicate the possible transitions that a nuclear system can undergo in the presence of an electromagnetic field, and we shall then treat in some detail the case where the nuclear system consists of a neutron and a proton. (See sections 8.6 and 8.7.)

In the similar atomic problem the emitted radiation is in the visible or ultraviolet region, so that the wavelength λ is some hundred or even thousand times larger than the linear dimensions of the system d, i.e. $d/\lambda \ll 0{\cdot}01$. The γ-rays emitted and absorbed in nuclear transitions often have energies of several MeV, which yield values of $0{\cdot}1$ to $0{\cdot}01$ for the ratio d/λ in this case. The methods of approximation commonly employed in the atomic case—which depend on the smallness of d/λ—can therefore still be used, but it is often necessary to take the approximation a stage further than is usual in the case of atoms.

When a nucleus emits or absorbs radiation, it changes its quantum mechanical state, so that we are not dealing here with a stationary state, but with a transition between states. The formalism for this is outlined in the appendix, to which reference will be made.

8.1 Absorption and Induced Emission of Radiation

We start by investigating the interaction of a nucleon with the electromagnetic field. To do this we have to determine the Hamiltonian (A.2) which now consists of a nuclear part H_0 and a part ϵH_1, due to the interaction between the nucleon and the field. We can then evaluate the transition probability (A.27) and interpret it in terms of the emission and absorption of quanta of the field by the nucleon.

The electromagnetic field is given by Maxwell's equations

$$\nabla \times \mathbf{H} = \frac{1}{c} \frac{\partial \mathbf{E}}{\partial t} + \frac{4\pi}{c} \mathbf{j} \qquad (8.1)$$

$$\nabla \times \mathbf{E} = -\frac{1}{c} \frac{\partial \mathbf{B}}{\partial t} \qquad (8.2)$$

$$\mathbf{B} = \mathbf{H} + 4\pi\mathbf{M} \qquad (8.3)$$

$$\nabla . \mathbf{B} = 0 \qquad (8.4)$$

$$\nabla . \mathbf{E} = 4\pi\rho \qquad (8.5)$$

$$\nabla . \mathbf{j} = -\frac{\partial \rho}{\partial t} \qquad (8.6)$$

where $\mathbf{H}$ and $\mathbf{E}$ are the magnetic and electric field vectors, $\mathbf{M}$ is the intensity of magnetization, and ρ and $\mathbf{j}$ are the charge and current densities. If $\mathbf{M} = 0$, i.e. if there is no magnetic material present, then $\mathbf{E}$ and $\mathbf{H}$ can be expressed in terms of the vector and scalar potential $\mathbf{A}$ and ϕ,

$$\mathbf{E} = -\frac{1}{c} \frac{\partial \mathbf{A}}{\partial t} - \nabla\phi, \quad \mathbf{H} = \nabla \times \mathbf{A}. \qquad (8.7)$$

These definitions do not determine the potentials uniquely, and we can choose $\mathbf{A}$ so that

$$\nabla . \mathbf{A} = 0 \qquad (8.8)$$

everywhere. The field equations then reduce to

$$-\nabla^2\mathbf{A} + \frac{1}{c^2} \frac{\partial^2 \mathbf{A}}{\partial t^2} + \frac{1}{c} \frac{\partial}{\partial t}(\nabla\phi) = \frac{4\pi}{c} \mathbf{j} \qquad (8.9)$$

$$\nabla^2\phi = -4\pi\rho. \qquad (8.10)$$

If $\rho = 0$ and $\mathbf{j} = 0$ everywhere, a further simplification is possible. In that case the only solution of (8.10) that is finite everywhere is $\phi = $ constant. Hence $\nabla\phi = 0$ throughout space and the term depending on ϕ in (8.9) drops out. The electromagnetic field in a vacuum is therefore completely determined by the vector potential $\mathbf{A}$ that satisfies the homogeneous wave equation

$$\nabla^2\mathbf{A} - \frac{1}{c^2} \frac{\partial^2 \mathbf{A}}{\partial t^2} = 0. \qquad (8.11)$$

We first calculate the probability of absorption of photons by a nucleon placed in an electromagnetic field. We assume that the effect of the nucleon on the field is negligible, so that the electromagnetic field is given by (8.11). Classically the Hamiltonian of a nucleon of mass M and electric charge e,† moving in an electromagnetic potential $\mathbf{A}(\mathbf{r}, t)$ as well as having some other potential energy $V(r)$, which in our case is due to nuclear forces, is

$$H = \frac{1}{2M}\left(\mathbf{p} - \frac{e}{c}\mathbf{A}\right)^2 + V. \tag{8.12}$$

(See for instance Corben and Stehle, *Classical Mechanics*, chapter 17.) The transition to quantum mechanics is carried out in the usual manner,

$$\mathbf{r} \to \mathbf{r}, \quad \mathbf{p} \to -i\hbar\nabla \tag{8.13}$$

so that (8.12) transforms into (see also example 8.8.1)

$$H = -\frac{\hbar^2}{2M}\nabla^2 + \frac{ie\hbar}{Mc}\mathbf{A}\cdot\nabla + \frac{e^2}{2Mc^2}\mathbf{A}^2 + V. \tag{8.14}$$

We are interested in the plane wave solution of (8.11)

$$\mathbf{A} = \mathbf{A}_0\, e^{i(\kappa\cdot\mathbf{r} - \kappa ct)} + \mathbf{A}_0^*\, e^{-(\kappa\cdot\mathbf{r} - \kappa ct)} \tag{8.15}$$

where the wave vector κ points in the direction of propagation of the wave, and its magnitude is the wave number κ. The circular frequency of the wave is of course given by $\omega = \kappa c$. Because of (8.8) we have

$$\mathbf{A}_0\cdot\kappa = 0 \tag{8.16}$$

i.e. the polarization of the wave is perpendicular to the direction of its propagation. On comparing (8.15) with (A.30) and (A.32) we see that the first term will lead to absorption and the second to emission of radiation.

The electric and magnetic vectors of the field are given by (8.7) with $\nabla\phi = 0$,

$$\left.\begin{aligned}
\mathbf{E} &= i\kappa\mathbf{A}_0\, e^{i(\kappa\cdot\mathbf{r} - \kappa ct)} - i\kappa\mathbf{A}_0^*\, e^{-i(\kappa\cdot\mathbf{r} - \kappa ct)} \\
\mathbf{H} &= i\kappa\times\mathbf{A}_0\, e^{i(\kappa\cdot\mathbf{r} - \kappa ct)} - i\kappa\times\mathbf{A}_0^*\, e^{-i(\kappa\cdot\mathbf{r} - \kappa ct)}.
\end{aligned}\right\} \tag{8.17}$$

The flow of energy across unit surface area perpendicular to κ in unit time is given by the Poynting vector

$$\mathbf{S} = \frac{c}{4\pi}\mathbf{E}\times\mathbf{H} \tag{8.18}$$

which when averaged over an oscillation reduces to

$$\bar{\mathbf{S}} = \frac{\kappa c}{2\pi}\,|\,\mathbf{A}_0\,|^2\,\kappa. \tag{8.19}$$

† We should really consider a particle with intrinsic magnetic moment as well as intrinsic electric charge, since elementary particles have both. For the sake of simplicity we shall not do this.

In applying perturbation theory to (8.14) we are going to restrict ourselves to first-order terms in the electric charge e, so that we neglect the terms $e^2\mathbf{A}^2/2Mc^2$ in (8.12) and finally take for the quantities in (A.2),

$$H_0 = -\frac{\hbar^2}{2M} \nabla^2 + V(r), \quad H_1(t) = \frac{i\hbar^{\frac{3}{2}}}{Mc^{\frac{1}{2}}} \mathbf{A} \cdot \nabla, \quad \epsilon = \frac{e}{\sqrt{(\hbar c)}}. \quad (8.20)$$

The expansion parameter ϵ must be chosen so as to be dimensionless. It is in fact the square root of the fine structure constant and equal to $137^{-\frac{1}{2}}$, which is small. Our use of perturbation theory is therefore justified.

To apply the same approach to the interaction of an electromagnetic field with a nucleus, the perturbation part of the Hamiltonian can be simply generalized to

$$H_1(t) = \frac{i\hbar^{\frac{3}{2}}}{Mc^{\frac{1}{2}}} \mathbf{A} \cdot \sum_{m=1}^{Z} \nabla_m \quad (8.21)$$

where the summation is over all the protons in the nucleus and ∇_m is the gradient operator for the co-ordinates of the mth proton. The centre of mass of the nucleus is again taken as the origin of co-ordinates.

In problems of absorption and emission of radiation by a nucleon we generally require both the initial and final states to be discrete stationary states, and it is then necessary to suppose that the radiation has a finite spread in energy. In practice this is of course always the case, as is seen from the finite width of spectral lines. If the total intensity of energy per unit volume in the frequency range $\triangle\omega$ in the neighbourhood of ω is $I(\omega)\triangle\omega$, then the flux of energy through unit area is

$$cI(\omega)\triangle\omega = \frac{\kappa^2 c}{2\pi} |\mathbf{A}_0|^2 \quad (8.22)$$

by (8.19). From (A.30) and (8.20) we have

$$H_1 = \frac{i\hbar^{\frac{3}{2}}}{Mc^{\frac{1}{2}}} \mathbf{A}_0 \cdot e^{i\mathbf{\kappa} \cdot \mathbf{r}} \quad (8.23)$$

and on substituting this in (A.42) we have for the absorption probability

$$w_{\text{abs}} = \frac{2\pi}{\hbar} \frac{e^2}{\hbar c} \frac{\hbar^3}{M^2 c} |\mathbf{A}_0|^2 \left| \int u_f^* e^{i\mathbf{\kappa} \cdot \mathbf{r}} \frac{\partial u_i}{\partial n_{\mathbf{a}}} d\tau \right|^2 \delta(E_f - E_i - \hbar\omega)$$

$$= \frac{4\pi^2 e^2 \hbar}{M^2 \omega^2} I(\omega)\triangle\omega \left| \int u_f^* e^{i\mathbf{\kappa} \cdot \mathbf{r}} \frac{\partial u_i}{\partial n} d\tau \right|^2 \delta(E_f - E_i - \hbar\omega) \quad (8.24)$$

by (8.22). Here u_i and u_f are the initial and final states of the nucleon, and $\partial/\partial n$ denotes differentiation along the direction $\mathbf{A}_0$. Integrating over ω results in

$$w_{\text{abs}} = \frac{4\pi^2 e^2}{M^2 \omega_{if}^2} I(\omega_{if}) \left| \int u_f^* \, e^{i\kappa \cdot \mathbf{r}} \frac{\partial u_i}{\partial n} \, d\tau \right|^2, \qquad (8.25)$$

where

$$\hbar \omega_{if} = E_f - E_i \qquad (8.26)$$

and κ is now equal to ω_{if}/c. Similarly for emission,

$$w_{\text{eml}} = \frac{4\pi^2 e^2 I(\omega_{if'})}{M^2 \omega_{if'}^2} \left| \int u_{f'}^* \, e^{-i\kappa \cdot \mathbf{r}} \frac{\partial u_i}{\partial n} \, d\tau \right|^2 \qquad (8.27)$$

where u_f and $u_{f'}$ are of course different final states. It is important to realize that (8.27) gives the transition probability for induced emission, i.e. the emission of quanta $\hbar \omega_{if'}$ in consequence of the presence of a radiation field of energy density $I(\omega_{if'})$.

8.2 Spontaneous Emission of Radiation

Spontaneous emission is the result of the interaction of a nucleon with the electromagnetic field due to its own charge, current and magnetic moment. It cannot be deduced from the theory as presented so far, since in the absence of an external field there is no reason why classically transitions should occur at all. The full quantum theory will yield the correct expression, but we shall see that it is possible to go quite a long way using a purely classical approach, the formulae at the end being translated correctly, though not very convincingly, into quantum mechanics.

Suppose the charge, current and magnetic moment densities of the nucleon are given by

$$\rho(\mathbf{r}, t) = \rho_0(\mathbf{r}) \, e^{-i\omega t} + \text{c.c.} \qquad (8.28)$$

$$\mathbf{j}(\mathbf{r}, t) = \mathbf{j}_0(\mathbf{r}) \, e^{-i\omega t} + \text{c.c.} \qquad (8.29)$$

$$\mathbf{M}(\mathbf{r}, t) = \mathbf{M}_0(\mathbf{r}) \, e^{-i\omega t} + \text{c.c.} \qquad (8.30)$$

These distributions generate electric and magnetic fields

$$\left. \begin{aligned} \mathbf{E}(\mathbf{r}, t) &= \mathbf{E}_0(\mathbf{r}) \, e^{-i\omega t} + \text{c.c.} \\ \mathbf{H}(\mathbf{r}, t) &= \mathbf{H}_0(\mathbf{r}) \, e^{-i\omega t} + \text{c.c.} \end{aligned} \right\} \qquad (8.31)$$

where it follows from (8.1) and (8.2) that

$$\nabla \times \mathbf{H}_0 = -i\kappa \mathbf{E}_0 + \frac{4\pi}{c} \mathbf{j}_0 \qquad (8.32)$$

and

$$\nabla \times \mathbf{E}_0 = i\kappa(\mathbf{H}_0 + 4\pi\mathbf{M}_0). \qquad (8.33)$$

We eliminate $\mathbf{E}_0$ and obtain for $\mathbf{H}_0$ the equation

$$\nabla \times \nabla \times \mathbf{H}_0 = \kappa^2(\mathbf{H}_0 + 4\pi\mathbf{M}_0) + \frac{4\pi}{c}\nabla \times \mathbf{j}_0. \qquad (8.34)$$

Now it is shown in books on vector analysis that, provided $\mathbf{H}_0$ is expressed in Cartesian components,

$$\begin{aligned}\nabla \times \nabla \times \mathbf{H}_0 &= \nabla(\nabla \cdot \mathbf{H}_0) - \nabla^2\mathbf{H}_0 \\ &= -4\pi\nabla(\nabla \cdot \mathbf{M}_0) - \nabla^2\mathbf{H}_0 \end{aligned} \qquad (8.35)$$

where we have used (8.3) and (8.4). Hence finally the equation of the magnetic field is the inhomogeneous wave equation

$$\nabla^2\mathbf{H}_0 + \kappa^2\mathbf{H}_0 = -\frac{4\pi}{c}\nabla \times \mathbf{j}_0 - 4\pi\kappa^2\mathbf{M}_0 - 4\pi\nabla(\nabla \cdot \mathbf{M}_0). \qquad (8.36)$$

The solution of this equation corresponding asymptotically to an outgoing spherical wave can be shown to be (see examples 8.8.2 and 8.8.3)

$$\mathbf{H}_0(\mathbf{r}) = \frac{1}{c}\int \frac{e^{i|\kappa\mathbf{r}-\mathbf{r}'|}}{|\mathbf{r}-\mathbf{r}'|}\{\nabla \times \mathbf{j}_0(\mathbf{r}') + c\kappa^2\mathbf{M}_0(\mathbf{r}') + c\nabla[\nabla \cdot \mathbf{M}_0(\mathbf{r}')]\}d\tau'. $$
$$(8.37)$$

The electric field is obtained by substituting this value of $\mathbf{H}_0$ into (8.32).

The energy radiated is given by the Poynting vector (8.18). Substituting (8.31) into this, we obtain for its time average

$$\begin{aligned}\bar{\mathbf{S}} &= \frac{\omega}{2\pi}\int_0^{2\pi/\omega} \frac{c}{4\pi}[\mathbf{E}_0(\mathbf{r})e^{-i\omega t} + \text{c.c.}] \times [\mathbf{H}_0(\mathbf{r})e^{-i\omega t} + \text{c.c.}]dt \\ &= \frac{c}{4\pi}[\mathbf{E}_0(\mathbf{r}) \times \mathbf{H}_0^*(\mathbf{r}) + \text{c.c.}]. \end{aligned} \qquad (8.38)$$

If this is evaluated on a large sphere of radius r, it gives the energy passing through one square centimetre of the sphere per second. The energy radiated into a solid angle $d\Omega$ in direction (θ, ϕ) is therefore given by

$$U(\theta, \phi)d\Omega = r^2\bar{S}(r, \theta, \phi)d\Omega. \qquad (8.39)$$

So far this is entirely classical. To obtain the corresponding quantum mechanical expression we first note that the energy is not emitted continuously, but in quanta of energy $\hbar\omega$. The transition probability per second for emission of a single quantum in direction (θ, ϕ) is therefore given by

$$w(\theta, \phi)\mathrm{d}\Omega = \frac{U(\theta, \phi)\mathrm{d}\Omega}{\hbar\omega}. \tag{8.40}$$

Also the classical expressions $\rho_0(\mathbf{r})$, $\mathbf{j}_0(\mathbf{r})$ and $\mathbf{M}_0(\mathbf{r})$ must be replaced by their quantum mechanical analogues. For a stationary system with wave function ψ the charge and current densities are given by

$$e\psi^*\psi \quad \text{and} \quad e\psi^*\mathbf{v}\psi = \frac{e}{M}\psi^*\mathbf{p}\psi \tag{8.41}$$

respectively. For the corresponding expressions for a system which makes a transition from state u_i to state u_f it is thus plausible to take

$$\rho_0(\mathbf{r}) = eu_f^*u_i \tag{8.42}$$

$$\mathbf{j}_0(\mathbf{r}) = \frac{e}{2M}\left\{u_f^*(\mathbf{p}u_i) + (\mathbf{p}u_f)^*u_i\right\} \tag{8.43}$$

where $\mathbf{p}$ is of course given by (8.13). It is necessary to symmetrize $\mathbf{j}_0(\mathbf{r})$ in the way indicated, as otherwise (8.6) would not be satisfied, i.e. charge would not be conserved (see example 8.8.4). Lastly $\mathbf{M}_0(\mathbf{r})$ arises from the intrinsic moment $(e\hbar/2Mc)\mu\boldsymbol{\sigma}$ of a nucleon, so that we have

$$\mathbf{M}_0(\mathbf{r}) = \frac{e\hbar}{2Mc}u_f^*\mu\boldsymbol{\sigma}u_i \tag{8.44}$$

where $\boldsymbol{\sigma}$ is the spin operator.

8.3 Multipole Transitions due to Absorption

We proceed to investigate the matrix element for absorption. Apart from a factor this is the integral in (8.25). However, instead of $A_0\partial/\partial n$ it is more convenient now to write $\mathbf{A}_0 \cdot \nabla$ and we then have

$$\langle f \mid \epsilon H_1 \mid i \rangle = \frac{ie\hbar}{Mc}\int u_f^*e^{i\boldsymbol{\kappa}\cdot\mathbf{r}}(\mathbf{A}_0 \cdot \nabla)u_i\mathrm{d}\tau. \tag{8.45}$$

To study the integral further we notice that the integrand vanishes for $r > R$, where R is the distance at which the nuclear wave functions become negligible. Now it was mentioned in the introduction to this chapter that the wavelength of the emitted or absorbed radiation is considerably greater than the nuclear dimensions so that for even the most energetic radiation $\boldsymbol{\kappa} \cdot \mathbf{r} \ll 1$ in the region where the nuclear wave functions u_i and u_f are large. The series obtained by expanding $e^{i\kappa \cdot r}$ in (8.45) is therefore rapidly convergent, and we shall only consider the first two terms,

$$\mathcal{M}_1 = \frac{ie\hbar}{Mc} \int u_f^*(\mathbf{A}_0 \cdot \nabla)u_i \mathrm{d}\tau \qquad (8.46)$$

and

$$\mathcal{M}_2 = -\frac{e\hbar}{Mc} \int u^*(\kappa \cdot \mathbf{r})(\mathbf{A}_0 \cdot \nabla)u_i \mathrm{d}\tau. \qquad (8.47)$$

(In the atomic case it is generally not necessary to go beyond $\mathcal{M}_1$.)

The interaction between the nucleon and the field is the result of two effects, an electric effect, due to the charge distribution ρ and a magnetic effect due to the moment of the current distribution $\mathbf{r} \times \mathbf{j}$. We must split up the matrix element accordingly, and quantum mechanically this amounts to splitting it up into terms depending on $u_f^* u_i$, and terms depending on $u_f^* \, \mathbf{r} \times \nabla u_i$. This we must now do.

We start by integrating $\mathcal{M}_1$ by parts,

$$\int u_f^*(\mathbf{A}_0 \cdot \nabla)u_i \mathrm{d}\tau = -\int u_i(\mathbf{A}_0 \cdot \nabla)u_f^* \mathrm{d}\tau$$

$$= \tfrac{1}{2} \int \{u_f^*(\mathbf{A}_0 \cdot \nabla)u_i - u_i(\mathbf{A}_0 \cdot \nabla)u_f^*\}\mathrm{d}\tau \qquad (8.48)$$

where we have added the left-hand side to both sides and divided by two. We now drop the brackets around $(\mathbf{A}_0 \cdot \nabla)$, replace $\mathbf{A}_0$ by the identical expression $\nabla(\mathbf{A}_0 \cdot \mathbf{r})$ and integrate by parts,

$$\int u_f^*(\mathbf{A}_0 \cdot \nabla)u_i \mathrm{d}\tau = \int u_f^* \mathbf{A}_0 \cdot \nabla u_i \mathrm{d}\tau$$

$$= \int u_f^* \nabla(\mathbf{A}_0 \cdot \mathbf{r}) \cdot \nabla u_i \mathrm{d}\tau$$

$$= -\int (\mathbf{A}_0 \cdot \mathbf{r})(\nabla u_f^* \cdot \nabla u_i + u_f^* \nabla^2 u_i)\mathrm{d}\tau. \qquad (8.49)$$

Hence

$$\mathcal{M}_1 = -\frac{ie\hbar}{2Mc} \int (\mathbf{A}_0 \cdot \mathbf{r})(u_f^* \nabla^2 u_i - u_i \nabla^2 u_f^*)\mathrm{d}\tau$$

$$= -\frac{ie}{\hbar c}(E_f - E_i) \int u^*(\mathbf{A}_0 \cdot \mathbf{r})u_i \mathrm{d}\tau \qquad (8.50)$$

where use has been made of the wave equation of the nucleon

$$-\nabla^2 u_i + \frac{2M}{\hbar^2} V u_i = \frac{2M}{\hbar^2} E_i u_i \qquad (8.51)$$

and similarly for u_f. But $E_f - E_i$ is the energy absorbed from the electromagnetic field, i.e.

$$E_f - E_i = \kappa c \hbar \qquad (8.52)$$

so that finally we obtain for the first term of the matrix element

$$\mathscr{M}_1 = - ie\kappa \mathbf{A}_0 . \int u_f^* \mathbf{r} u_i d\tau \qquad (8.53)$$

which is of the required form, depending only on the charge distribution $u_f^* u_i$. The structure of this term is closely related to that of the electric dipole moment (2.41), and so we say that it is the matrix element of an electric dipole transition.

We next split $\mathscr{M}_2$ into two parts,

$$\mathscr{M}_2 = \mathscr{M}_2^{(1)} + \mathscr{M}_2^{(2)} \qquad (8.54)$$

where

$$\mathscr{M}_2^{(1)} = - \frac{e\hbar}{2Mc} \int u_f^* [(\mathbf{\kappa} . \mathbf{r})(\mathbf{A}_0 . \nabla) - (\mathbf{A}_0 . \mathbf{r})(\mathbf{\kappa} . \nabla)] u_i d\tau \quad (8.55)$$

and

$$\mathscr{M}_2^{(2)} = - \frac{e\hbar}{2Mc} \int u_f^* [(\mathbf{\kappa} . \mathbf{r})(\mathbf{A}_0 . \nabla) + (\mathbf{A}_0 . \mathbf{r})(\mathbf{\kappa} . \nabla)] u_i d\tau. \quad (8.56)$$

The reason for this is that

$$(\mathbf{\kappa} . \mathbf{r})(\mathbf{A}_0 . \nabla) - (\mathbf{A}_0 . \mathbf{r})(\mathbf{\kappa} . \nabla) = (\mathbf{\kappa} \times \mathbf{A}_0) . (\mathbf{r} \times \nabla) \qquad (8.57)$$

which is of the correct form for an effect due to the current distribution. Now

$$- i\mathbf{r} \times \nabla = \mathbf{L} \qquad (8.58)$$

the angular momentum operator in units of $\hbar$, and from (2.26) we see that the corresponding magnetic dipole operator (in nuclear magnetons) is

$$\mathbf{\mu}_l = \mathbf{L}. \qquad (8.59)$$

Hence

$$\mathscr{M}_2^{(1)} = - \frac{ie\hbar}{2Mc} (\mathbf{\kappa} \times \mathbf{A}_0) . \int u_f^* \mathbf{\mu}_l u_i d\tau \qquad (8.60)$$

giving a magnetic dipole transition.

Finally we treat $\mathscr{M}_2^{(2)}$ in the same way as $\mathscr{M}_1$.

$$\int u_f^* [(\mathbf{\kappa} . \mathbf{r})(\mathbf{A}_0 . \nabla) + (\mathbf{A}_0 . \mathbf{r})(\mathbf{\kappa} . \nabla)] u_i d\tau$$

$$= \int u_f^* \nabla [(\mathbf{A}_0 . \mathbf{r})(\mathbf{\kappa} . \mathbf{r})] . \nabla u_i d\tau$$

$$= - \int (\mathbf{A}_0 . \mathbf{r})(\mathbf{\kappa} . \mathbf{r})(\nabla u_f^* . \nabla u_i + u_f^* \nabla^2 u_i) d\tau \quad (8.61)$$

and also

$$\int u_j^*[(\kappa \cdot \mathbf{r})(\mathbf{A}_0 \cdot \nabla) + (\mathbf{A}_0 \cdot \mathbf{r})(\kappa \cdot \nabla)]u_i d\tau$$

$$= - \int u_i[(\kappa \cdot \mathbf{r})(\mathbf{A}_0 \cdot \nabla) + (\mathbf{A}_0 \cdot \mathbf{r})(\kappa \cdot \nabla)]u_j^* d\tau. \quad (8.62)$$

Combining these results we obtain

$$\mathscr{M}_2^{(2)} = \frac{e\hbar}{4Mc} \int (\mathbf{A}_0 \cdot \mathbf{r})(\kappa \cdot \mathbf{r})(u_j^*\nabla^2 u_i - u_i\nabla^2 u_j^*)d\tau$$

$$= \tfrac{1}{2}e\kappa \int u_j^*(\mathbf{A}_0 \cdot \mathbf{r})(\kappa \cdot \mathbf{r})u_i d\tau. \quad (8.63)$$

This is again a charge distribution effect, but since the integrand now contains r^2 as a factor, we have an electric quadrupole transition. Higher-order terms will contain successively higher powers of r. We shall not derive these, but merely quote the final result for the complete expansion of the matrix element (see example 8.8.5),

$$\langle f \mid \epsilon H_1 \mid i \rangle = - i \sum_{l=1}^{\infty} \left\{ \frac{e\kappa}{l!} \int u_j^*(\mathbf{A}_0 \cdot \mathbf{r})(i\kappa \cdot \mathbf{r})^{l-1}u_i d\tau \right.$$

$$\left. + \frac{e\hbar}{2Mc} \cdot \frac{2l}{(l+1)!} \int u_j^*(i\kappa \cdot \mathbf{r})^{l-1}(\kappa \times \mathbf{A}_0) \cdot \boldsymbol{\mu}_l u_i d\tau \right\}. \quad (8.64)$$

We have succeeded in our task of splitting up the matrix element into a part due to static charge effects and one due to current effects. It is now also possible to give a more direct physical interpretation of the power series expansion, successive terms of which are referred to as multipole moments of order l (dipole, quadrupole, etc.). The expression $(\mathbf{A}_0 \cdot \mathbf{r})$ $(i \cdot \mathbf{r})^{l-1}$ is proportional to $\mathbf{r}^l$ and hence can be expressed in terms of Legendre polynomials of order up to l. Hence an electric 2^l-pole carries angular momentum l and can change the angular momentum of the nuclear state by up to l units. This is true too of the magnetic 2^l-pole, for although the expression, $(i\kappa \cdot \mathbf{r})^{l-1}(\kappa \times \mathbf{A}_0) \cdot \boldsymbol{\mu}_l$ is proportional to only $\mathbf{r}^{l-1}$, $\boldsymbol{\mu}_l$ is proportional to the angular momentum *operator* $\mathbf{L}$ and this operator carries unit angular momentum. [Feenberg and Pake, *Notes on the Quantum Theory of Angular Momentum*, chapter 4.] The fact that the series (8.64) is rapidly convergent now means that transitions of nuclear systems due to interaction with an electromagnetic field become progressively less likely, the larger the change in angular momentum of the system.

8.4 Multipole Transitions due to Spontaneous Emission

We now turn to spontaneous emission and consider (8.37). For large r the vectors $\mathbf{r}$ and κ are parallel, since the electromagnetic wave is propagated away from the origin. Let θ be the angle between $\mathbf{r}$ and $\mathbf{r}'$. Then $r' \ll r$ in the region where the integrand is large, and we can write

$$
\frac{e^{i\kappa|\mathbf{r}-\mathbf{r}'|}}{|\mathbf{r}-\mathbf{r}'|} = (r^2 - 2rr'\cos\theta + r'^2)^{-\frac{1}{2}} \exp\left[i\kappa(r^2 - 2rr'\cos\theta + r'^2)^{\frac{1}{2}}\right]
$$

$$
\sim \frac{1}{r}\left(1 - \frac{r'}{r}\cos\theta\right) \exp\left[i\kappa r\left(1 - \frac{r'}{r}\cos\theta\right)\right]
$$

$$
\sim \frac{1}{r} e^{i(\kappa r - \mathbf{\kappa}\cdot\mathbf{r}')}. \tag{8.65}
$$

Hence

$$
\mathbf{H}_0(\mathbf{r}) \sim \frac{e^{i\kappa r}}{r} \int \left\{\frac{1}{c}\nabla \times \mathbf{j}_0(\mathbf{r}') + \kappa^2\mathbf{M}_0(\mathbf{r}') + \nabla[\nabla\cdot\mathbf{M}_0(\mathbf{r}')]\right\} e^{-i\mathbf{\kappa}\cdot\mathbf{r}'}\,d\tau'.
$$

This can be integrated by parts with the use of the formulae

$$
\int S\nabla \times \mathbf{V}d\tau = \int \mathbf{V} \times \nabla S d\tau \tag{8.66}
$$

$$
\int S\nabla T d\tau \quad = -\int T\nabla S d\tau \tag{8.67}
$$

$$
\int \mathbf{V}\nabla\cdot\mathbf{U}d\tau \quad = -\int (\mathbf{U}\cdot\nabla)\mathbf{V}d\tau \tag{8.68}
$$

where it is assumed that all integrated parts vanish, as is true in our case. Then

$$
\mathbf{H}_0(\mathbf{r}) \sim \frac{e^{i\kappa r}}{r} \int \left\{\frac{i}{c}\mathbf{\kappa} \times \mathbf{j}_0(\mathbf{r}') + \kappa^2\mathbf{M}_0(\mathbf{r}') - \mathbf{\kappa}[\mathbf{\kappa}\cdot\mathbf{M}_0(\mathbf{r}')]\right\} e^{-i\mathbf{\kappa}\cdot\mathbf{r}'}d\tau'
$$

$$
= \frac{e^{i\kappa r}}{r} \int \left\{\frac{i}{c}\mathbf{\kappa} \times \mathbf{j}_0(\mathbf{r}') - \mathbf{\kappa} \times [\mathbf{\kappa} \times \mathbf{M}_0(\mathbf{r}')]\right\} e^{-i\mathbf{\kappa}\cdot\mathbf{r}'}d\tau'. \tag{8.69}
$$

The brace in (8.69) is a vector at right angles to $\mathbf{\kappa}$, and its direction defines the direction $(\mathbf{\kappa} \times \hat{\mathbf{A}}_0)/\kappa$ of the emitted magnetic field. [See (8.17).] Here $\hat{\mathbf{A}}_0$ is the unit vector along the polarization direction. It then follows that

$$
\mathbf{H}_0(\mathbf{r}) \sim \frac{e^{i\kappa r}}{r}\mathbf{\kappa} \times \hat{\mathbf{A}}_0 \int \hat{\mathbf{A}}_0 \cdot \left\{\frac{i}{c}\mathbf{j}_0(\mathbf{r}') - \mathbf{\kappa} \times \mathbf{M}_0(\mathbf{r}')\right\} e^{-i\mathbf{\kappa}\cdot\mathbf{r}'}\,d\tau'. \tag{8.70}
$$

Next (8.69) is substituted into (8.32) to yield

$$
\mathbf{E}_0(\mathbf{r}) \sim \frac{\mathbf{\kappa}}{\kappa} \times \mathbf{H}_0(\mathbf{r})
$$

$$
= \frac{e^{i\kappa r}}{r}\kappa\hat{\mathbf{A}}_0 \int \hat{\mathbf{A}}_0 \cdot \left\{\frac{i}{c}\mathbf{j}_0(\mathbf{r}') - \mathbf{\kappa} \times \mathbf{M}_0(\mathbf{r}')\right\} e^{-i\mathbf{\kappa}\cdot\mathbf{r}'}\,d\tau'. \tag{8.71}
$$

Hence

$$\mathbf{E}_0(\mathbf{r}) \times \mathbf{H}_0^*(\mathbf{r}) + \text{c.c.} \sim \frac{2\kappa\kappa}{r^2} \left| \int \mathbf{\hat{A}}_0 \cdot \left\{ \frac{i}{c} \mathbf{j}_0(\mathbf{r}') - \kappa \times \mathbf{M}_0(\mathbf{r}') \right\} e^{-i\kappa \cdot \mathbf{r}'} d\tau'. \right. \tag{8.72}$$

This must now be substituted into (8.40) for the transition probability of a quantum $\hbar\omega$ to be emitted in direction κ into solid angle $d\Omega$

$$w d\Omega = \frac{\kappa}{2\pi\hbar} \left| \int \mathbf{\hat{A}}_0 \cdot \left\{ \frac{i}{c} \mathbf{j}_0(\mathbf{r}') - \kappa \times \mathbf{M}_0(\mathbf{r}') \right\} e^{-i\kappa \cdot \mathbf{r}'} d\tau' \right|^2 d\Omega \tag{8.73}$$

We translate into quantum mechanics according to (8.43) and (8.44)—

$$w d\Omega = \frac{\kappa}{2\pi\hbar} \left| \int \mathbf{\hat{A}}_0 \cdot \left\{ \frac{e\hbar}{2Mc} (u_f^* \nabla u_i - u_i \nabla u_f^*) \right. \right.$$

$$\left. \left. -\kappa \times \frac{e\hbar\mu}{2Mc} u_f^* \boldsymbol{\sigma} u_i \right\} e^{-i\kappa \cdot \mathbf{r}} d\tau' \right|^2 d\Omega. \tag{8.74}$$

When $e^{-i\kappa \cdot \mathbf{r}'}$ is expanded in powers of $\kappa \cdot \mathbf{r}'$, we shall again obtain matrix elements of multipole transitions. We shall confine ourselves to dipole transitions, so that we need the first two terms in the expansion, since, as before, the terms in $\kappa \cdot \mathbf{r}'$ contain a mixture of dipole and quadrupole transitions. We therefore have the following integrals, where we have dropped the prime—

$$A: \frac{e\hbar}{2Mc} \int (u_f^* \nabla u_i - u_i \nabla u_f^*) d\tau = -e\kappa \int u_f^* \mathbf{r} u_i d\tau \tag{8.75}$$

using (8.48) and (8.53).

$$B: -\kappa \times \frac{e\hbar\mu}{2Mc} \int u_f^* \boldsymbol{\sigma} u_i d\tau. \tag{8.76}$$

$$C: -\frac{ie\hbar}{2Mc} \int (\kappa \cdot \mathbf{r})(u_f^* \nabla u_i - u_i \nabla u_f^*) d\tau = -\frac{ie\hbar}{Mc} \int (\kappa \cdot \mathbf{r}) u_f^* \nabla u_i d\tau$$

using (8.48). This must now be split up in the same way as $\mathcal{M}_2$ in (8.54), so that we obtain for the dipole contribution,

$$-\frac{ie\hbar}{2Mc} \int u_f^*[(\kappa \cdot \mathbf{r})\nabla - \mathbf{r}(\kappa \cdot \nabla)]u_i d\tau = \frac{ie\hbar}{2Mc} \int u_f^*[\kappa \times (\mathbf{r} \times \nabla)]u_i d\tau$$

$$= -\frac{e\hbar}{2Mc} \kappa \times \int u_f^* \mu_l u_i d\tau. \tag{8.77}$$

$$D: i\frac{e\hbar}{2Mc} \int (\kappa \cdot \mathbf{r}) u_f^* \kappa \times \mu \boldsymbol{\sigma} u_i d\tau.$$

This is split up in the same way as C and yields the dipole contribution

$$\tfrac{1}{2}i \frac{e\hbar\mu}{2Mc} \kappa \times \int u_f^*[(\kappa \cdot \mathbf{r})\sigma - \mathbf{r}(\kappa \cdot \sigma)]u_i d\tau$$

$$= \frac{ie\hbar\mu}{4Mc} \kappa \times \int u_f^*[\kappa \times (\mathbf{r} \times \sigma)]u_i d\tau$$

$$= -\frac{ie\hbar\mu}{4Mc} \kappa^2 \int u_f^*(\mathbf{r} \times \sigma)u_i d\tau + \frac{ie\hbar\mu}{4Mc} \kappa \int u_f^* \kappa \cdot (\mathbf{r} \times \sigma)u_i d\tau.$$

$$(8.78)$$

The last term does not contribute to the matrix element, since $\hat{\mathbf{A}}_0 \cdot \kappa = 0$.

We thus have four contributions to the dipole transition,

A : Electric dipole due to electric charge distribution   ($E1$),

B : Magnetic dipole due to magnetic intensity   ($M1$),

C : Magnetic dipole due to electric charge distribution   ($M'1$),

D : Electric dipole due to magnetic intensity.   ($E'1$).

The affix 1 denotes that these are 2^1-poles.

We shall see in the next section that because of parity assignments electric and magnetic multipole transitions of the same order cannot interfere with each other. The transition probabilities for electric and magnetic dipole radiation in a given direction $\kappa(\theta, \phi)$ are therefore given by

$$w_{\mathrm{E}}(\theta, \phi) = \frac{\kappa^3}{2\pi\hbar} |\langle E1 + E'1 \rangle|^2 d\Omega \qquad (8.79)$$

$$w_{\mathrm{M}}(\theta, \phi) = \frac{\kappa^3}{2\pi\hbar} |\langle M1 + M'1 \rangle|^2 d\Omega \qquad (8.80)$$

where

$$\langle E1 + E'1 \rangle = \int u_f^* \hat{\mathbf{A}}_0 \cdot \left(e\mathbf{r} + i\kappa \frac{e\hbar\mu}{4Mc} \mathbf{r} \times \sigma\right) u_i d\tau \qquad (8.81)$$

$$\langle M1 + M'1 \rangle = \frac{e\hbar}{2Mc} \int u_f^* \hat{\mathbf{A}}_0 \cdot \left\{\frac{\kappa}{\kappa} \times (\mu\sigma + \mu_l)\right\} u_i d\tau$$

$$= \frac{e\hbar}{2Mc} \int u_f^* \frac{\hat{\mathbf{A}}_0 \times \kappa}{\kappa} \cdot (\mu\sigma + \mu_l) u_i d\tau. \qquad (8.82)$$

Now it follows from (8.70) that the electric dipole vector lies in the plane of κ and $\hat{\mathbf{A}}_0$, while the magnetic dipole vector lies in the plane of κ and $\hat{\mathbf{A}}_0 \times \kappa$. We now take the z-axis in each case along the respective vector. Then

$$\langle E1 + E1' \rangle = \int u_f^* \left\{ ez + i\kappa \frac{e\hbar\mu}{4Mc} (x\sigma_y - y\sigma_x) \right\} u_i \, d\tau \sin\theta_E \quad (8.83)$$

$$\langle M1 + M1' \rangle = \frac{e\hbar}{2Mc} \int u_f^* (\mu\sigma_z + \mu_{lz}) u_i \, d\tau \sin\theta_M \quad (8.84)$$

where θ_E and θ_M are the angles between the direction of propagation and the respective dipole directions. It is seen that dipoles do not radiate along their axes, and that the spatial distribution of the intensity of the radiation is the same for an electric and a magnetic dipole. Multipole radiation of higher order leads of course to quite different spatial distributions (see e.g. example 8.8.6). To distinguish between magnetic and electric multipoles of the same order it is necessary to measure the polarization of the radiation, i.e. to measure the actual fields and not just the energy carried by the fields.

The total probabilities for emission are obtained by integrating (8.79) and (8.80) over all angles,

$$\int w_E(\theta, \phi) d\Omega = \frac{\kappa^3}{2\pi\hbar} |\langle E1 + E'1 \rangle|^2 \int \sin^2\theta \, d\cos\theta \, d\phi$$

$$= \frac{4\kappa^3}{3\hbar} |\langle E1 + E'1 \rangle|^2 \quad (8.85)$$

$$\int w_M(\theta, \phi) d\Omega = \frac{4\kappa^3}{3\hbar} |\langle M1 + M'1 \rangle|^2. \quad (8.86)$$

Up to now we have dealt with transitions affecting one nucleon only. When we are dealing with a nucleus, we must replace the operators z and μ_{lz} by sums over all protons, i.e. by

$$\sum_{n=1}^{Z} z_n \quad \text{and} \quad \sum_{n=1}^{Z} \mu_{lz}^{(n)} \quad (8.87)$$

and the operators $\mu\sigma_z$ and $\mu(x\sigma_y - y\sigma_x)$ by sums over all nucleons, i.e. by

$$\sum_{n=1}^{A} \mu_n \sigma_{nz} \quad \text{and} \quad \sum_{n=1}^{A} \mu_n (x_n \sigma_{ny} - y_n \sigma_{nx}). \quad (8.88)$$

The wave functions u_i and u_f will now be functions of all $3A$ co-ordinates, and the integration will be taken over all these. This simple generalization is of course only possible because we have referred the co-ordinates of each nucleon to the mass centre of the nucleus as origin. A formulation in relative co-ordinates does not end itself to this generalization.

8.5 Selection Rules

We now investigate the angular momentum and parity properties of the multipole moments.

We have already mentioned that an electric 2^l-pole corresponds to a spherical harmonic of order l and a magnetic 2^l-pole to a spherical harmonic of order $l - 1$ multiplied by the operator μ_l, which in itself carries unit angular momentum. Thus any 2^l-pole carries orbital angular momentum l in units of $\hbar$. However while the parity of an lth order spherical harmonic is $(-1)^l$, that of μ_l, which is an axial vector, is even. Thus an electric 2^l-pole has parity $(-1)^l$, while a magnetic one has parity $(-1)^{l-1}$.

It will be noticed that no multipole moment has zero angular momentum. If we call the total angular momentum of the initial and final states $\mathbf{I}_i$ and $\mathbf{I}_f$, and the angular momentum carried away by the radiation $\mathbf{l}$, then we must have

$$\mathbf{I}_f = \mathbf{I}_i + \mathbf{l}. \tag{8.89}$$

As $l \neq 0$, it follows that a transition from a state with $I_i = 0$ to one with $I_f = 0$ is absolutely forbidden.†

The probabilities of successive multipole transitions of the same type are in the ratio $\kappa^2 R^2$, where R is the nuclear radius. For a heavy nucleus this is about 6 fm, i.e. $R \simeq 0.015\,\lambda_0$, where $\lambda_0 = \hbar/m_e c$ is the reduced Compton wavelength. Even the most energetic γ-rays have energies below about $E = 2$ Mev $\simeq 4\,m_e c^2$, so that their reduced wavelength is

$$\lambda = \frac{1}{\kappa} = \frac{\hbar c}{E} < \tfrac{1}{4}\frac{\hbar}{m_e c}.$$

Hence in all cases $\kappa R < 0.06$. On the other hand, the ratio of the transition probability of a magnetic multipole transition to the electric multipole transition of the same order is indicated by the dipole ratios, which to an order of magnitude is best obtained from (8.75) and (8.77),

$$\left(\frac{\text{magnetic dipole transition}}{\text{electric dipole transition}}\right)^2 = \left(\frac{e\hbar/Mc}{eR}\right)^2.$$

Now

$$\frac{\hbar/Mc}{R} = \frac{(m_e/M)\lambda_0}{0.015\,\lambda_0} \simeq 0.03$$

† It should be pointed out however that electric monopole transitions, in which the total angular momentum and parity of the nucleus are unchanged by the transition, can arise from an interaction between the nucleus and the atomic negatons surrounding it. In such an interaction the nuclear excitation energy is transferred to the negaton, which is ejected with zero angular momentum and positive parity. No photon is emitted. In particular, the transition $0 \to 0$ has been observed in this way.

so that this ratio is of the same order as κR, though as a rule somewhat larger. It follows that if the most important multipole moment is an electric one, the competing magnetic one, which because of parity requirements must be one order higher, is in general negligible, but that if the most important multipole moment is magnetic, then the competing electric one of one order higher may have to be taken into consideration. That there are exceptions to these order of magnitude estimates we shall see in the next section.

We can now write down the lowest-order multipole radiation which will allow a transition to take place between a state of angular momentum I_i and parity Π_i and one of angular momentum I_f and parity Π_f.

When $I_i \neq I_f$ and neither vanishes, then considerations of parity lead to the following two possibilities—

(i) If $\Pi_i \Pi_f = (-1)^{I_i - I_f}$, then the dominant radiation is electric multipole of order $l = |I_i - I_f|$ and the magnetic multipole radiation, which is of order $l = |I_i - I_f| + 1$ is generally negligible ;

(ii) if $\Pi_i \Pi_f = (-1)^{I_i - I_f + 1}$, then the electric multipole radiation of order $l = |I_i - I_f| + 1$ and the magnetic multipole radiation of order $l = |I_i - I_f|$ compete.

Clearly the transition probability is in general much greater in (i), which for that reason is called parity-favoured.

When either I_i or I_f vanish, but not the other, the transitions with $l = |I_i - I_f| + 1$ are forbidden by (8.89), but those with $l = |I_i - I_f|$ can occur.

When $I_i = I_f$, but neither vanishes, then the transitions with $l = |I_i - I_f|$ cannot occur, since the lowest-order radiation has $l = 1$. The two above cases then reduce to (i) electric quadrupole with magnetic dipole radiation when $\Pi_i = \Pi_f$, and (ii) electric dipole with magnetic quadrupole radiation when $\Pi_i = -\Pi_f$. In this case (ii) is therefore parity-favoured.

From the point of view of the emitted radiation the selection rules can be summarized as in Table 8.1, where a transition is progressively less likely, the lower down in the table it is. In the table we have put $\triangle I$ for $I_f - I_i$, and " yes " and " no " mean " change of parity " and " no change of parity " respectively.

TABLE 8.1. ELECTRIC AND MAGNETIC MULTIPOLE TRANSITIONS

		$I_i, I_f \neq 0$	I_i or $I_f = 0$	$I_i = I_f = 0$
$E1$	$\Delta I = $	$\pm 1, 0$; yes	$\Delta I = \pm 1$; yes	
$M1$		$\pm 1, 0$; no	± 1 ; no	absolutely
$E2$		$\pm 2, \pm 1, 0$; no	± 2 ; no	forbidden
$M2$		$\pm 2, \pm 1, 0$; yes	± 2 ; yes	
		etc.		

8.5 Photodisintegration of the Deuteron

Our first application of the foregoing theory is to the disintegration of the deuteron through incident radiation of given frequency

$$\mathrm{d} + \hbar\omega \to \mathrm{n} + \mathrm{p}. \tag{8.90}$$

As the neutron is uncharged, the incident radiation interacts with the proton only, so that the sum in (8.87) is over one term only. The differential cross-section for this reaction is given by (A.41), where the matrix element has been evaluated in (8.25) and S is given by (8.22). Hence

$$\frac{\mathrm{d}\sigma}{\mathrm{d}\Omega} = \frac{4\pi^2\omega}{\kappa^2 c \, |\mathbf{A}_0|^2} \frac{e^2\hbar^2 \, |\mathbf{A}_0|^2}{M^2 c^2} \left| \int u_f^* \, \mathrm{e}^{\mathrm{i}\kappa \cdot \mathbf{r}} \frac{\partial u_i}{\partial n} \mathrm{d}\tau \right|^2 \rho(E_f). \tag{8.91}$$

Now $\rho(E_f)$ is given by (A.34) and (A.35), where the reduced mass of the proton is $\frac{1}{2}M$. Hence

$$\frac{\mathrm{d}\sigma}{\mathrm{d}\Omega} = \frac{4\pi^2 e^2 \hbar^2}{M^2\omega c} \left| \int u_f^* \, \mathrm{e}^{\mathrm{i}\kappa \cdot \mathbf{r}} \frac{\partial u_i}{\partial n} \mathrm{d}\tau \right|^2 \frac{Mk}{16\hbar^2\pi^3}. \tag{8.92}$$

The final energy is $E_f = \hbar^2 k^2/M$. The final wave function consists of a free neutron and proton, i.e. we neglect the proton-neutron interaction. Then

$$u_f = \mathrm{e}^{\mathrm{i}\mathbf{k}_p \cdot \mathbf{r}_p} \mathrm{e}^{\mathrm{i}\mathbf{k}_n \cdot \mathbf{r}_n} \tag{8.93}$$

Now in the c.m. system,

$$\mathbf{k}_p = -\mathbf{k}_n = \mathbf{k}, \quad \mathbf{r}_p = -\mathbf{r}_n = \mathbf{r}, \tag{8.94}$$

where $\hbar\mathbf{k}$ is is the relative momentum and $2\mathbf{r}$ the relative co-ordinate. Hence†

$$u_f = \mathrm{e}^{2\mathrm{i}\mathbf{k} \cdot \mathbf{r}}. \tag{8.95}$$

† Actually, if the centre of mass of the system is at rest before the interaction, it cannot be so afterwards, as a momentum $\hbar K = \hbar\omega/c$ in the direction of the incident photon has been given to the system. The final wave function u_f thus contains another factor

$$\mathrm{e}^{\mathrm{i}\mathbf{K} \cdot \mathbf{R}},$$

where $\mathbf{R}$ is the co-ordinate of the moving centre of mass relative to its original rest position. This factor does not contribute to the matrix element for the transition probability and we shall simply omit it.

We must now be very careful about the system of co-ordinates which we are employing. Since in it the mass centre is at rest, we must use it as the origin of the integration variable. On the other hand the wave function u_i, being that of the deuteron, is invariably given in the relative co-ordinates of the two particles. We therefore change to relative co-ordinates, which is done simply by changing the integration variable from $\mathbf{r}$ to $\mathbf{r}_{\mathrm{rel}} = 2\mathbf{r}$. Then u_i will be given in standard fashion, $u_f = e^{i\mathbf{k}\cdot\mathbf{r}}$ and $e^{i\mathbf{\kappa}\cdot\mathbf{r}}$ is transformed to $e^{\frac{1}{2}i\mathbf{\kappa}\cdot\mathbf{r}}$. (We drop the subscript.) Note that the wave vector $\mathbf{k}$ is unchanged (see example 3.10.12).

Following our programme, we shall only evaluate the contribution of the most important term of (8.91) which is the $E1$ term. The matrix element then reduces essentially to $\mathscr{M}_1$ (see (8.47) and (8.53)), and the final result is

$$\frac{\mathrm{d}\sigma_e}{\mathrm{d}\Omega} = \frac{Mk\kappa e^2}{4\pi\hbar^2} \left| \int u_f^* \cdot \tfrac{1}{2} \hat{\mathbf{A}}_0 \cdot \mathbf{r}\, u_i \mathrm{d}\tau \right|^2. \tag{8.96}$$

The initial wave function is of course the ground state wave function of the deuteron. This is given by (3.49) and example 3.10.3, but we shall use the expression for it outside the nuclear range,

$$u_i = \sqrt{\left\{ \frac{\alpha_t}{2\pi} (1 + b_t\alpha_t) \right\}} \frac{e^{-\alpha_t r}}{r} \tag{8.97}$$

as if it were valid inside the range too. Here b_t is the triplet range of the nuclear force, $\alpha_t = (MB_t)^{\frac{1}{2}}/\hbar$ and B_t is the binding energy of the deuteron. As we shall see below, nearly all the contributions to the integral come from beyond the nuclear range, so that the approximation is a good one.

We next expand $u_f = e^{i\mathbf{k}\cdot\mathbf{r}}$ in spherical harmonics. The result was obtained in (3·31). Since u_i is spherically symmetric and $\hat{\mathbf{A}}_0 \cdot \mathbf{r}$ is proportional to the $l = 1$ spherical harmonic, only the $l = 1$ term of this series will contribute. This is also clear from the selection rules for $E1$, which are $\triangle I = \pm 1, 0$; yes. As the ground state of the deuteron is a ^{3}S-state, the final state must be ^{3}P. It cannot be ^{1}P, since the electric dipole operator does not operate on the spin part of the wave function, which must therefore be unchanged.

As a P-state vanishes at the origin, little contribution to the integral will come from near the origin. This result was required above in our approximation for u_i. Furthermore, for low energies a P-state is practically uninfluenced by the potential between neutron and proton. We are therefore here quite justified in putting for u_f a free particle wave function and can write, using (3.31) and (3.61),

$$u_f = \frac{3i}{kr}\left(\frac{\sin kr}{kr} - \cos kr\right)\cos\theta' \qquad (8.98)$$

where θ' is the angle between the direction of ejection of the proton and the radius vector of the integration variable (see Fig. 8.1). If χ is the angle between the direction of ejection of the proton and

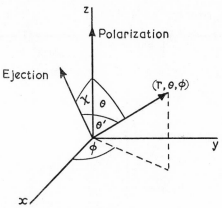

Fɪɢ. 8.1.

that of polarization of the photon, which we take as z-axis, then in accordance with Fig. 8.2

$$\cos\theta' = \cos\chi\cos\theta + \sin\chi\sin\theta\cos\phi.$$

The integration over $\cos\phi$ will make the latter term vanish and we are left with

$$\frac{\mathrm{d}\sigma_e}{\mathrm{d}\Omega} = \frac{Mk\kappa e^2}{4\pi\hbar^2}\left|\iiint \frac{3i}{kr}\left(\frac{\sin kr}{kr} - \cos kr\right)\cos\chi\cos\theta \cdot \tfrac{1}{2}r\cos\theta\right.$$

$$\left.\sqrt{\left\{\frac{\alpha_t}{2\pi}(1+\alpha_t b_t)\right\}}\frac{e^{-\alpha_t r}}{r} \cdot r^2\sin\theta \mathrm{d}r\mathrm{d}\theta\mathrm{d}\phi\right|^2$$

$$= \frac{2e^2k^3\alpha_t(1+\alpha_t b_t)}{\hbar c(k^2+\alpha_t^2)^3}\cos^2\chi \qquad (8.99)$$

since $\qquad\qquad \hbar\omega = E_f - E_i = \frac{\hbar^2}{M}(k^2+\alpha_i^2). \qquad (8.100)$

The angular distribution of ejected protons for an unpolarized incident beam is obtained by averaging $\cos^2\chi$ over all directions of polarization perpendicular to the direction of propagation of the incident beam. Let this latter make angle ϑ with the direction of ejection and let the normal to the plane defined by these two directions make angle ζ with the polarization direction (see Fig. 8.2).

Then $$\overline{\cos^2\chi} = \frac{1}{2\pi}\int_0^{2\pi}\sin^2\zeta\,\sin^2\vartheta\,d\zeta = \tfrac{1}{2}\sin^2\vartheta$$

so that for unpolarized photons

$$\frac{d\sigma_e}{d\Omega} = \frac{e^2k^3\alpha_t(1+\alpha_tb_t)}{\hbar c(k^2+\alpha_t^2)^3}\sin^2\vartheta. \tag{8.101}$$

The complete cross-section is obtained by integrating over all $d\Omega$

$$\sigma_e = \frac{2\pi e^2k^3\alpha_t(1+\alpha_tb_t)}{\hbar c(k^2+\alpha_t^2)^3}\int_0^\pi\sin^2\vartheta\,d\cos\vartheta = \frac{8\pi e^2k^3\alpha_t(1+\alpha_tb_t)}{3\hbar c(k^2+\alpha_t^2)^3}. \tag{8.102}$$

Analogously to the electric dipole transition we expect there to

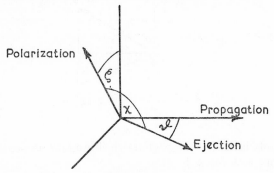

Fig. 8.2.

be a magnetic dipole transition in which the matrix element

$$e\int u_f^* \cdot \tfrac{1}{2}\hat{\mathbf{A}}_0 \cdot \mathbf{r}u_i d\tau \tag{8.103}$$

in (8.96) is replaced by

$$\frac{e\hbar}{2Mc}\int u_f^* \frac{\hat{\mathbf{A}}_0 \times \boldsymbol{\kappa}}{\kappa} \cdot (\mu_p\boldsymbol{\sigma}_p + \mu_n\boldsymbol{\sigma}_n)u_i d\tau. \tag{8.104}$$

This transition cannot be derived from the theory as outlined so far, since to avoid complications, we did not consider particles with intrinsic magnetic moments in our theory of absorption. We shall assume that the replacement is permissible, which is certainly true.

As an $M1$ transition does not change parity, the most likely transition is one from one S-state to another. In a $^3S - {}^3S$ transition the matrix element vanishes, since the space parts of two ^3S-states of different energies are orthogonal to each other and the $M1$ operator has no space dependence. This argument does not hold for a $^3S - {}^1S$ transition, since the triplet and singlet forces in the deuteron are not the same, and so ^3S and ^1S-states are not necessarily orthogonal to each other. The only possible transition is therefore to the virtual ^1S-state of the deuteron.

Making the necessary replacement in (8.96), we at once obtain for the magnetic dipole differential cross-section

$$\frac{d\sigma_m}{d\Omega} = \frac{k\kappa e^2}{16\pi Mc^2} \left| \int u_f^* \frac{\hat{\mathbf{A}}_0 \times \mathbf{\kappa}}{\kappa} \cdot (\mu_p\mathbf{\sigma}_p + \mu_n\mathbf{\sigma}_n)u_i \, d\tau \right|^2. \quad (8.105)$$

Here u_i is again given by (8.97), but as we are now dealing with spin dependent operators, we must specify its spin state,

$$u_i = \sqrt{\left\{ \frac{\alpha_t}{2\pi}(1 + \alpha_t b_t) \right\}} \frac{e^{-\alpha_t r}}{r} \, {}^3\chi_{1,\,0,\,-1} \quad (8.106)$$

where $^3\chi_{1,\,0,\,-1}$ are the triplet spin wave functions (2.81). The final state is the ^1S-state. An S-state is influenced by the interaction potential even at the lowest energies, and hence we must not use the free particle wave function here. A solution of the wave equation is obtained by adding to $e^{i\mathbf{k}\cdot\mathbf{r}}$ the scattered wave, so that asymptotically the final state is given by the S-component of

$$e^{i\mathbf{k}\cdot\mathbf{r}} + f(\theta)\frac{e^{ikr}}{r} \quad (8.107)$$

[see (3.21)]. The addition of the scattered wave does not affect the normalization. Also, since at infinity the intensity of the scattered wave vanishes, (8.107) represents asymptotically a plane wave in direction $\mathbf{k}$.

The S-component of (8.107) is obtained from (3.40) and is asymptotically equal to

$$u_f \sim \frac{1}{kr} e^{i\,{}^1\eta_0} \sin(kr + {}^1\eta_0) {}^1\chi_0 \quad (8.108)$$

where $^1\eta_0$ is the ^1S phase shift. We shall take this expression for u_f at all distances, an approximation we have already made for u_i. It is equivalent to taking the range of nuclear forces to be zero, which at low energies $(k^{-1} \gg b_s, b_t)$ is quite justifiable.

The phase shift $^1\eta_0$ is obtained by combining formulae analogous to (3.71) and (3.75),

$$\cot {}^1\eta_0 = -\frac{\alpha_s}{k}(1 - \tfrac{1}{2}\alpha_s b_s) \simeq -\frac{\alpha_s}{k} \quad (8.109)$$

since $\tfrac{1}{2}\alpha_s b_s \ll 1$. The spin wave function $^1\chi_0$ is given by (2.82).

The integration over $d\Omega$ in (8.105) can be performed at once, since the matrix element is clearly angle independent. Averaging over the three possible initial states, we have

$$\sigma_m = \frac{1}{3} \sum_{m=-1}^{1} \frac{k\kappa e^2}{4Mc^2} \left| {}^1\chi_0{}^* \frac{\hat{\mathbf{A}}_0 \times \boldsymbol{\kappa}}{\kappa} \cdot (\mu_p \boldsymbol{\sigma}_p + \mu_n \boldsymbol{\sigma}_n) \, {}^3\chi_m \right|^2$$

$$\times \, 16\pi^2 \left| \int_0^\infty \frac{1}{k} \sin (kr + {}^1\eta_0) \sqrt{\left\{ \frac{\alpha_t}{2\pi} (1 + \alpha_t b_t) \right\}} e^{-\alpha_t r} \, dr \right|^2 . \quad (8.110)$$

We take the incident polarization direction as z-axis. Then only the $m = 0$ initial state gives a non-zero contribution (see example 8.8.7) and

$$\begin{aligned}
{}^1\chi_0{}^*(\mu_p \sigma_{pz} &+ \mu_n \sigma_{nz}) {}^3\chi_0 \\
&= \tfrac{1}{2}(\alpha_p \beta_n - \alpha_n \beta_p)^*(\mu_p \sigma_{pz} + \mu_n \sigma_{nz})(\alpha_p \beta_n + \alpha_n \beta_p) \\
&= \tfrac{1}{2}(\mu_p - \mu_n) \mid \alpha_p \beta_n - \alpha_n \beta_p \mid^2 \\
&= \mu_p - \mu_n
\end{aligned} \quad (8.111)$$

using (2.74) and (2.75). Hence

$$\begin{aligned}
\sigma_m &= \frac{2\pi\kappa e^2 \alpha_t}{3Mkc^2}(\mu_p - \mu_n)^2 \frac{(k \cos {}^1\eta_0 + \alpha_t \sin {}^1\eta_0)^2}{(k^2 + \alpha_t{}^2)^2}(1 + \alpha_t b_t) \\
&= \frac{2\pi e^2 \hbar}{3M^2 c^3}(\mu_p - \mu_n)^2 \frac{k\alpha_t(\alpha_t - \alpha_s)^2}{(k^2 + \alpha_t{}^2)(k^2 + \alpha_s{}^2)}(1 + \alpha_t b_t). \quad (8.112)
\end{aligned}$$

From (8.102) and (8.112) we have

$$\begin{aligned}
\frac{\sigma_e}{\sigma_m} &= \frac{4M^2 c^2}{\hbar^2(\mu_p - \mu_n)^2(\alpha_t - \alpha_s)^2} \cdot \frac{k^2(k^2 + \alpha_s{}^2)}{(k^2 + \alpha_t{}^2)^2} \quad (8.113) \\
&= 70 \times \frac{E(E + \mid B_s \mid)}{(E + B_t)^2}
\end{aligned}$$

where $E = \hbar^2 k^2/M$ is the energy of the final state of the nuclear system and $\mid B_s \mid$ is the binding energy of the virtual singlet state of the deuteron. E is of course the difference between the energy $\hbar\omega$ of the incident photon and the threshold energy for disintegration, which is equal to B_t.

We now investigate the behaviour of σ_e and σ_m as functions of the energy E. For small E, i.e. for incident energies just above threshold, σ_e is proportional to $E^{3/2}$ and σ_m to $E^{1/2}$. The photomagnetic cross-section is therefore much more important at such energies. For energies much larger than the binding energy of the deuteron, but still sufficiently small for the P-phase shift to be negligible, both σ_e and σ_m are proportional to $E^{-3/2}$. (8.113) shows that the ratio σ_e/σ_m becomes energy independent and equal to about

70. The general behaviour is shown in Fig. 8.3. It is interesting to note that for small E our rule that an electric transition is much more probable than a magnetic one of the same order is upset by

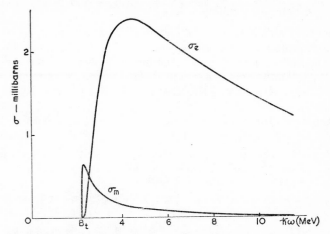

Fig. 8.3. Photoelectric and Photomagnetic Disintegration Cross-sections of the Deuteron as a Function of the Energy of the Incident Photon
B_t is the binding energy of the deuteron.

the difference in the wave functions, caused by the opposite parities of the transitions. This may serve as a warning against the too glib acceptance of order of magnitude assessments.

8.7 Radiative Capture of Neutrons by Protons

The inverse process to photodisintegration of the deuteron is that in which a proton captures a neutron and emits a γ-ray,

$$n + p \rightarrow d + \hbar\omega. \tag{8.114}$$

This process competes with elastic neutron-proton scattering, and has a very small cross-section except for very slow incident neutrons, when the neutrons spend a sufficiently long time near the protons for capture to be probable. At such energies only S-wave neutrons interact, and it then follows from the selection rules, which are the same as for photodisintegration, that the transition must be a magnetic dipole one, from a ^{1}S-state of the free neutron-proton system to the ^{3}S-ground state of the deuteron.

The cross-section for this process is obtained by dividing the transition probability (8.86) by the incident flux velocity v and then dividing by four, since with an unpolarized beam only one-quarter of the states will be singlet states. The result is

$$\sigma_{\text{cap}} = \frac{1}{4} \cdot \frac{4\kappa^3}{3\hbar v} \sum_{m=-1}^{1} \left| \frac{e\hbar}{2Mc} \int u_f^* \frac{\hat{\mathbf{A}}_0 \times \mathbf{\kappa}}{\kappa} \cdot (\mu_p \sigma_p + \mu_n \sigma_n) u_i d\tau \right|^2 \quad (8.115)$$

where the z-axis is along the direction of the magnetic dipole of the neutron-proton system, and u_i and u_f of (8.105) and (8.108) are now u_f and u_i respectively. Another difference, compared with (8.110), is that we now sum over final states instead of averaging over initial ones. Also $\hbar k = \frac{1}{2}Mv$, since v is the relative velocity of the particles.

Our z-axis is now in the direction in which we measure the magnetic quantum number m of the deuteron, while the direction $(\hat{\mathbf{A}}_0 \times \mathbf{\kappa})/\kappa$ is that of the polarization of the emitted photon. This is not of course fixed in space, and its direction relative to the z-axis for a given m is obtained from the fact that, for a given m, (8.115) vanishes unless the photon is polarized in a particular way. Thus by considering the expression

$$^3\chi_m^* (\mu_p \sigma_{pw} + \mu_w \sigma_{nw})^1 \chi_0, \quad m = 1, \quad 0, -1; \quad w = x, y, z$$

(see example 8.8.8) we see that for $m = 0$ the photon is plane polarized along the z-axis, since only σ_z leads to a non-vanishing matrix element. When $m = \pm 1$, there are equal contributions, $90°$ out of phase, from σ_x and σ_y, and none from σ_z, so that the photon is circularly polarized in the (x, y)-plane. Our operator $\hat{\mathbf{A}}_0 \times \mathbf{\kappa} \cdot \mathbf{\sigma}/\kappa$ is therefore equal to σ_z and $2^{-\frac{1}{2}}(\sigma_x \pm i\sigma_y)$ corresponding to $m = 0$ and ± 1. The resulting integrals are actually identical, which is not surprising since this simply expresses the fact that the final deuteron is equally likely to have $m = 0, +1$ or -1, and we thus obtain

$$\sigma_{\text{cap}} = \frac{e^2 \kappa^3}{8 M c^2 k} \left| \int u_f^* \frac{\hat{\mathbf{A}}_0 \times \mathbf{\kappa}}{\kappa} \cdot (\mu_p \sigma_p + \mu_n \sigma_n) u_i d\tau \right|^2$$

$$= \frac{3}{2} \frac{\kappa^2}{k^2} \sigma_m \quad (8.116)$$

from (8.110).

Since the radiative capture and the photomagnetic disintegration are inverse processes, we need not have calculated them separately. Instead we could have obtained one from the other by the principle of detailed balance (6.24). In this formula let the deuteron be X, the photon x, the neutron B and the proton b. The angular momenta of the deuteron, neutron and proton are

$$I_X = 1, I_B = \frac{1}{2}, I_b = \frac{1}{2}.$$

Although the photon has an intrinsic angular momentum 1, it only has two states for a given energy, given by the two possible directions of polarizations. (Light cannot be polarized along its direction of propagation.) Hence $I_x = \frac{1}{2}$ effectively. If we take the deuteron to be at rest in the photo-disintegration, then the momentum $\hbar k_\alpha$ is that of the photon, $\hbar\kappa$. The momentum in the inverse reaction is $\frac{1}{2}Mv = \hbar k$. Substituting these values into (6.24), we at once obtain (8.116). This agreement serves to confirm the correctness of the result for spontaneous emission, obtained by a semi-classical method in section 8.2.

8.8. EXAMPLES

8.8.1. Show that $\mathbf{p}$ and $\mathbf{A}$ in (8.12) commute, even when they are treated as quantum mechanical operators. Why is this important?

8.8.2. By substituting back show that

$$G(\mathbf{r}) = -\frac{1}{4\pi} \int \frac{e^{\pm i\kappa|\mathbf{r}-\mathbf{r}'|}}{|\mathbf{r}-\mathbf{r}'|} F(\mathbf{r}')d\tau' \tag{8.117}$$

where the integral is taken over all space, is a solution of the inhomogeneous wave equation

$$\nabla^2 G(\mathbf{r}) + \kappa^2 G(\mathbf{r}) = F(\mathbf{r}) \tag{8.118}$$

provided that $F(\mathbf{r}) \to 0$, as $r \to \infty$.
[Hint : Use Green's theorem on an infinitesimal spherical volume surrounding the point $\mathbf{r} = \mathbf{r}'$.]

8.8.3. Use (8.65) to show that asymptotically (8.37) corresponds to an outgoing wave.

8.8.4. Use (A.1) to show that (8.42) and (8.43) satisfy the continuity equation (8.6).

8.8.5. Show that for $l > 1$

$$\int u \ (\kappa . \mathbf{r})^{l-1}(\mathbf{A}_0 . \nabla)u_i . d\tau = -\frac{\kappa Mc}{l\hbar} \int u_f^*(\mathbf{A}_0 . \mathbf{r})(\kappa . \mathbf{r})^{l-1}u_i d\tau$$
$$+ \frac{l-1}{l} \int u_f^*(\kappa . \mathbf{r})^{l-2}(\kappa \times \mathbf{A}_0) . (\mathbf{r} \times \nabla)u_i . d\tau \tag{8.119}$$

and hence verify (8.64).
[Hint : Put

$$l(\kappa . \mathbf{r})(\mathbf{A}_0 . \nabla) = (l-1)\{(\kappa . \mathbf{r})(\mathbf{A}_0 . \nabla) - (\mathbf{A}_0 . \mathbf{r})(\kappa . \nabla)\}$$
$$+ \{(\kappa . \mathbf{r})(\mathbf{A}_0 . \nabla) + (l-1)(\mathbf{A}_0 . \mathbf{r})(\kappa . \nabla)\}.]$$

8.8.6. Show that the matrix element for electric quadrupole radiation due to an electric charge distribution is

$$\langle E2 \rangle = \frac{1}{2}ie \int u_f^*(\hat{\mathbf{A}}_0 . \mathbf{r})(\kappa . \mathbf{r})u_i d\tau \tag{8.120}$$

and that the spatial distribution of the radiation is proportional to $\sin^2 \theta \cos^2 \theta$, where θ is the angle between the axis of symmetry of the quadrupole and the direction of the emitted radiation.

8.8.7. Use the orthonormality properties of the spin wave functions to show that

$$^1\chi_0^*(\mu_p\sigma_{pz} + \mu_n\sigma_{nz})^3\chi_1 = 0. \tag{8.121}$$

8.8.8. Show that

$$^3\chi_{1,\,0,\,-1}^*(\mu_p\sigma_{px} + \mu_n\sigma_{nx})^1\chi_0 = [-2^{-\frac{1}{2}},\, 0,\, 2^{-\frac{1}{2}}](\mu_p - \mu_n)$$

$$^3\chi_{1,\,0,\,-1}^*(\mu_p\sigma_{py} + \mu_n\sigma_{ny})^1\chi_0 = [i2^{-\frac{1}{2}},\, 0,\, i2^{-\frac{1}{2}}](\mu_p - \mu_n) \tag{8.122}$$

$$^3\chi_{1,\,0,\,-1}^*(\mu_p\sigma_{pz} + \mu_n\sigma_{nz})^1\chi_0 = [0,\, 1,\, 0](\mu_p - \mu_n).$$

CHAPTER 9

Beta-decay

9.1 Relativistic Wave Equation

UP to now we have never had to deal with particles of very great velocity and we have therefore been able to work throughout in the non-relativistic approximation. This will not be possible in the present chapter, and we therefore precede our discussion of β-decay by a brief description of the relativistic wave equation.†

Relativistically, the energy E and momentum p of a free particle of mass m are connected by the equation ‡

$$E^2 = p^2c^2 + m^2c^4. \tag{9.1}$$

To translate this equation into quantum mechanics we use (8.13) substituting the result into the time-dependent Schrödinger equation

$$H\Psi = i\hbar\frac{\partial\Psi}{\partial t} \tag{9.3}$$

where H is of course the energy operator corresponding to E in (9.1). It is apparent that difficulties will arise owing to the occurrence of the term E^2 in (9.1). To avoid this difficulty Dirac postulated that the right-hand side of (9.1) must have an exact square root, i.e. that

$$\sqrt{(p^2 + m^2c^2)} = \alpha_1 p_x + \alpha_2 p_y + \alpha_3 p_z + \beta mc \tag{9.4}$$

where α_1, α_2, α_3 and β are quantities still to be determined. On squaring (9.4) it is immediately obvious that these cannot be ordinary numbers, but if we assume that they are quantities that commute with p_x, p_y, p_z, although not necessarily with each other, we obtain the following equations which they must satisfy

$$\left.\begin{array}{l} \alpha_1^2 = \alpha_2^2 = \alpha_3^2 = \beta^2 = 1 \\ \alpha_2\alpha_3 + \alpha_3\alpha_2 = 0, \quad \alpha_3\alpha_1 + \alpha_1\alpha_3 = 0, \quad \alpha_1\alpha_2 + \alpha_2\alpha_1 = 0 \\ \alpha_1\beta + \beta\alpha_1 = 0, \quad \alpha_2\beta + \beta\alpha_2 = 0, \quad \alpha_3\beta + \beta\alpha_3 = 0. \end{array}\right\} \tag{9.5}$$

† Sections 9.2, 9.3 and the introductions to sections 9.4, 9.5 require a knowledge of only equations (9.1) and (9.2).

‡ This has to replace the non-relativistic equation for the kinetic energy

$$T = E - mc^2 = p^2/2m. \tag{9.2}$$

These equations are very similar to those satisfied by σ_x, σ_y, σ_z [see (2.93)], except that we now have four quantities to consider. It is found that the simplest matrix representation of α_1, α_2, α_3, β is in terms of matrices of order four. One possible representation is

$$
\alpha_1 = \begin{pmatrix} 0 & 0 & 0 & 1 \\ 0 & 0 & 1 & 0 \\ 0 & 1 & 0 & 0 \\ 1 & 0 & 0 & 0 \end{pmatrix} \quad
\alpha_2 = \begin{pmatrix} 0 & 0 & 0 & -i \\ 0 & 0 & i & 0 \\ 0 & -i & 0 & 0 \\ i & 0 & 0 & 0 \end{pmatrix}
$$

$$
\alpha_3 = \begin{pmatrix} 0 & 0 & 1 & 0 \\ 0 & 0 & 0 & -1 \\ 1 & 0 & 0 & 0 \\ 0 & -1 & 0 & 0 \end{pmatrix} \quad
\beta = \begin{pmatrix} 1 & 0 & 0 & 0 \\ 0 & 1 & 0 & 0 \\ 0 & 0 & -1 & 0 \\ 0 & 0 & 0 & -1 \end{pmatrix} \tag{9.6}
$$

In terms of the spin matrices (2.92) this can be written in the form of partitioned matrices,

$$
\alpha = \left(\begin{array}{c|c} 0 & \sigma \\ \hline \sigma & 0 \end{array} \right), \qquad
\beta = \left(\begin{array}{c|c} I & 0 \\ \hline 0 & -I \end{array} \right) \tag{9.7}
$$

where I and 0 are the unit and zero matrices of order two. We use the vector notation α to denote the three matrices α_1, α_2, α_3.

The free particle solutions of (9.3) have constant energy E and can therefore be written

$$
\Psi(\mathbf{r}, t) = \psi(\mathbf{r}) \exp\left(-\frac{i}{\hbar} Et \right). \tag{9.8}
$$

With the help of (8.13), (9.3), (9.4) and (9.8) the free-particle wave equation can then be written

$$
(-i\hbar c\alpha \cdot \nabla + \beta mc^2)\psi(\mathbf{r}) = E\,\psi(\mathbf{r}) \tag{9.9}
$$

where $\alpha \cdot \nabla = \alpha_1 \partial/\partial x + \alpha_2 \partial/\partial y + \alpha_3 \partial/\partial z$.

Since α and β are 4×4 matrices, $\psi(\mathbf{r})$ must be a column matrix,

$$
\psi(\mathbf{r}) = \begin{pmatrix} \psi_1(\mathbf{r}) \\ \psi_2(\mathbf{r}) \\ \psi_3(\mathbf{r}) \\ \psi_4(\mathbf{r}) \end{pmatrix}. \tag{9.10}
$$

Hence this is really only a shorthand way of writing the four simultaneous equations

$$\left.\begin{aligned}
(E - mc^2)\psi_1 \qquad\qquad + i\hbar c\,\frac{\partial\psi_3}{\partial z} + i\hbar c\left(\frac{\partial}{\partial x} - i\frac{\partial}{\partial y}\right)\psi_4 &= 0 \\[2mm]
(E - mc^2)\psi_2 + i\hbar c\left(\frac{\partial}{\partial x} + i\frac{\partial}{\partial y}\right)\psi_3 - i\hbar c\,\frac{\partial\psi_4}{\partial z} &= 0 \\[2mm]
i\hbar c\,\frac{\partial\psi_1}{\partial z} + i\hbar c\left(\frac{\partial}{\partial x} - i\frac{\partial}{\partial y}\right)\psi_2 + (E + mc)^2\psi_3 \qquad &= 0 \\[2mm]
i\hbar c\left(\frac{\partial}{\partial x} + i\frac{\partial}{\partial y}\right)\psi_1 - i\hbar c\,\frac{\partial\psi_2}{\partial z} \qquad\qquad + (E + mc^2)\psi_4 &= 0.
\end{aligned}\right\} \quad (9.11)$$

It is clear that we have overcome the difficulty of the square root at the expense of replacing one wave equation by four.

To interpret the four-component wave function (9.10) physically, we go back to the time-dependent wave equation which can be written

$$i\hbar\,\frac{\partial\Psi}{\partial t} = -i\hbar c\boldsymbol{\alpha}\,.\,\nabla\Psi + \beta mc^2\Psi. \qquad (9.12)$$

The Hermitian conjugate of this equation is formed by transposing the matrices and taking their complex conjugates.‡ Now it is a fundamental postulate of quantum mechanics that operators that correspond to physical observables must be " real", since their eigenvalues correspond to physical measurements. This means that they must be equal to their complex conjugates, which in the case of matrices is generalized to Hermitian conjugates. As $\boldsymbol{\alpha}$ and β are part of the energy operator, they must therefore be Hermitian, i.e.

$$\boldsymbol{\alpha}^\dagger = \boldsymbol{\alpha} \quad\text{and}\quad \beta^\dagger = \beta. \qquad (9.13)$$

It is easily seen that this is in agreement with (9.6).

Hence we have

$$-i\hbar\,\frac{\partial\Psi^\dagger}{\partial t} = i\hbar c\nabla\Psi^\dagger\,.\,\boldsymbol{\alpha} + \Psi^\dagger\beta mc^2 \qquad (9.14)$$

where

$$\Psi^\dagger = (\Psi_1^* \ \ \Psi_2^* \ \ \Psi_3^* \ \ \Psi_4^*). \qquad (9.15)$$

We premultiply (9.12) by $\Psi^\dagger$, postmultiply (9.14) by Ψ and subtract. Then

$$\frac{\partial}{\partial t}\,(\Psi^\dagger\Psi) + c\nabla\,.\,\Psi^\dagger\boldsymbol{\alpha}\Psi = 0. \qquad (9.16)$$

‡ The Hermitian conjugate of a matrix $A = \{a_{ij}\}$ is given by $A^\dagger = \{a_{ji}\}^*$. Note that $(AB)^\dagger = B^\dagger A^\dagger$.

This is a continuity equation of the form (6.93). If it is to denote the fact that the total probability is constant, we must interpret it through

$$\text{Position probability density} = \Psi^\dagger\Psi, \tag{9.17}$$

$$\text{Probability current density} = \Psi^\dagger c\alpha\Psi. \tag{9.18}$$

The former, which can be written

$$\Psi^\dagger\Psi = \sum_{j=1}^{4} \Psi_j^* \Psi_j, \tag{9.19}$$

is an obvious generalization of the non-relativistic formula. The latter shows that $c\alpha$ is a velocity operator, since it gives a current.

For any momentum $\mathbf{p}$, we can obtain plane wave solutions of (9.11)

$$\psi_j(\mathbf{r}) = u_j \exp\left(\frac{\mathrm{i}}{\hbar}\mathbf{p} \cdot \mathbf{r}\right) \tag{9.20}$$

where u_j is an ordinary number. Here $\mathbf{p}$ is the eigenvalue corresponding to the operator $-\mathrm{i}\hbar\nabla$ in (9.11).

Now

$$-\mathrm{i}\hbar\frac{\partial}{\partial x}\psi_j(\mathbf{r}) = p_x u_j \exp\left(\frac{\mathrm{i}}{\hbar}\mathbf{p} \cdot \mathbf{r}\right), \text{ etc.} \tag{9.21}$$

so that the four simultaneous differential equations (9.11) reduce to the four ordinary simultaneous equations

$$\left.\begin{aligned}
(E - mc^2)u_1 \qquad\qquad\quad - cp_z u_3 - c(p_x - \mathrm{i}p_y)u_4 &= 0 \\
(E - mc^2)u_2 - c(p_x + \mathrm{i}p_y)u_3 + cp_z u_4 &= 0 \\
- cp_z u_1 - c(p_x - \mathrm{i}p_y)u_2 + (E + mc^2)u_3 \qquad\qquad\quad &= 0 \\
- c(p_x + \mathrm{i}p_y)u_1 + cp_z u_2 \qquad\qquad + (E + mc^2)u_4 &= 0.
\end{aligned}\right\} \tag{9.22}$$

These equations have a non-zero solution only if the determinant of the coefficients vanishes. This gives

$$(E^2 - p^2 c^2 - m^2 c^4)^2 = 0. \tag{9.23}$$

Hence there are two possible values of the energy E corresponding to a given momentum $\mathbf{p}$,

$$E_+ = +\sqrt{(p^2 c^2 + m^2 c^4)}, \quad E_- = -\sqrt{(p^2 c^2 + m^2 c^4)}. \tag{9.24}$$

We are thus led to the negative energy solutions first mentioned in section 1.9.

Because of the square in (9.23) there are in fact four independent solutions of (9.22). If we put $E_+ = |E_-| = W$, these can be written

$$
\left.
\begin{array}{cccccc}
 & u_1 & u_2 & u_3 & u_4 \\[4pt]
E > 0, \uparrow & 1 & 0 & \dfrac{cp_z}{W + mc^2} & \dfrac{c(p_x + ip_y)}{W + mc^2} \\[12pt]
\downarrow & 0 & 1 & \dfrac{c(p_x - ip_y)}{W + mc^2} & -\dfrac{cp_z}{W + mc^2} \\[12pt]
E < 0, \uparrow & -\dfrac{cp_z}{W+mc^2} & -\dfrac{c(p_x+ip_y)}{W + mc^2} & 1 & 0 \\[12pt]
\downarrow & -\dfrac{c(p_x - ip_y)}{W + mc^2} & \dfrac{cp_z}{W + mc^2} & 0 & 1
\end{array}
\right\}
\tag{9.25}
$$

We have here anticipated a result to be proved below that, non-relativistically, of the two solutions for a given energy, one corresponds to z-component of spin $+\frac{1}{2}\hbar$ and the other to $-\frac{1}{2}\hbar$. If (9.20) is to be normalized to unit volume, then it follows from (9.19) that (9.25) must be multiplied by

$$
\left[1 + \frac{c^2 p^2}{(W + mc^2)^2}\right]^{-\frac{1}{2}} = \left(\frac{W + mc^2}{2W}\right)^{\frac{1}{2}}.
\tag{9.26}
$$

It is interesting to see what happens to (9.25) in the non-relativistic limit. Then

$$
W \simeq mc^2 \gg cp
\tag{9.27}
$$

so that u_3 and u_4 are of order v/c times u_1 and u_2 for positive energy solutions, and conversely for negative energy solutions. The wave functions then effectively have only two components, corresponding to the two spin directions.

Since our wave functions now have four components, our spin operators must be 4×4 matrices. It is easily seen that the three matrices

$$
\sigma' = \left(
\begin{array}{c|c}
\sigma & 0 \\
\hline
0 & \sigma
\end{array}
\right)
\tag{9.28}
$$

satisfy (2.93) and we shall see that they can be taken to represent the spin operator. In the non-relativistic limit we have from (9.25) that

$$
\sigma_z'\psi(E > 0, \uparrow) = \begin{pmatrix} 1 & 0 & 0 & 0 \\ 0 & -1 & 0 & 0 \\ 0 & 0 & 1 & 0 \\ 0 & 0 & 0 & -1 \end{pmatrix} \begin{pmatrix} 1 \\ 0 \\ 0 \\ 0 \end{pmatrix} = \begin{pmatrix} 1 \\ 0 \\ 0 \\ 0 \end{pmatrix}
$$

and

$$\sigma_z'\psi(E > 0, \ \downarrow\,) = \begin{pmatrix} 1 & 0 & 0 & 0 \\ 0 & -1 & 0 & 0 \\ 0 & 0 & 1 & 0 \\ 0 & 0 & 0 & -1 \end{pmatrix} \begin{pmatrix} 0 \\ 1 \\ 0 \\ 0 \end{pmatrix} = - \begin{pmatrix} 0 \\ 1 \\ 0 \\ 0 \end{pmatrix}$$

thus confirming our spin assignments.

It is interesting to observe that the intrinsic spin of an elementary particle is a natural consequence of the Dirac equation. We know that a quantity is a constant of motion if it commutes with H. For the z-component of orbital angular momentum this gives

$$L_z H - H L_z = (xp_y - yp_x)(c\boldsymbol{\alpha} \cdot \mathbf{p} + \beta mc^2)$$
$$- (c\boldsymbol{\alpha} \cdot \mathbf{p} + \beta mc^2)(xp_y - yp_x)$$

$$= - c\hbar^2 \left(x\frac{\partial}{\partial y} - y\frac{\partial}{\partial x} \right)\left(\alpha_1 \frac{\partial}{\partial x} + \alpha_2 \frac{\partial}{\partial y} + \alpha_3 \frac{\partial}{\partial z} \right)$$

$$- c\hbar^2 \left(\alpha_1 \frac{\partial}{\partial x} + \alpha_2 \frac{\partial}{\partial y} + \alpha_3 \frac{\partial}{\partial z} \right)\left(x\frac{\partial}{\partial y} - y\frac{\partial}{\partial x} \right)$$

$$= - c\hbar^2 \left(\alpha_2 \frac{\partial}{\partial x} - \alpha_1 \frac{\partial}{\partial y} \right) \tag{9.29}$$

since the Dirac matrices $\boldsymbol{\alpha}$, β clearly commute with the co-ordinate and momentum operators. Similarly σ_z' commutes with these and it is also easily shown (example 9.8.1) that σ_z' commutes with α_3 and β, but that

$$\sigma_z'\alpha_1 - \alpha_1\sigma_z' = 2i\alpha_2, \quad \sigma_z'\alpha_2 - \alpha_2\sigma_z' = - 2i\alpha_1. \tag{9.30}$$

Hence

$$\sigma_z'H - H\sigma_z' = \sigma_z'(c\alpha_1 p_x + c\alpha_2 p_y) - (c\alpha_1 p_x + c\alpha_2 p_y)\sigma_z'$$
$$= 2\hbar c \left(\alpha_2 \frac{\partial}{\partial x} - \alpha_1 \frac{\partial}{\partial y} \right) \tag{9.31}$$

Combining (9.29) and (9.31) we see that

$$L_z + \tfrac{1}{2}\hbar\sigma_z' \tag{9.32}$$

commutes with H. Similarly for the x and y components. Hence

$$\mathbf{L} + \tfrac{1}{2}\hbar\boldsymbol{\sigma}' \tag{9.33}$$

is a constant of motion. For that reason $\tfrac{1}{2}\hbar\boldsymbol{\sigma}'$ is interpreted as the intrinsic spin of the particle which must be added to its orbital angular momentum. Only the resultant total angular momentum is in general a constant of motion, although it has been shown that in the non-relativistic limit both $\mathbf{L}$ and $\tfrac{1}{2}\hbar\boldsymbol{\sigma}'$ separately are constants of motion.

Lastly, for a particle of charge e in a potential $(\mathbf{A}, \phi)$ we have with the usual substitution

$$E \to E - e\phi, \quad \mathbf{p} \to \mathbf{p} - \frac{e}{c}\mathbf{A} \tag{9.34}$$

the wave equation

$$\left[c\boldsymbol{\alpha} \cdot \left(-i\hbar\nabla - \frac{e}{c}\mathbf{A} \right) + \beta mc^2 + e\phi \right]\psi = E\,\psi. \tag{9.35}$$

9.2 Beta-Decay (Descriptive)

The phenomena covered by β-decay are those in which a nucleus makes an isobaric transition (mass number A constant), the charge number Z increasing or decreasing by one. A brief account of these phenomena was given in section 1.6. In calculating the energies available for them we have to be careful, since as was stated in section 1.3, it is not possible here to use atomic masses instead of nuclear ones without due caution. In the lines below we shall distinguish between the two by means of suffixes a and n. We must further include in our considerations the binding energy of the negatons in the atom, so that for an atom of mass number A and charge number Z, denoted by Z^A, we have

$$M_a(Z^A) = M_n(Z^A) + Zm_e - B(Z) \tag{9.36}$$

where $B(Z)$ is the binding energy of the Z negatons.

9.2.1 NEGATON EMISSION

The decay can be written symbolically as

$$Z^A \to (Z+1)^A + e^- + \bar{\nu} \tag{9.37}$$

where we have included the emission of the unobservable anti-neutrino. As far as we are concerned at present, there is of course no difference between a neutrino and an anti-neutrino, and the emission of an anti-neutrino is equivalent to the absorption of a neutrino. However, recently a new conservation law has been tentatively put forward, the conservation of leptons. According to this the difference in the number of leptons and anti-leptons in a system is constant. This is certainly true—because of the conservation law of electric charge—for reactions in which only negatons and positons are involved. If, as is now suggested, it is also true for the neutrino, and if we take the negaton to be a lepton and the positon the corresponding anti-lepton, then the particle that in β-decay is emitted together with a negaton must be an anti-neutrino.

In considering the maximum kinetic energy T_0 available for the negaton and the anti-neutrino in reaction (9.37) we shall assume that the anti-neutrino has zero mass. Then

$$T_0(e^-) = M_n(Z^A) - M_n(Z+1)^A - m_e - B(Z) + B(Z+1)^*$$
$$= M_a(Z^A) - Zm_e - M_a(Z+1)^A + (Z+1)m_e$$
$$\qquad - B(Z+1) + B(Z+1)^* - m_e$$
$$= M_a(Z^A) - M_a(Z+1)^A + I \qquad (9.38)$$

where $B(Z+1)^*$ is the binding energy of the singly ionized $(Z+1)^A$ atom and $I = -B(Z+1) + B(Z+1)^*$ is the energy of single ionization of the $(Z+1)^A$ atom. In practice this is quite negligible.

9.2.2 POSITON EMISSION

In this case we have

$$(Z+1)^A \to Z^A + e^+ + \nu. \qquad (9.39)$$

It is easily seen that

$$T_0(e^+) = M_a(Z+1)^A - M_a(Z^A) - 2m_e - I. \qquad (9.40)$$

9.2.3 NEGATON CAPTURE

Finally we have the possibility of the capture of an orbital negaton e_K by the nucleus,

$$(Z+1)^A + e_K \to Z^{A*} + \nu \qquad (9.41)$$
$$\downarrow$$
$$Z^A + \gamma.$$

Here the Z^A atom is left in an excited state, since it lacks a negaton in the K-shell and has one too many in the least bound shell. It decays to the ground state by the emission of photons produced by the rearrangement of the negatons in the shells. If the energy of the photons is $E(\gamma)$ and the original binding energy of the K-negaton in the $(Z+1)^A$ atom is $B(K)$, then

$$T_0(e_K) = M_n(Z+1)^A + m_e - B(K) - M_n(Z^A)$$
$$= M_a(Z+1)^A - (Z+1)m_e + B(Z+1) + m_e - B(K)$$
$$\qquad - M_a(Z^A) + Zm_e - B(Z+1) - E(\gamma)$$
$$= M_a(Z+1)^A - M_a(Z^A) - B(K) - E(\gamma). \qquad (9.42)$$

Negaton capture from other shells is also possible, but less likely.

The results obtained can be displayed on energy diagrams, originally due to Fermi (Figs. 9.1—9.4), which clearly show the energies available. These diagrams also show the minimum mass differences between the initial and final nuclei for which a particular decay is possible.

Although electrons appear to come out of nuclei in β-decay, they do not in fact form a constituent part of nuclei. One argument which supports this statement is based on the intrinsic spins of protons and electrons. This was given in section 2.3, but the matter is so important that we shall present here two further arguments.

It follows from the uncertainty principle that if electrons are located in nuclei, then their wavelength must be of the order of nuclear dimensions. If we take these to be of the order 10 fm $\simeq$ 0·025 λ_0, where $\lambda_0 = \hbar/m_e c$ is the Compton wavelength, then we have for the electron momentum

$$p = \frac{\hbar}{\lambda} \simeq 40 \; m_e c.$$

The corresponding energy is obtained from (9.1) and is

$$E \simeq 40 \; m_e c^2 \simeq 20 \text{ MeV}$$

which gives a kinetic energy of 39 $m_e c^2$. There are very good reasons why electrons with such large kinetic energies are exceedingly unlikely to exist inside nuclei. For one thing, such high energies have never been observed in β-decays. It might be argued that in the decay process the electrons lose energy because of a strong interaction with the nuclei. Such a strong nuclear attraction would also have to be postulated to keep the electrons in the nuclei before decay, but no such interaction has ever been observed in experiments in which electrons were scattered by nuclei. It can also be

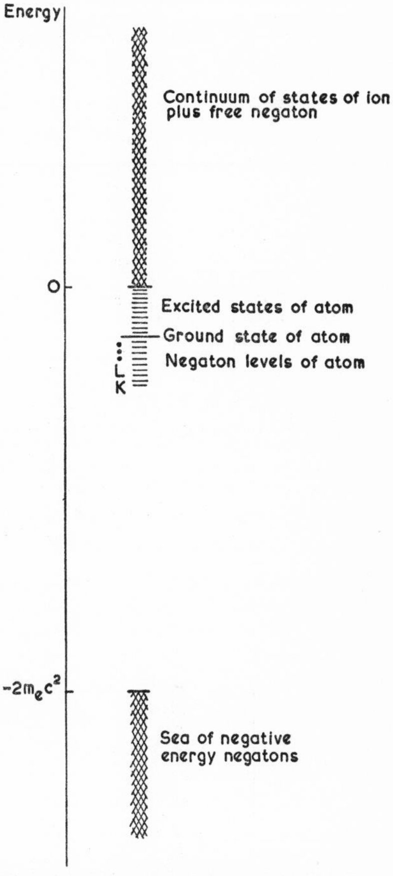

FIG. 9.1. ENERGY STATES OF $(Z + 1)^A$ ATOM

This diagram is used in Figs. 9.2-9.4. The zero of energy corresponds to the singly ionized $(Z + 1)^A$ atom plus a free negaton with zero kinetic energy. (Energies not to scale.) See also section 1.9 for the idea of negative energy negatons.

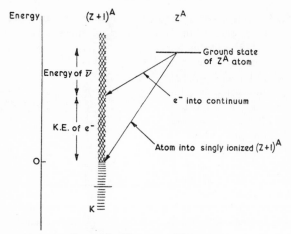

FIG. 9.2. NEGATON EMISSION

The negaton goes into the continuum. The remaining atom has only Z orbital negatons and so goes into the ground state of the singly ionized $(Z + 1)^A$ atom. The negaton could also go to one of the empty discrete levels of $(Z + 1)^A$. In that case the $(Z + 1)^A$ atom is formed in an excited state and no negaton is emitted. Because of the small energy range available for this process, this is very much less likely.

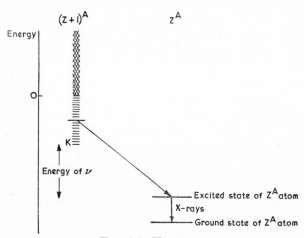

FIG. 9.3. K-CAPTURE

The atom goes into an excited state of Z^A, since it has a vacancy in the K-shell. It goes to the ground state by X-ray emission. See also example 9.8.4.

shown that such an attraction would strongly influence the K-shell energies in heavy atoms. No such effect has ever been found.

A final argument is based on the size of the nuclear magnetic moments. These are all of the order of a few nuclear magnetons and so about a thousand times smaller than the electron magnetic

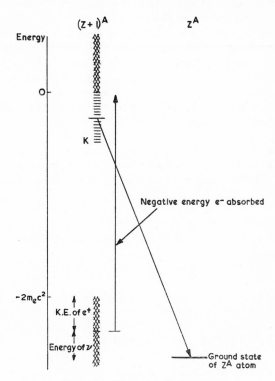

FIG. 9.4. POSITON EMISSION

This is equivalent to the absorption by $(Z + 1)^A$ of a negative energy negaton. K-capture is of course also possible in this case.

moment. If nuclei contain electrons, then there should be at least some with magnetic moments of the order of the electron magnetic moment.

We are led then to the assumption that the electron and the neutrino are created at the moment the nucleus decays. Before going into this, however, we want to say a few more words about the neutrino. The requirement of conservation of both energy and linear momentum in any particular decay will determine the mass of the neutrino for that decay. Should different masses be required for different decays, the whole neutrino hypothesis would be very unsatisfactory indeed.

There are many decays in which the energy balance has been determined and all of these require very small neutrino masses. It is much more difficult to establish a momentum balance since this requires a measurement of the recoil velocity of the nucleus. This is of course very small, since the nuclear mass is so much larger than the masses of the electron and neutrino. In particular, the evaluation of the results becomes extremely unreliable if the decaying nucleus is embedded in a solid or forms part of a molecule. The best results are therefore obtained with monatomic gases.

A further simplification can be achieved if only two-body decays are considered, since in these the decay products do not have varying velocities and they move in opposite directions to each other. In three-body decays the final velocities depend on the angles between the final directions and therefore vary from decay to decay. Now while an electron decay is a three-body process, K-capture is a two-body process, in which a nucleus at rest captures a negaton with effectively zero linear momentum. The decay products are then the daughter nucleus and the neutrino.

A decay which satisfies all the above requirements is the K-capture of argon,

$$A^{37} + e_K = Cl^{37} + \nu.$$

In this the momentum of the recoil nucleus was found to be (Kofoed-Hansen, 1955) 806 ± 8 keV/c.† The energy available for the decay is obtained from the reaction $Cl^{37}(p, n)A^{37}$ and is found to be 816 ± 4 keV. Substituting these values in (9.1) we see that the neutrino mass must be small. It is clear that no very accurate value of it can ever be obtained from recoil experiments, since (9.1) gives the square of the small mass as the difference of two large quantities. Better evidence for the zero mass of the neutrino will be given later.

Other reactions requiring a light neutral particle concern the decays of the pion and the muon. There is no *a priori* reason why this neutral particle, which we shall denote by ν_μ, should be the same as the neutrino that arises from nuclear beta decays, although for the sake of economy and simplicity this was at one time hoped to be the case. However, the fact that certain predicted modes of muon decay did not occur indicated that the two types of neutral

† Since momentum × c has the dimensions of energy, it is permissible to measure momentum in units of energy divided by c. This is particularly convenient when working at relativistic energies.

particle were not identical. As the pion decays into a muon of constant energy, we have here a two-body decay, given by

$$\pi^- \to \mu^- + \bar{\nu}_\mu, \quad \pi^+ \to \mu^+ + \nu_\mu \qquad (9.43)$$

It will be noted that these decays conserve muon-type leptons. The muon decays further into an electron of variable energy, so that this is a three-body decay. If we assume conservation laws to exist for both muon and electron-type leptons, then we must have

$$\mu^- \to e^- + \nu_\mu + \bar{\nu}, \quad \mu^+ \to e^+ + \nu + \bar{\nu}_\mu. \qquad (9.44)$$

The existence of the muon-neutrino was finally settled by a remarkable experiment (Danby, 1962) in which use was made of the powerful pion beam of the Brookhaven synchrotron. Some of the pions decay in flight according to (9.43), and after the charged particles are filtered out, the remaining neutral particles enter a spark chamber. If the ν_μ are identical with electron-neutrinos, then they should interact with the nuclei in the spark chamber and produce electrons according to equation (1.12). No such electrons were observed, which showed that the muon-neutrino was in fact a different particle. The excitement of the scientific chase for this most elusive particle is well caught in Ledermann's article in the *Scientific American* of March, 1963.

The mass of the muon-neutrino is not as well known as that of the electron-neutrino. It is obtained in the following way (Dudziak, 1959). The muon in (9.44) decays at rest and the kinetic energy of the resulting electron is $52\cdot4 \pm 0\cdot1$ MeV. From a knowledge of the mass of the muon, the maximum mass of the neutral particles can be calculated (see example 9.8.5) and it turns out to be less than 8–9 m_e and may well be zero within the limits of experimental error. A similar calculation for the pion decay (example 9.8.5) gives the same result, but with less accuracy.

9.3 Spectrum Shape for Allowed Transitions

So far we have dealt with T_0, the maximum kinetic energy available to both the leptons in a β-decay. We now concentrate on the charged lepton, and for the sake of definiteness consider negaton emission. If the probability of a negaton being emitted in an energy interval dE_e at total energy E_e, is plotted against the energy, then the resulting curve is known as the energy spectrum of the decay. Now it is a remarkable fact that most experimentally observed decays have, apart from a Coulomb correction discussed below, exactly the same spectrum shape, which can be fitted to the formula

$$\text{const.} \times p_e E_e (E_0 - E_e)^2$$

which can be written

$$\text{const.} \times E_e(E_0 - E_e)^2(E_e^2 - m_e^2 c^4)^{1/2} \tag{9.45}$$

where the constant is different for different decays and

$$E_0 = T_0 + m_e c^2. \tag{9.46}$$

It must be the main aim of β-decay theory to explain this fact.

The detailed theory of β-decay, due to Fermi, is based on an analogy with photon emission. Just as in photon emission a quantum mechanical system makes a transition during which a photon is created, so in β-decay a neutron makes a transition to a proton with the creation of two leptons, a negaton and an anti-neutrino. It will actually be more convenient to treat the latter as the destruction of a negative energy neutrino. This makes the mathematical treatment more symmetrical and it makes no difference physically. The basic reaction then is

$$n + \nu \rightarrow p + e^-. \tag{9.47}$$

The theory of positon decay is of course basically the same as that of negaton decay.

We again use time-dependent perturbation theory, as outlined in the appendix. In (A.27) the density of states is now given by the product of the densities of states of the electron and anti-neutrino. Each of these is of the form (A.34),

$$\rho(E)\,dE = (2\pi\hbar)^{-3}\,p^2 dp d\Omega \tag{9.48}$$

where p denotes the momentum, which was previously denoted by $\hbar k$. Instead of (A.35) we have to use the relativistic formula (9.1), which gives

$$E dE = c^2 p dp, \tag{9.49}$$

and a further complication arises from the fact that the final negaton energy is not unique. We shall therefore calculate a transition probability $w dE_e$ for negaton emission in the energy interval E_e to $E_e + dE_e$. This is then given by†

$$w(E_e)dE_e = \frac{2\pi}{\hbar}\,|\,\langle f\,|\,H_1\,|\,i\rangle\,|^{\,2}\,(2\pi\hbar)^{-6}c^{-4}\,p_e E_e p_\nu E_\nu \delta(E_0 - E_e - E_\gamma)$$
$$\times\;dE_e dE_\nu d\Omega_e d\Omega_\gamma. \tag{9.50}$$

(We omit the bar on the anti-neutrino suffix for the sake of convenience.)

This expression must now be integrated over dE_ν, and as we shall not discuss angular correlations between the negaton and the anti-

---

† It is more convenient now to write H_1 for the perturbation Hamiltonian, where H_1 is small, instead of ϵH_1 as in the appendix.

neutrino, we may also integrate over $d\Omega_e d\Omega_\nu$. We further eliminate p_ν by means of (9.1) and write the whole expression in dimensionless form by defining

$$\epsilon = \frac{E_e}{m_e c^2}, \quad \epsilon_0 = \frac{E_0}{m_e c^2}, \quad \mu = \frac{m_\nu}{m_e}. \qquad (9.51)$$

The transition probability per unit energy range is then

$$w = C^2 \epsilon (\epsilon_0 - \epsilon) \sqrt{(\epsilon^2 - 1)} \sqrt{[(\epsilon_0 - \epsilon)^2 - \mu^2]} \qquad (9.52)$$

where the quantity C is given by

$$C = \frac{|\langle f | H_1 | i \rangle | m_e^2 c}{(2\pi^3 \hbar^7)^{1/2}}. \qquad (9.53)$$

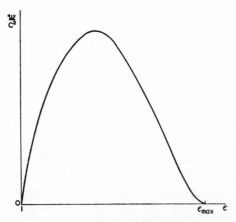

FIG. 9.5. ENERGY SPECTRUM FOR ALLOWED TRANSITIONS

On comparing (9.52) with (9.45) we see that for transitions with spectrum shape (9.45) the matrix element must be independent of the energy, provided the neutrino mass is small, as we know it is. A plot of (9.52) for $\mu \ll 1$ is shown in Fig. 9.5. The maximum energy of the electron is given by

$$\epsilon_{\max} = \epsilon_0 - \mu. \qquad (9.54)$$

The minimum is of course $\epsilon = 1$.

The energy spectrum enables us to estimate the mass of the neutrino. For small ϵ, (9.52) is clearly very insensitive to small variations in μ, but for $\epsilon \simeq \epsilon_{\max}$ this is not so. If we put $\epsilon_{\max} - \epsilon = x$, then

$$w = C^2 (\epsilon_{\max} - x)(\mu + x) \sqrt{[(\epsilon_{\max} - x)^2 - 1]} \sqrt{[x(2\mu + x)]}. \quad (9.55)$$

For small x, we have therefore

$$w \propto \begin{cases} x^2 & \text{for } \mu = 0 \\ x^{1/2} & \text{for } \mu \neq 0. \end{cases} \tag{9.56}$$

The part of the energy spectrum near the maximum energy for the two cases is shown in Fig. 9.6. From an investigation of the decay of H^3, Hamilton (1953) concluded that $\mu < 0{\cdot}001$.

Another way of plotting the energy spectrum is due to Kurie. For $\mu = 0$, (9.52) reduces to

$$w = C^2 \epsilon (\epsilon_0 - \epsilon)^2 \sqrt{(\epsilon^2 - 1)} \tag{9.57}$$

so that a plot of $F(\epsilon, \alpha) = [w/\epsilon \sqrt{(\epsilon^2 - 1)}]^{1/2}$ against ϵ should be a straight line cutting the ϵ-axis at $\epsilon = \epsilon_0 = \epsilon_{\max}$. Any deviation from

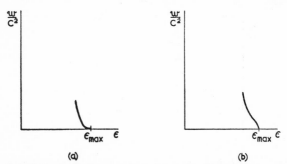

(a) (b)

FIG. 9.6. ENERGY SPECTRUM FOR ALLOWED TRANSITIONS NEAR $\epsilon_{\max}$ FOR (a) $m_\nu = 0$, (b) $m_\nu \neq 0$

a straight line near the high-energy end of the plot is an indication of a finite neutrino mass. This method is clearly more suitable for determining $\epsilon_{\max}$ than the ordinary spectrum plot.

We shall now assume that the neutrino has zero mass and obtain the total decay probability λ by integrating (9.57) over all energies. Then, since $\mathrm{d}E_e = m_e c^2 \mathrm{d}\epsilon$,

$$\lambda = \frac{1}{\tau} = m_e c^2 \int_1^{\epsilon_0} C^2 \epsilon (\epsilon_0 - \epsilon)^2 \sqrt{(\epsilon^2 - 1)} \mathrm{d}\epsilon = m_e c^2 C^2 f(\epsilon_0) \tag{9.58}$$

where

$$f(\epsilon_0) = \tfrac{1}{4}\epsilon_0 \cosh^{-1}\epsilon_0 - \tfrac{1}{4}\epsilon_0^2(\epsilon_0^2 - 1)^{1/2} + \tfrac{1}{6}\epsilon_0^2(\epsilon_0^2 - 1)^{3/2} - \tfrac{2}{15}(\epsilon_0^2 - 1)^{5/2}. \tag{9.59}$$

Here τ is the lifetime of the decay. The quantity $f\tau$, therefore, rather than τ, is significant for a particular decay. Since experimentally it is the half-life $t = \tau \ln 2$ that is measured,† we shall in

† This was denoted by T in section 1.6, but in β-decay theory, where matters of notation are frequently a law unto themselves, t is used invariably. We shall try to avoid confusion with t meaning simply time.

future speak of ft-values. Decays that have spectra of the form (9.45) tend to have lower ft-values than those that have spectra of different form. They are called " allowed " decays, while the others are forbidden. This is so far an experimental classification, but we shall see that it agrees with our theoretical definition, introduced in the appendix.

So far we have said nothing about the Coulomb effect of the nucleus on the emitted negaton or positon. It will be significant only at low negaton or positon energies. Then the negaton will be appreciably retarded by the Coulomb force, and the positon acceler-

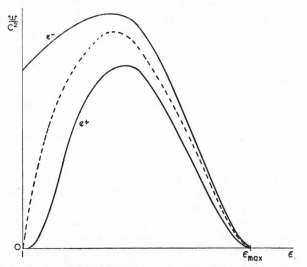

FIG. 9.7. EFFECT OF COULOMB INTERACTION ON β-DECAY
SPECTRUM SHAPES

The dotted line gives the allowed spectrum without Coulomb effect.

ated. There will therefore be an excess of low energy negatons and a deficiency of low energy positons, compared with the theory which neglects the Coulomb effect. The resulting spectrum shapes are shown schematically in Fig. 9.7. The value of f in (9.59) was of course calculated without taking the Coulomb effect into consideration and is valid only for values of the charge number Z of the daughter nucleus less than about 15.

We now proceed to formulate the detailed theory of β-decay and turn to an expression for the matrix element in (9.53). In the case of photon emission we obtained an expression for the interaction energy (8.20) from classical considerations and found it proportional to the vector potential $\mathbf{A}$. Now in β-decay there is no classical analogue, but as the vector potential can be thought of as the wave function of the photon (it satisfies a wave equation !) we postulate that the β-decay interaction energy is proportional to the negaton and neutrino wave functions ϕ_e and ϕ_ν. In addition it will contain operators, analogous to ∇ in (8.20), which operate on the initial and final wave functions ψ_p and ψ_n of the nucleon and perhaps also on ϕ_e and ϕ_ν. (We have used here a notation by which ψ or ϕ denote the space and spin parts of a wave function, while the suffix denotes the i-spin part. Clearly, the i-spin formalism can be applied to the negaton-neutrino pair in the same way as to the proton-neutron pair.) As we have no classical theory to guide us, these operators are restricted only by general requirements of invariance, similar to those that restricted the nuclear potential terms in section 4.1. Lastly, final states will again appear in complex conjugate form, i.e. the proton and negaton wave functions will occur as $\psi_p^\dagger$ and $\phi_e^\dagger$ respectively. Positon emission would correspond to the absorption of a negaton and the emission of a neutrino. This is given by the complex conjugate of the matrix element for negaton emission.

The complete matrix element is therefore of the form

$$\langle f \mid H_1 \mid i \rangle = g \int \psi_p^\dagger(\mathbf{r})\phi_e^\dagger(\mathbf{r})\tau_+\tau_+' Oo\phi_\nu(\mathbf{r})\psi_n(\mathbf{r})\mathrm{d}\tau \qquad (9.60)$$

where O and o are the above-mentioned operators operating on the heavy and light particles respectively and g is a constant corresponding to e in photon emission. The i-spin operators τ_+, τ_+' respectively turn the neutron into a proton and the neutrino into a negaton. For the negaton and neutrino wave functions we shall take plane waves. This is always correct for the neutrino, since it does not interact with other particles, but is justified for the negaton only at comparatively high energies when the Coulomb interaction between it and the nucleus can be neglected. This point has already been noted. We then put

$$\phi_e = \exp\left(\frac{\mathrm{i}}{\hbar}\mathbf{p}_e \,.\, \mathbf{r}\right)u_e, \quad \phi_\nu = \exp\left(\frac{\mathrm{i}}{\hbar}\mathbf{p}_\nu \,.\, \mathbf{r}\right)u_\nu \qquad (9.61)$$

where we have normalized to unit volume and u_e and u_ν are column matrices defined by (9.25). Now in practice the momenta are such that $(\mathbf{p}_e \,.\, \mathbf{r})/\hbar$ and $(\mathbf{p}_\nu \,.\, \mathbf{r})/\hbar$ are always very small compared with unity inside the nuclear volume and never greater than about 0·1. It is therefore permissible to expand the exponentials as in (8.45). The first terms will give the allowed transitions. For these we have then the matrix element

$$g\mathcal{M}_\text{all} = g \int \psi_p^\dagger(\mathbf{r})u_e^\dagger\tau_+\tau_+' Oou_\nu\psi_n(\mathbf{r})\mathrm{d}\tau. \qquad (9.62)$$

This is independent of the energy of the emitted negaton provided the operator *o* does not contain any differentiation. Another way of putting this is to say that the β-decay interaction must be velocity independent. The fact that for experimentally allowed spectra the matrix element is energy independent shows that this is so. Matrix elements of forbidden transitions will be energy dependent, since they contain terms of the form $\mathbf{p}_e$. $\mathbf{r}$. Finally we must sum the matrix element over all nucleons in the nucleus that can take part in the

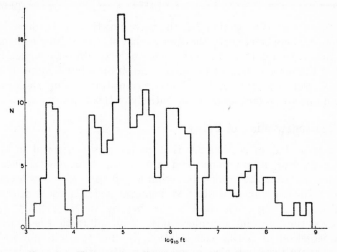

FIG. 9.8. FREQUENCY DISTRIBUTION OF EXPERIMENTAL $\log_{10} ft$ VALUES

[After Feenberg and Trigg, *Revs. Mod. Phys.*, **22**, p. 399 (1950).]

β-transition. For the sake of convenience we shall omit the summation sign until we actually come to evaluate particular matrix elements.

We can now say something more about *ft*-values. It follows from (9.58) and (9.53) that *ft* is inversely proportional to the square of the matrix element. Now matrix elements should be of the same size for all allowed decays and successively smaller for forbidden decays of increasing order. One might think that experimental *ft*-values should therefore fall into groups according to allowed and first, second, etc., forbidden transitions, so that the *ft*-value of a decay would at once give its order of forbiddenness. As long as there were only a few experimental values, there seemed indeed to be some hope of this, but as more experimental *ft*-values were determined, this hope faded, the present position being indicated by Fig. 9.8. It is clear that apart from a group of decays with *ft*-values given by $\log_{10} ft \simeq 3.5$, the so-called super-allowed transitions, there is little if any significant grouping.

The reason for the blurring of the groups is not difficult to find. The *ft*-value of a decay depends not only on the degree of forbiddenness, but also on the form of the nuclear wave functions, and these are not the same for different decays. An exception are the mirror nuclei (see section 2.2) which have β-decays of the form

$$_{z+1}^{Z}\mathrm{X}^{2Z+1} \rightarrow {}_{Z}^{Z+1}\mathrm{Y}^{2Z+1} + \mathrm{e}^{+}. \tag{9.63}$$

As was explained in section 2.2, the wave function of the decaying proton will here be virtually the same as that of the resulting neutron. For that reason $\psi_n(\mathbf{r})$ and $\psi_p^\dagger(\mathbf{r})$ in (9.62) overlap almost completely, so that the matrix element for such a transition is much larger than matrix elements for other allowed transitions. Super-allowed transitions are in fact found to be entirely of this type.

9.4 Non-conservation of Parity

We indicated in section 2.6 that parity was conserved in the strong nuclear interactions, and also in electromagnetic interactions, but that the weak interaction of β-decay did not conserve parity. The experiment which first demonstrated this was suggested by Lee and Yang (1956) and carried out by Wu (1957). It was based on the following considerations. If an interaction is to lead to a violation of parity conservation, it must contain not only scalar quantities, but also pseudoscalar quantities. These latter behave like scalars under co-ordinate rotation, but, unlike scalars, they change sign under co-ordinate reflexion. A well-known example of a pseudoscalar is the scalar triple product of three polar vectors $\mathbf{a} \cdot (\mathbf{b} \times \mathbf{c})$. Now in a normal β-decay experiment we measure the momentum of the electron $\mathbf{p}_e$ and, by means of the recoil of the nucleus, the neutrino momentum $\mathbf{p}_\nu$. This can only yield information on a term in the interaction depending on $\mathbf{p}_e \cdot \mathbf{p}_\nu$, which is a scalar. If however the nuclei that are β-active are polarized, so that all their intrinsic angular momenta $\mathbf{I}$ point in the same direction, then we have an additional vector entering into our measurements. The important point is that $\mathbf{I}$ is not an ordinary polar vector that changes sign under co-ordinate reflexion, but an axial vector that does not. This is most easily seen from the fact that part of it is due to orbital angular momentum, which is the vector product of position and linear momentum vectors $\mathbf{r} \times \mathbf{p}$, and such a vector product is an axial vector. The rest is due to spin angular momentum, which too is an axial vector. A scalar product of the form $\mathbf{I} \cdot \mathbf{p}_e$ is therefore a pseudoscalar and, if such a term exists in the β-decay interaction, then the latter is clearly not invariant under space reflexion, i.e. the interaction does not conserve parity. Experimentally one measures the angle θ between $\mathbf{I}$ and $\mathbf{p}_e$. As the parity operation changes $\mathbf{p}_e$ to $-\mathbf{p}_e$, but $\mathbf{I}$ to $\mathbf{I}$, it changes θ to $\pi - \theta$, and so, if parity is conserved, electron emission will be symmetric about a plane perpendicular to $\mathbf{I}$. The experiment was performed using the negaton decay from Co^{60} which had been cooled down to about $0.01°$K.

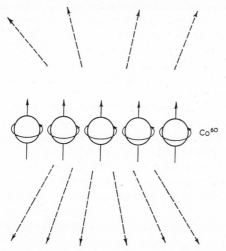

FIG. 9.9. NEGATON DECAY FROM POLARIZED Co^{60} NUCLEI (schematic)

Under these circumstances the spins of the nuclei align in a magnetic field and it was then found that more negatons were emitted against the spin direction than with it (see Fig. 9.9). The asymmetry, i.e. the ratio of the difference of the negatons emitted downwards and upwards to the sum of these two, was about 30 per cent.

A possible explanation of the breakdown of parity conservation in β-decay lies in the zero mass of the neutrino. A spinning particle moving in space has attached to it two vectors, its velocity $\mathbf{v}$ and its spin $\boldsymbol{\sigma}$. Now it might be thought that a measurement of $\boldsymbol{\sigma} . \mathbf{v}$, which is a pseudoscalar, would determine whether the particle had a definite parity or not. However, in general this is not so, since there is an arbitrariness about $\mathbf{v}$, which depends on the velocity of the observer. If a particle moves forward with a velocity $\mathbf{v}$ relative to a stationary observer, then as seen by an observer, whose velocity relative to the first observer is greater than $\mathbf{v}$ and in the same direction as $\mathbf{v}$, the particle will appear to move backwards. The product $\boldsymbol{\sigma} . \mathbf{v}$ does not therefore have a definite sign at any given moment. Another way of putting this is that if $\boldsymbol{\sigma}$ and $\mathbf{v}$ are parallel, it is not possible to state whether the particle is spinning clockwise or anti-clockwise relative to its direction of motion. An exception to the above is a particle of zero mass. Such a particle moves with the velocity of light, and therefore no observer can move as fast as it. For it, the product $\boldsymbol{\sigma} \cdot \mathbf{v}$ has a definite sign. In fact, it can be shown that for a particle of spin $\frac{1}{2}$ and zero mass $\boldsymbol{\sigma}$ and $\mathbf{v}$ are always parallel, so that the particle moves in a screw motion of definite left-handed or right-handed sense. Since such a screw motion changes from left-handed to right-handed under space reflexion, an individual particle of zero mass must violate parity conservation. It would still be possible for overall parity to be conserved, since in any given β-decay there might be as many left-handed as right-handed neutrinos emitted. The experimental results indicate that this is not so.

The above considerations can be put on a firm quantum mechanical basis. Let us go back to the relativistic wave equation (9.9). We had expressed the matrices $\boldsymbol{\alpha}$ and β in one particular representation, given in partitioned form by (9.7), and this representation turned out to be especially convenient in the non-relativistic limit, since it enabled us to separate the wave functions into " large " and " small " components in this limit. We are now interested in the extreme relativistic limit, since neutrinos move with the velocity of light, and another representation then turns out more useful. This is given by

$$\boldsymbol{\alpha} = \left(\begin{array}{c|c} \boldsymbol{\sigma} & 0 \\ \hline 0 & -\boldsymbol{\sigma} \end{array} \right), \qquad \beta = \left(\begin{array}{c|c} 0 & \mathsf{I} \\ \hline \mathsf{I} & 0 \end{array} \right). \qquad (9.64)$$

It is easily shown that these matrices, too, satisfy (9.5). If we now write the wave function in partitioned form,

$$\psi(\mathbf{r}) = \left(\begin{array}{c} \phi_1(\mathbf{r}) \\ \hline \phi_2(\mathbf{r}) \end{array} \right), \text{ where } \phi_1(\mathbf{r}) = \left(\begin{array}{c} \psi_1(\mathbf{r}) \\ \psi_2(\mathbf{r}) \end{array} \right), \ \phi_2(\mathbf{r}) = \left(\begin{array}{c} \psi_3(\mathbf{r}) \\ \psi_4(\mathbf{r}) \end{array} \right) \qquad (9.65)$$

then (9.9) reduces to

$$\left\{ -i\hbar c \left(\begin{array}{c|c} \boldsymbol{\sigma} \cdot \nabla & 0 \\ \hline 0 & -\boldsymbol{\sigma} \cdot \nabla \end{array} \right) + mc^2 \left(\begin{array}{c|c} 0 & \mathsf{I} \\ \hline \mathsf{I} & 0 \end{array} \right) \right\} \left(\begin{array}{c} \phi_1 \\ \hline \phi_2 \end{array} \right)$$

$$= E \left(\begin{array}{c} \phi_1 \\ \hline \phi_2 \end{array} \right). \qquad (9.66)$$

This can be written as a pair of coupled equations in ϕ_1 and ϕ_2,

$$\left.\begin{aligned} - i\hbar c\boldsymbol{\sigma} \cdot \nabla \phi_1 + mc^2\phi_2 &= E\phi_1 \\ i\hbar c\boldsymbol{\sigma} \cdot \nabla \phi_2 + mc^2\phi_1 &= E\phi_2 \end{aligned}\right\} \qquad (9.67)$$

For vanishing rest mass, these equations uncouple, and since to every positive energy eigenvalue E, there is a corresponding negative eigenvalue $- E$, they are in fact equivalent. We consider the upper equation. It describes a particle with Hamiltonian

$$H = - i\hbar c\boldsymbol{\sigma} \cdot \nabla \qquad (9.68)$$

and it will be noticed that this is a pseudoscalar quantity, given by the scalar product of the axial spin vector $\boldsymbol{\sigma}$ and the polar momentum vector $\mathbf{p} = -i\hbar\nabla$. The parity operator (2.59) does not commute with such a Hamiltonian and parity is therefore not a constant of motion for a particle described by (9.67). It is for this reason that such equations were rejected by Pauli as " unphysical " in a famous remark.†

Now that we know that neutrinos do not conserve parity, we can see that the two-component equation

$$c\boldsymbol{\sigma} \cdot \mathbf{p}\phi = - i\hbar c\boldsymbol{\sigma} \cdot \nabla \phi = E\phi \qquad (9.68)$$

admirably describes a neutrino and anti-neutrino of strictly zero rest-mass.

Neutrinos and anti-neutrinos differ through the fact that the former have the spin vector opposite to the direction of motion, while the latter have it along it, or alternatively that the one describes a left-handed screw and the other a right-handed one. (Which particle describes which kind of screw can only be settled by experiment. It turns out that it is the neutrino which is left-handed.) The operator for this " handedness " or *helicity* is

$$Q = \frac{\boldsymbol{\sigma} \cdot \mathbf{p}}{|\mathbf{p}|}, \qquad (9.69)$$

and it is clear from (9.68) that the eigenvalues of Q are

$Q = + 1$ for $E > 0$ (right-handedness) anti-neutrino

$Q = - 1$ for $E < 0$ (left-handedness) neutrino

A word of caution must be added. The first suspicion that there might be reactions which did not conserve parity did not come from β-decay, but from the different decays of the heavy K-meson, which is

† " Indessen sind diese Wellengleichungen nicht invariant gegenüber Spiegelungen (Vertauschung von links und rechts) und infolgedessen sind sie auf die physikalische Wirklichkeit nicht anwendbar." (*Handbuch der Physik*, 2nd ed., Vol. 24, Part 1, page 226.)

created in the bombardment of nucleons by very energetic pions. This can decay into either two pions or three pions and it can be shown that only one of these decays can conserve parity while and the other must violate it. Unfortunately there is no room for neutrinos in either of these decays, so that it looks as if the zero mass of the neutrino cannot be the only possible cause of parity violation.

Although parity is not conserved in β-decay, we know from many experiments that it is conserved in the strong nuclear interactions. For that reason even in β-decay the parity of the nucleus must be unchanged by the decay if the leptons are emitted in an even angular momentum state and changed if they are emitted in an odd angular momentum state. The emitted electron, on the other hand, violates parity in just such a way as to compensate for the parity violation of the neutrino. This means that it too must be emitted with a definite polarization, and this has been observed.

9.5 Selection Rules for Allowed Transitions

So far we have said nothing about the selection rules which govern the angular momentum of the nucleus before and after decay. This depends of course on the angular momentum carried away by the emitted leptons.† One of the complications of relativistic theory is that we can no longer split this up into orbital and spin angular momentum, and therefore we shall at first employ a non-relativistic approach, in spite of the obvious absurdity of treating the neutrino non-relativistically. At least we shall in this way obtain some physical insight into the problem before getting down to the mathematical difficulties of the relativistic approach.

Non-relativistically, two particles, having spin $\frac{1}{2}$, can be emitted with spins anti-parallel or parallel, and for allowed transitions the orbital angular momentum of the state is zero, corresponding to the first term in the expansion of a plane wave. The parity of a state with $l = 0$ is of course even. We have then the following selection rules :

$$\triangle I = 0, \text{ no,} \qquad \text{for spins anti-parallel (Fermi)} \qquad (9.70)$$

$$\triangle I = \pm 1 \text{ or } 0 \text{ (except } 0 \to 0\text{), no,} \qquad \text{for spins parallel (Gamow-Teller).} \qquad (9.71)$$

---

† As before there is no difference between the emission of an anti-neutrino and the absorption of a neutrino.

The names in brackets are those by which the selection rules are usually known. The reason for the absence of $0 \to 0$ transitions in (9.71) is that the equation

$$\triangle I = I_f - I_i = S$$

where $S = 1$ is the total spin angular momentum of the leptons cannot be satisfied with $I_f = I_i = 0$.

It is of course quite likely that β-decay mixes states with spins anti-parallel or parallel in definite proportions. That this is the true state of affairs is shown by the experimentally observed decays. Thus

$$\text{He}^6 \to \text{Li}^6 + \text{e}^-, \quad \log_{10} ft = 2 \cdot 77$$
$$(I = 0) \qquad (I = 1)$$

which is impossible by Fermi rules, and

$$\text{O}^{14} \to \text{N}^{14*} + \text{e}^+, \quad \log_{10} ft = 3 \cdot 49$$
$$(I = 0) \qquad (I = 0)$$

which is impossible by Gamow-Teller rules. The small values of $\log_{10} ft$ show that these are certainly allowed transitions. Unfortunately the angular momentum assignments in these and many similar cases are never absolutely certain for both nuclei, the assignment for the parent nucleus in particular being often based on indirect evidence. Nevertheless, the case for mixed selection rules is pretty firmly established.

The different selection rules must of course come out of different choices of the operators O and o in (9.60). As the β-decay interaction does not depend on the velocities of the particles, O and o do not contain space derivatives, but merely spin operators. The only possible ones are 1 and $\boldsymbol{\sigma}$, and since the complete Hamiltonian must be invariant under rotations, we must have either $Oo = 1$ or $Oo = \boldsymbol{\sigma}_{\text{nucleon}} \cdot \boldsymbol{\sigma}_{\text{lepton}}$. We therefore have from (9.62) the following two possible matrix elements for allowed transitions,

$$\mathscr{M}_{\text{all}}^{(1)} = \int \psi_p^{\dagger} \tau_+ \psi_n u_e^{\dagger} \tau_+' u_\nu \mathrm{d}\tau \tag{9.72}$$

$$\mathscr{M}_{\text{all}}^{(2)} = \int \psi_p^{\dagger} \tau_+ \boldsymbol{\sigma} \psi_n \cdot u_e^{\dagger} \tau_+' \boldsymbol{\sigma} u_\nu \mathrm{d}\tau. \tag{9.73}$$

Since the operators 1 and $\boldsymbol{\sigma}$ carry respectively angular momentum 0 and 1, these matrix elements obey respectively Fermi and Gamow-Teller selection rules.

It may be instructive to prove the above statement directly. Since we are dealing with the non-relativistic approximation, the wave functions have of course only two components, and u_e and u_ν are given by the large components of (9.25) for $E > 0$,

$$u_e = \begin{pmatrix} 1 \\ 0 \end{pmatrix} \text{ or } \begin{pmatrix} 0 \\ 1 \end{pmatrix}, \quad u_\nu = \begin{pmatrix} 1 \\ 0 \end{pmatrix} \text{ or } \begin{pmatrix} 0 \\ 1 \end{pmatrix}. \tag{9.74}$$

These are the familiar spin wave functions α and β of section 2.7.

Now $u_e^\dagger \tau_+' u_\nu \neq 0$ only if u_e and u_ν correspond to the same spin direction, i.e. if the spin direction of the emitted negaton is the same as that of the absorbed neutrino. This is the singlet state. On the other hand

$$\psi_p^\dagger \tau_+ \boldsymbol{\sigma} \psi_n \cdot u_e^\dagger \tau_+' \boldsymbol{\sigma} u_\nu = \sum_w \psi_p^\dagger \tau_+ \sigma_w \psi_n u_e^\dagger \tau_+' \sigma_w u_\nu \tag{9.75}$$

where $w = x, y, z$, and this corresponds to the triplet state. To see this we must also write the nucleon wave functions as products of space and spin functions and we then consider the spin dependent part of the matrix element, which is

$$\sum_w u_p^\dagger \tau_+ \sigma_w u_n u_e^\dagger \tau_+' \sigma_w u_\nu. \tag{9.76}$$

If for instance $u_e = \alpha$, $u_\nu = \beta$, then this vanishes unless $u_p = \beta$ and $u_n = \alpha$, i.e. the angular momentum of the nucleus changes by one.

The rigorous generalization to a relativistic theory is beyond the scope of this book. Our operators must now be invariant under what are called proper Lorentz transformations (rotations in the four-dimensional space-time continuum) and there result ten invariants, corresponding to our two non-relativistic ones, (9.72) and (9.73). Like these they are scalar products and because of the transformation properties of their factors they are referred to as scalar, vector, tensor, axial vector and pseudoscalar. Each one of these contains two terms, known as even and odd, the odd terms being denoted by primed letters. The relative sign of these terms is changed under space reflexion, and so parity non-conservation will show up from a measurement of the interference between even and odd terms. The reason why this could not happen in our non-relativistic treatment was that the idea of maximum velocities of particles of zero and non-zero mass have no meaning in a non-relativistic theory, where there is no upper bound to velocity. Hence in a non-relativistic theory not even the neutrino would have a definite spin sense.

In terms of 4×4 matrices the interactions corresponding to the ten invariants can be written (see also examples 9.8.2 and 9.8.3)

$$S = g_S \psi_p^\dagger \tau_+ \beta \psi_n \phi_e^\dagger \tau_+' \beta \phi_\nu \tag{9.77}$$

$$S' = g_S' \psi_p^\dagger \tau_+ \beta \psi_n \phi_e^\dagger \tau_+' \beta \gamma \phi_\nu \tag{9.78}$$

$$V = g_V \psi_p^\dagger \tau_+ \psi_n \phi_e^\dagger \tau_+' \phi_\nu \quad - g_V \psi_p^\dagger \tau_+ \alpha \psi_n \cdot \phi_e^\dagger \tau_+' \alpha \phi_\nu \tag{9.79}$$

$$V' = g_V' \psi_p^\dagger \tau_+ \psi_n \phi_e^\dagger \tau_+' \gamma \phi_\nu - g_V' \psi_p^\dagger \tau_+ \alpha \psi_n \cdot \phi_e^\dagger \tau_+' \boldsymbol{\sigma}' \phi_\nu \tag{9.80}$$

$$T = g_T \psi_p^\dagger \tau_+ \beta \boldsymbol{\sigma}' \psi_n \cdot \phi_e^\dagger \tau_+' \beta \boldsymbol{\sigma}' \phi_\nu + g_T \psi_p^\dagger \tau_+ \beta \alpha \psi_n \cdot \phi_e^\dagger \tau_+' \beta \alpha \phi_\nu \tag{9.81}$$

$$T' = g_T' \psi_p^\dagger \tau_+ \beta \boldsymbol{\sigma}' \psi_n \cdot \phi_e^\dagger \tau_+' \beta \alpha \phi_\nu + g_T' \psi_p^\dagger \tau_+ \beta \alpha \psi_n \cdot \phi_e^\dagger \tau_+' \beta \boldsymbol{\sigma}' \phi_\nu \tag{9.82}$$

$$A = g_A \psi_p^\dagger \tau_+ \boldsymbol{\sigma}' \psi_n \cdot \phi_e^\dagger \tau_+' \boldsymbol{\sigma}' \phi_\nu - g_A \psi_p^\dagger \tau_+ \gamma \psi_n \phi_e^\dagger \tau_+' \gamma \phi_\nu \tag{9.83}$$

$$A' = g_A' \psi_p^\dagger \tau_+ \boldsymbol{\sigma}' \psi_n \cdot \phi_e^\dagger \tau_+' \alpha \phi_\nu - g_A' \psi_p^\dagger \tau_+ \gamma \psi_n \phi_e^\dagger \tau_+' \phi_\nu \tag{9.84}$$

$$P = g_P \psi_p^\dagger \tau_+ \beta \gamma \psi_n \phi_e^\dagger \tau_+' \beta \gamma \phi_\nu \tag{9.85}$$

$$P' = g_P' \psi_p^\dagger \tau_+ \beta \gamma \psi_n \phi_e^\dagger \tau_+' \beta \phi_\nu \tag{9.86}$$

where γ is defined by

$$\gamma = -i\alpha_1 \alpha_2 \alpha_3. \tag{9.87}$$

The g's are numbers giving the strengths of the interaction.

Although it is convenient to express the above terms in matrix form, it is not essential. They are in fact simply bilinear expressions in the components of the wave functions, e.g. in representation (9.7),

$$\left. \begin{array}{l} \psi^\dagger \beta \psi = \psi_1^* \psi_1 + \psi_2^* \psi_2 - \psi_3^* \psi_3 - \psi_4^* \psi_4 \\ \psi^\dagger \gamma \psi = \psi_1^* \psi_3 + \psi_2^* \psi_4 + \psi_3^* \psi_1 + \psi_4^* \psi_2 \end{array} \right\} \tag{9.88}$$

and similarly for all others. It may be noticed that $\psi^\dagger \psi$ is not a scalar, but a component of a four-vector. The explanation of this is given in example 9.8.2.

Fortunately not all the interactions contribute to the allowed transitions. In first approximation it is still possible to treat the nucleons non-relativistically, so that their wave functions can be written in the form

$$\psi = \left(\begin{array}{c} L \\ \hline S \end{array} \right), \quad L = \left(\begin{array}{c} \psi_1 \\ \psi_2 \end{array} \right), \quad S = \left(\begin{array}{c} \psi_3 \\ \psi_4 \end{array} \right) \tag{9.89}$$

where L and S are the large and small components. Now the matrices between nuclear wave functions in (9.77)—(9.86) can be divided into two groups,

$$\beta, \, 1, \, \beta\boldsymbol{\sigma}', \, \boldsymbol{\sigma}', \tag{9.90}$$

which in partitioned form have 0 matrices in the non-leading diagonal, and

$$\alpha, \, \beta\alpha, \, \gamma, \, \beta\gamma, \tag{9.91}$$

which have 0 matrices in the leading diagonal. As is exemplified in (9.88), the former lead to large components being multiplied by large components, while the latter lead to the mixing of large and small components. Terms containing them are therefore smaller by order v/c than the others, where v is the velocity of the nucleon in the nucleus. This is of the order 0·2 for heavy nuclei, so that these terms are comparable with those arising from the next term in the expansion of the lepton wave functions. The situation is very similar to that in photon emission, where the magnetic dipole term is comparable with the electric quadrupole. In β-decay the terms due to (9.91) are included among the forbidden transitions and will be dealt with in the next section. The allowed transitions are then due to (9.77), (9.78) and the first terms of (9.79)—(9.84).

In the non-relativistic limit the 4×4 matrices are represented by their top-left-hand 2×2 matrices in the partitioned form, since all other elements of the matrices are multiplied by the small components of the wave functions, which of course vanish in the non-relativistic limit. Thus

$$\beta, \, 1, \, \beta\sigma', \, \sigma' \, (4 \times 4) \rightarrow 1, \, 1, \, \sigma, \, \sigma \, (2 \times 2). \tag{9.92}$$

As was to be expected, we are back with our two non-relativistic invariants, and on comparing (9.92) with (9.70) and (9.71) we find for the selection rules, which must be independent of the velocity of the nucleons,

$$\left.\begin{array}{l} S, \, S' : \int\beta \\[2mm] V, \, V' : \int 1 \end{array}\right\} \triangle I = 0, \text{ no (Fermi)}, \tag{9.93}$$

$$\left.\begin{array}{l} T, \, T' : \int\beta\sigma' \\[2mm] A, \, A' : \int\sigma' \end{array}\right\} \triangle I = \pm 1 \text{ or } 0 \text{ (except } 0 \rightarrow 0) \text{ no (Gamow-Teller).} \tag{9.94}$$

The notation for the matrix elements, using the integral sign, is very convenient and self-explanatory.

9.6 Forbidden Transitions

The selection rules for first forbidden transitions can now be obtained at once. We must of course distinguish between the two types of forbiddenness and we shall deal first with that due to the expansion of the lepton wave functions. This brings a factor **r** into the integrand, corresponding to the emission of a P-wave. As P-waves have negative parity and angular momentum $l = 1$, the selection rules (9.93) and (9.94) must clearly be modified by increasing $\triangle I$ by one and changing the parity assignment. Thus for first forbidden transitions we have

$$\left.\begin{array}{l} S,\ S' : \int\beta\mathbf{r} \\[2ex] V,\ V' : \int\mathbf{r} \end{array}\right\} \triangle I = \pm\ 1,\ 0,\ (\text{except}\ 0 \rightarrow 0),\ \text{yes} \qquad (9.95)$$

$$\left.\begin{array}{l} T,\ T' : \int\beta\boldsymbol{\sigma}'\mathbf{r} \\[2ex] A,\ A' : \int\boldsymbol{\sigma}'\mathbf{r} \end{array}\right\} \triangle I = \pm\ 2,\ \pm\ 1,\ 0,\ \text{yes}. \qquad (9.96)$$

The product of $\boldsymbol{\sigma}'\mathbf{r}$ is a tensor product and has nine components

$$\sigma_m' r_n (m,\ n = x,\ y,\ z).$$

[For fuller details see example 9.8.7.] The reason why in (9.96) transitions $0 \rightarrow 0$ may now be allowed is easiest seen non-relativistically. We now have

$$\triangle \mathbf{I} = \mathbf{I}_f - \mathbf{I}_i = \mathbf{S} + \mathbf{L}$$

where $S = 1$, $L = 1$ are the spin and orbital angular momenta of the leptons. This is clearly possible for $I_f = I_i = 0$.

We next turn to the forbiddenness arising from the relativistic correction. As was pointed out after (9.19), $\boldsymbol{\alpha}$ is a velocity vector, i.e. a polar vector which, unlike an axial vector like $\boldsymbol{\sigma}'$, changes sign under space inversion. Its angular momentum selection rules are therefore the same as those of $\boldsymbol{\sigma}'$, but it has opposite parity. Similarly γ, which is a pseudoscalar [see example 9.8.2], has the same angular momentum selection rules and opposite parity to β. We then have from those terms of (9.79)—(9.86) which we have so far neglected,

$$\left.\begin{array}{l} V,\ V' : \int\boldsymbol{\alpha} \\[2ex] T,\ T' : \int\beta\boldsymbol{\alpha} \end{array}\right\} \triangle I = \pm\ 1,\ 0\ (\text{except}\ 0 \rightarrow 0),\ \text{yes} \qquad (9.97)$$

$$\left.\begin{array}{l} A,\ A' : \int\gamma \\[2ex] P,\ P' : \int\beta\gamma \end{array}\right\} \triangle I = 0,\ \text{yes}. \qquad (9.98)$$

The selection rules for these transitions are therefore included in (9.95) and (9.96), but are in contradiction with (9.93) and (9.94). This is the real justification for including these transitions among the first forbidden ones. Selection rules for higher-order forbiddenness can be obtained in a similar manner.

The spectrum shapes and lifetimes of forbidden transitions are a good deal more troublesome to evaluate then those of allowed transitions and will not be dealt with here.

9.7 The Coupling Constants

So far we have dealt with possible forms of the β-decay interaction. We now turn to the experimental data to see which of the ten interactions are actually present and what their relative strengths are. We shall only be able to give some of the evidence.

The first simplification arises from our belief in the neutrino wave equation (9.68). From this it follows that the neutrino must be described by a two-component wave function. Now the general wave function ϕ_ν in (9.77–9.86) is a four-component wave function. To investigate these interaction terms further, we note that in the representation (9.64), which is suitable for extremely relativistic particles, we have

$$\gamma = \left(\begin{array}{c|c} -I & 0 \\ \hline 0 & I \end{array} \right). \tag{9.99}$$

Hence the matrices $I + \gamma$ and $I - \gamma$ will both project out two of the four components, and we therefore deduce that

$$g'_s = \pm\, g_s, \text{ etc.} \tag{9.100}$$

It is not possible to go into the details of how further information reduces the uncertainties about the coupling constants, but experiments on the longitudinal polarization of emitted electrons and on the helicity of the neutrino show that the $+$ sign in (9.100) is correct and that the dominant terms in the interaction are A and V. If this is accepted, then we can obtain g_V and g_A from any two decays for which the matrix elements are particularly simple.

It follows from (9.58) and (9.53) that for an allowed transition,

$$\frac{1}{ft} = \frac{m^5 c^4}{\pi^3 \hbar^7 \ln 2} \left\{ \left| \int I \right|^2 + \left| \int \sigma' \right|^2 \right\} \tag{9.101}$$

where we have only used the V and A terms in (9.93) and (9.94). It should be noted that a factor $\frac{1}{2}$ has disappeared, as there are two terms for each interaction. The simplest decay is that of the neutron, for which the nuclear matrix elements are clearly unity, so that

$$n \to p : \left| \int I \right|^2 = g_V^2, \quad \left| \int \sigma' \right|^2 = g_A^2. \tag{9.102}$$

We also assume that for a decay within an i-spin multiplet, such as $O^{14} \to N^{14}$ (see Fig. 2.7), there is complete overlap of the wave function, so that the nuclear matrix element is again unity. Now this is a $0^+ \to 0^+$ transition and thus completely forbidden by Gamow-Teller rules. Further, we have to scan over the two protons in the last shell which can β-decay, so that we have (see also ex. 9.8.8)

$$O^{14} \to N^{14} : \quad \left|\int I\right|^2 = 2g_V{}^2, \quad \left|\int \sigma'\right| = 0. \qquad (9.103)$$

The most recent ft-values for the above decays (Blin-Stoyle, 1961) are

$$ft(n \to p) = 1180 \pm 35 \quad ft(O^{14} \to N^{14}) = 3071 \pm 16, \qquad (9.104)$$

from which,

$$\begin{aligned} g_V &= (1\cdot415 \pm 0\cdot004) \times 10^{-49}\text{erg cm}^3, \\ g_A &= (1\cdot55 \pm 0\cdot10) \times 10^{-49}\text{erg cm}^3. \end{aligned} \qquad (9.105)$$

In terms of the nucleon rest mass and Compton wavelength, the coupling constants are of the order

$$g \simeq 10^{-5} Mc^2 . \left(\frac{\hbar}{Mc}\right)^3. \qquad (9.106)$$

We might compare this with the nuclear forces derived in section 3.7. From there we find that

$$V_{ot} b_t{}^3 = 73 Mc^2 \left(\frac{\hbar}{Mc}\right)^3, \quad V_{os} b_s{}^3 = 60 Mc^2 \left(\frac{\hbar}{Mc}\right)^3 \qquad (9.107)$$

which gives a good idea of the smallness of the β-decay interaction.

9.8. EXAMPLES

9.8.1. If α_1, α_2, α_3, β are any four quantities satisfying (9.5), show that there are just exactly twelve independent other quantities that can be obtained from the above four by multiplication. Obtain expressions for them and for the matrix γ in the representations (9.7) and (9.64), and show that

$$\alpha_2\alpha_3 = i\sigma_x' \text{ (cycl.).}$$

Hence prove that σ_x' commutes with α_3 and β.

9.8.2. By considering the physical meaning of $\Psi^\dagger \Psi$ [see (9.16)], show that it must be the time-like part of a four-vector and cannot be a scalar. Similarly show that $\Psi^\dagger \alpha \Psi$ is the space-like part of the same four-vector, and that $\Psi^{-\dagger}\sigma'\Psi$ is the space-like part of an axial four-vector.

Prove that

$$\sigma' = \gamma\alpha$$

and hence that the time-like part of the above axial four-vector is $\Psi^\dagger \gamma \Psi$. What can be deduced about the behaviour of γ under space reflexion from the nature of the vectors σ' and α?

9.8.3. Use the scalar product of the two four-vectors $(\alpha, 1)$ and $(c\nabla, \partial/\partial t)$ to show that $\Psi^\dagger \beta \Psi$ is a scalar. Verify, with the help of (9.25), that it is invariant under space reflexions, and that its value is $(1 - v^2/c^2)^{1/2}$. What can be said about $\Psi^\dagger \beta \gamma \Psi$?

9.8.4. Show that if the ground state of the Z_i^A atom in Fig. 9.3 lies between the K-and L-levels of the $(Z + 1)^A$ atom, then L-capture is possible, but K-capture is not.

What happens if the ground state of the Z^A atom lies (i) between the highest filled and the lowest unfilled negaton levels of the $(Z + 1)^A$ atom, (ii) between two unfilled levels of the $(Z + 1)^A$ atom?

9.8.5. If the maximum kinetic energy of the electron in the μ-decay (9.44) is denoted by T_e, show that the total mass of the neutral particles, m_ν, is given by

$$m_\nu^2 = (m_\mu - m_e)^2 - \frac{2m_\mu T_e}{c^2}.$$

The measured value of T_e (Dudziak, 1959) is $52 \cdot 4 \pm 0 \cdot 1$ MeV. Show that the sum of the masses of the neutral particles is less than about $8\,m_e$.

The kinetic energy of the muon in the π-decay (9.43) is $4 \cdot 12 \pm 0 \cdot 02$ MeV (Barkas, 1956). Estimate the limits on the neutrino mass from this reaction.

[Take $m_\pi = 273 \cdot 3 \pm 0 \cdot 2\,m_e$, $m_\mu = 206 \cdot 9 \pm 0 \cdot 1\,m_e$.]

9.8.6. Show that

 (a) $f(\epsilon_0) \to \frac{2}{105}(\epsilon_0^2 - 1)^{7/2}$ as $\epsilon_0 \to 1$,

 (b) $f(\epsilon_0) \to \frac{1}{30}\epsilon_0^5$ for $\epsilon_0 \gg 1$.

Evaluate the $\log_{10} ft$-values of the following decays and comment on the results:

	H³	C¹¹	Ne²³	S³⁷	Sc⁴¹
Half-life	$3 \cdot 93 \times 10^8$	1230	40·7	302	0·87 sec
Max. kinetic energy of electron	0·0186	0·981	4·1	4·3	4·94 MeV.

9.8.7. Show that the nine terms of the tensor product $\sigma' \mathbf{r}$ can be rearranged into three invariant combinations:

 (a) a scalar $\sigma' \cdot \mathbf{r}$,

 (b) a vector $\sigma' \times \mathbf{r}$,

 (c) a symmetrical tensor $B_{mn} = \sigma_m' r_n + \sigma_n' r_m$, m, $n = x$, y, z, with the restriction

$$\sum_m B_{mm} = 2\sigma' \cdot \mathbf{r}.$$

Hence show that the more detailed selection rules for $\int \sigma' \mathbf{r}$ are:

$\int \sigma' \cdot \mathbf{r}$: $I = 0$, yes,

$\int \sigma' \times \mathbf{r}$: $I = \pm 1$, 0, yes (except $0 \to 0$),

$\int B_{mn}$: $I = \pm 2$, ± 1, 0, yes (except $0 \to 0$, $\frac{1}{2} \to \frac{1}{2}$, $0 \longleftrightarrow 1$).

[Hint: The intrinsic angular momentum j of each operator is obtained from the fact that the number of its independent components is $2j + 1$.]

CHAPTER 10

Meson Theory of Nuclear Forces

THE way we have so far described the forces acting between two particles has been by means of a potential which was a function of the distance between the particles. Another way to describe this force is by means of a force field due to the one particle in which the other finds itself. The former description is essentially non-relativistic, since the force is propagated instantaneously and space is treated on a different footing from time. A field theory on the other hand does not suffer from this defect and it will now be our task to devise a field theory of nuclear forces. The first attempt at such a theory was due to Yukawa (1935).

10.1 Yukawa's Theory

The field theory with which we are most familiar is Maxwell's theory of the electromagnetic field. In this theory the field is described by a vector potential $\mathbf{A}$ and a scalar potential ϕ which satisfy the equations †

$$\nabla^2\mathbf{A} - \frac{1}{c^2}\frac{\partial^2\mathbf{A}}{\partial t^2} = -\frac{4\pi}{c}\mathbf{j}, \quad \nabla^2\phi - \frac{1}{c^2}\frac{\partial^2\phi}{\partial t^2} = -4\pi\rho \quad (10.1)$$

where $\mathbf{j}$ and ρ are the electric current and charge density respectively. It will often be useful to write these and subsequent equations in a form in which space and time co-ordinates are treated in the same way, and we therefore define the following four-vectors,‡

$$\mathbf{x}_\mu = (\mathbf{r},\ ict) = (x,\ y,\ z,\ ict) = (x_1,\ x_2,\ x_3,\ x_4) \quad (10.2)$$

$$\mathbf{A}_\mu = (\mathbf{A},\ i\phi) = (A_x,\ A_y,\ A_z,\ i\phi) = (A_1,\ A_2,\ A_3,\ A_4) \quad (10.3)$$

$$\mathbf{j}_\mu = (\mathbf{j},\ ic\rho) = (j_x,\ j_y,\ j_z,\ ic\rho) = (j_1,\ j_2,\ j_3,\ j_4) \quad (10.4)$$

† We have here chosen $\mathbf{A}$ and ϕ to satisfy the equation

$$\nabla\cdot\mathbf{A} + \frac{1}{c}\frac{\partial\phi}{\partial t} = 0 \quad (10.1')$$

(so-called Lorentz gauge) instead of (8.8), which is called the Coulomb gauge.
‡ We distinguish four-vectors from three-vectors by giving them a Greek suffix.

and generalize the operator ∇ to

$$\Box = \left(\frac{\partial}{\partial x_1}, \frac{\partial}{\partial x_2}, \frac{\partial}{\partial x_3}, \frac{\partial}{\partial x_4}\right). \tag{10.5}$$

The operator $\Box$ is pronounced "dal" after d'Alembert, who first studied wave equations of the type (10.1).

The field equations (10.1) can then be written

$$\Box^2 \mathbf{A}_\mu = -\frac{4\pi}{c} \mathbf{j}_\mu \tag{10.6}$$

and it will be noticed that the continuity equation (8.41) can be written

$$\Box \cdot \mathbf{j}_\mu = 0 \tag{10.7}$$

where the scalar product of two four-vectors is formed in exactly the same way as that of two three-vectors, i.e.

$$\mathbf{A}_\mu \cdot \mathbf{B}_\mu = A_1 B_1 + A_2 B_2 + A_3 B_3 + A_4 B_4.$$

Equations (10.6) and (10.7) are of course merely another way of writing Maxwell's equations, but they have the advantage of clearly demonstrating their relativistic form.

There are two very familiar solutions of (10.6) for special cases. The first is the plane electromagnetic wave solution in free space, i.e. for $\mathbf{j}_\mu = 0$, given by (8.15), which in the present notation reads

$$\mathbf{A}_\mu = \mathbf{A}_{0\mu}\, e^{i\kappa_\mu \cdot x_\mu}, \quad \kappa_\mu = (\kappa, i\kappa). \tag{10.8}$$

It follows from (10.8) that $\kappa_\mu^2 = 0$. We note here that the modulus of a four-vector with complex components can vanish, even though its components do not. The three-vector κ is of course the familiar wave propagation vector of Chapter 8.

The other special case is the field due to static charges constant in time. The moment we speak of static charges we have of course fixed our system of reference in the space-time continuum, and can no longer express our equations in a relativistically invariant way. In fact we have taken the x_4-axis along the direction $\mathbf{j}_\mu$, so that $j_1 = j_2 = j_3 = 0$. If furthermore the charges are constant in time, then (10.1) reduces to Poisson's equation

$$\nabla^2 \phi = -4\pi\rho(\mathbf{r}) \tag{10.9}$$

and the most general solution of this, that vanishes at infinity is

$$\phi(\mathbf{r}) = \int \frac{\rho(\mathbf{r}')}{|\mathbf{r} - \mathbf{r}'|}\, d\tau'. \tag{10.10}$$

If the field is due to a point charge e at $\mathbf{r}_1$ then $\rho(\mathbf{r})$ vanishes everywhere except near $\mathbf{r}_1$ where it varies very rapidly. The integral in (10.10) can then be replaced by an integral over a small volume

$\Omega(\mathbf{r})$, containing the point $\mathbf{r}_1$, and $|\mathbf{r} - \mathbf{r}_1|$ can be taken to be constant over this volume. Hence in this case

$$\phi(\mathbf{r}) = \frac{1}{|\mathbf{r} - \mathbf{r}_1|} \int_{\Omega(\mathbf{r}_1)} \rho(\mathbf{r}') d\tau' = \frac{e}{|\mathbf{r} - \mathbf{r}_1|}. \qquad (10.11)$$

This is of course the Coulomb potential.

The task that Yukawa set himself was to find a similar formalism which would yield nuclear forces. The main difference between nuclear and electromagnetic forces lies in their range. The electrostatic potential between two protons 2 fm apart is only 0·7 MeV, which is of course much less than the corresponding nuclear potential. But if we double the distance, the nuclear potential is quite negligible, while the electrostatic one is still 0·35 MeV. In fact the electrostatic potential is still significant at atomic distances—the ionization potential of hydrogen is 13·6 eV—which are a hundred thousand times greater than nuclear ones. There is no distance, however large, at which the electrostatic potential is zero or in other words the range is infinite. Thus a description of nuclear forces must include a measure of their range, while a description of electromagnetic forces does not include such a measure, since the range is infinite. A field equation for nuclear forces must therefore include a parameter which has the dimensions of a length. On the other hand, the structure of the field for nuclear forces may well be simpler than that of the electromagnetic field, which is described by a four-vector. This is so because electromagnetic radiation has not only a magnitude, but also a direction, given by its polarization. On the principle that one should start with the simplest assumptions possible, we shall assume the field for nuclear forces to be given by a scalar, Φ, and the equation of this field will be taken to be

$$\Box^2\Phi - \mu^2\Phi = -4\pi\eta(\mathbf{r}, t). \qquad (10.12)$$

Here μ is a constant which has the dimensions of (length)$^{-1}$, and $\eta(\mathbf{r}, t)$ measures the strength of the sources of the field, in the same way as $\mathbf{j}_\mu(\mathbf{r}, t)$ gave the sources of the electromagnetic field. It is conventional to take the sign of the source strength negative, in agreement with the electromagnetic case (10.6).

The above equation, which is due to Yukawa, is the simplest possible generalization of the wave equation (10.1) which is relativistically invariant. Its plane wave solution in free space can be written down at once and is

$$\Phi = \Phi_0 e^{ik_\mu \cdot x_\mu}, \quad \mathbf{k}_\mu^2 = -\mu^2. \qquad (10.13)$$

The significance of this equation will be discussed below.

10

Corresponding to Poisson's equation (10.9) we have the equation for a static source distribution

$$\nabla^2 \Phi - \mu^2 \Phi = -4\pi\eta(\mathbf{r}). \tag{10.14}$$

The solution of this equation which vanishes at infinity is

$$\Phi(\mathbf{r}) = \int \frac{e^{-\mu|\mathbf{r}-\mathbf{r}'|}}{|\mathbf{r}-\mathbf{r}'|}\, \eta(\mathbf{r}')\mathrm{d}\tau'. \tag{10.15}$$

[See the solution (8.117) to the similar equation (8.118) and also example 10.4.2.] If the source distribution consists of a point source of strength g at $\mathbf{r}_1$, then, just as in (10.11), we obtain

$$\Phi(\mathbf{r}) = g\, \frac{e^{-\mu|\mathbf{r}-\mathbf{r}_1|}}{|\mathbf{r}-\mathbf{r}_1|}. \tag{10.16}$$

The potential energy of a source g at $\mathbf{r}_2$ in a field $\Phi(\mathbf{r})$ is given by

$$V = -g\Phi(\mathbf{r}_2), \tag{10.17}$$

where the negative sign arises from our choice of sign in (10.12). If the potential Φ is due to another source g at $\mathbf{r}_1$, then we obtain the interaction energy between two sources,

$$V = -g^2\, \frac{e^{-\mu|\mathbf{r}_1-\mathbf{r}_2|}}{|\mathbf{r}_1-\mathbf{r}_2|}. \tag{10.18}$$

It is interesting to note that it follows from (10.6) and (10.12) that like electric charges repel, while like mesic charges attract. The interaction energy between a charge and the corresponding field is given by the product of the charge and the scalar potential. In the mesic case, this leads to (10.18), which is negative and thus represents an attraction. In the electric case we require the product of the fourth components of the two four-vectors $\mathbf{A}_\mu$ and $\mathbf{j}_\mu$, instead of the product of two scalars. This introduces an additional factor $i^2 = -1$, which leads to a repulsion.

Comparing (10.16) with (10.11), we see that the nuclear potential decreases more rapidly with distance from the source than the Coulomb potential by an exponential factor, so that it will lead to short range forces. It is of course the Yukawa potential (3.137). For the singlet interaction $b_Y \simeq 1 \cdot 18\,\mathrm{fm}$, so that $\mu = 0 \cdot 85\,\mathrm{fm}^{-1}$.

So far the treatment of our fields has been entirely classical. We know however that the electromagnetic radiation field can be quantized into photons and that the energy and momentum of each photon are given respectively by

$$E = \hbar c\kappa, \quad \mathbf{p} = \hbar\kappa \tag{10.19}$$

so that the condition $\kappa_\mu^2 = 0$ is equivalent to $E = pc$. According to de Broglie, the relations (10.19) hold quite universally, and it is well known that they give the numerical relationship between the particle and wave aspects of matter. We now use them to derive properties of the quanta of our new field. It follows, since $k_2 = -\mu^2$, that the energy and momentum of these quanta obey the relationship

$$E^2 = p^2c^2 + \hbar^2c^2\mu^2. \tag{10.20}$$

If we compare this with (9.1), we see at once that our new quanta have a mass given by

$$m = \frac{\hbar\mu}{c} \tag{10.21}$$

which for $\mu = 0\cdot85$ fm^{-1} leads to $m \simeq 330\,m_e$. The triplet range would lead to $m \simeq 270\,m_e$. Now we must not take the numerical values of these ranges too seriously, since they were calculated from a very much simplified theory, employing only central forces, but it is clear that these quanta have a mass which is between the mass of the electron and that of the proton. For that reason they are called mesons (from the Greek for middle), the field is called the meson field, and the source strength g the mesic charge. In the same way in which the source e of the electromagnetic field is a property of the electron, and is used to describe interactions between electrons, so the source g of the mesic field is a property of the nucleon, and is used to describe interactions between nucleons. The source strength on each nucleon can be estimated from the fact that, as we saw in (10.18), the interaction potential between two nucleons is $-g^2\mathrm{e}^{-\mu r}/r$ and this is equivalent to (3.137). This leads to the dimensionless value

$$\frac{g^2}{\hbar c} \simeq 0\cdot3. \tag{10.22}$$

The strength of the mesic charge is therefore very considerably greater than that of the electric charge, which is given by $e^2/\hbar c = 137^{-1}$.

Another way to obtain (10.21) derives from the uncertainty principle, according to which the uncertainties of simultaneous measurements of energy and time for a given system are related by the equation

$$\triangle E \, . \, \triangle t \sim \hbar.$$

Hence, if a nucleon emits a meson of mass m, this must be absorbed by another nucleon within a time interval $\triangle t$ given by $\triangle t \sim \hbar/mc^2$. The maximum distance that the meson can have travelled in this time is $c\triangle t$ and this gives the force range μ^{-1}. Hence $\mu^{-1} \sim \hbar/mc$, as before.

To treat the problem of the interaction of nucleons through the mesic field it is necessary to solve a Schrödinger equation in which the Hamiltonian consists of three parts,

(i) the Hamiltonian of the free field,

(ii) the Hamiltonian of the free nucleons,

(iii) the interaction Hamiltonian between the field and the particles.

The usual method of solving this problem is to treat the last of these as a perturbation, the coupling parameter being $g^2/\hbar c$. This procedure has been extremely successful in quantum electrodynamics where the corresponding constant $e^2/\hbar c$ is so small that successive terms of the resulting power series decrease rapidly. This is fortunate, since the calculation of successive terms soon becomes prohibitively difficult. In the corresponding problems in meson field theory the second term is often larger than the first, and it is not at all certain whether the series converge at all. Although it is therefore difficult to obtain numerical results to be compared with experiment, we shall see that quite a lot of useful information can nevertheless be obtained from the conservation laws.

We found in Chapter 8 that an electrically charged particle in the presence of an electromagnetic field absorbs and emits photons, first-order perturbation theory corresponding to the absorption and emission of single photons. An interaction between two electrically charged particles arises when one of the particles absorbs a photon † which had been emitted by the other or vice versa. Since an interaction therefore corresponds to an emission followed by an absorption, each of which is proportional to e, the interaction is proportional to e^2 in first-order perturbation theory. Higher-order perturbations correspond to the simultaneous absorption and emission of several photons. The ideas outlined above for electromagnetic interactions transfer at once to nuclear ones, an important difference being that the contribution to the nuclear force from the absorption and emission of several mesons is almost certainly not negligible. In the same way in which the exchange between two nucleons of one meson led to a force of range μ^{-1}, so that of two mesons will lead to a force of range $\frac{1}{2}\mu^{-1}$ and so on. The total nucleon-nucleon force is then

† The word photon is used here in a more general sense than is usual, to denote the quanta of the Coulomb field as well as those of the electromagnetic radiation field. The latter, which are the well-known ones, correspond to the components of the vector potential **A** perpendicular to the propagation vector κ and are called transverse photons. The former correspond to the component of **A** along κ and to the scalar potential ϕ and are called longitudinal and scalar photons. This distinction is a consequence of the zero mass of the photons and need not concern us here.

the result of a superposition of these forces. At low energies, when the nucleons do not approach each other closely, the experiments should therefore give information on the one-meson-exchange force, while at higher energies contributions from the exchange of several mesons are important. This exchange of several mesons also leads to the probable existence of many-body forces, mentioned in section 4.7.

The processes of emission and absorption of mesons of mass $\simeq 300 \ m_e$ in the interaction between nucleons are not what are usually understood by real physical processes. Normally the energy needed for the creation of such a heavy particle is not available, and such processes that do not conserve energy are termed *virtual*. They are of extremely short duration and in consequence they have a very considerable energy uncertainty. The nucleon, so to speak, borrows the energy from a bank run by the uncertainty principle, and long before the deficiency is detected in the audit, the debt is repaid on the absorption of the meson by the second nucleon!

In our further discussions we shall restrict ourselves to the emission and absorption of single mesons. As was pointed out in the case of photons, this is equivalent to a first-order perturbation theory correct to order g^2. The classical calculation which led to (10.18) is therefore equivalent to a first-order perturbation theory only, and the numerical value obtained for g in (10.22) by comparison with experiment may well be far from correct.

The emission and absorption of virtual mesons can lead to either direct or exchange forces between nucleons. In the case of direct forces the nucleons are unchanged by the emission or absorption of a meson, and so the meson must be neutral in order that charge be conserved. If on the other hand a neutron emits a negative meson which is then absorbed by a proton, then the neutron will change into a proton and the proton into a neutron, i.e. we are dealing with exchange forces. It may be noted that between like nucleons even exchange forces only involve neutral mesons. In that case the only possible exchange is one of spin direction.

In anticipation of the results of the next section we now denote the mesons by π. We then have the following possibilities :

Direct forces

$$
\begin{array}{cccc}
\pi^{\circ} & \pi^{\circ} & \pi^{\circ} & \pi^{\circ} \\
n \rightarrow n & p \rightarrow p & n \rightarrow p & p \rightarrow n
\end{array}
$$

Exchange forces

$$
\begin{array}{cccc}
\pi^{\circ} & \pi^{\circ} & \pi^{-} & \pi^{+} \\
n \rightarrow n & p \rightarrow p & n \rightarrow p & p \rightarrow n.
\end{array}
$$

$$(10.23)$$

Since exchange forces undoubtedly exist, we see that we shall require both charged and uncharged mesons. It should be noted that the quanta of the electromagnetic field are always neutral. It is now possible to list the corresponding properties of the electromagnetic and meson fields. This is done in Table 10.1.

TABLE 10.1. CORRESPONDING PROPERTIES OF ELECTROMAGNETIC AND SCALAR MESON FIELDS

	e.m. field	meson field
static potential	$\dfrac{e}{r}$	$-g\,\dfrac{e^{-\mu r}}{r}$
charge on F.-D. particle	e (on electron)	g (on nucleon)
quantum of field	photon	meson
mass of quantum	0	$\sim 300\, m_e$
electric charge of quantum	0	$0, + e, - e$
free field equation	$\Box^2 A_\mu = 0$	$(\Box^2 - \mu^2)\Phi = 0$

The potential (10.16) is clearly singular at $\mathbf{r} = \mathbf{r}_1$. This singularity arises from our assumption of a point source at $\mathbf{r}_1$, and it will disappear when we consider a source which extends over a small volume in the neighbourhood of $\mathbf{r}_1$. Physically, this corresponds to the recoil of the source as it emits a meson, which makes its position uncertain by a small amount. We therefore define a shape function $\zeta(\mathbf{r} - \mathbf{r}_1)$ which has the following properties :

$$\zeta(\mathbf{r} - \mathbf{r}_1) = 0 \qquad \text{unless } |\,\mathbf{r} - \mathbf{r}_1\,| \text{ is very small}$$

$$\int \zeta(\mathbf{r} - \mathbf{r}_1)\mathrm{d}\tau = 1 \text{ over all space.} \qquad\qquad (10.24)$$

It is not necessary to specify an exact functional form for $\zeta(\mathbf{r} - \mathbf{r}_1)$, since it is clear that, if the above conditions are satisfied, $g\zeta(\mathbf{r} - \mathbf{r}_1)$ represents a source of strength g, which is spread out over a small volume in the neighbourhood of $\mathbf{r}_1$.

The potential due to this source satisfies the equation

$$\nabla^2\Phi - \mu^2\Phi = -\,4\pi g\zeta(\mathbf{r} - \mathbf{r}_1) \qquad\qquad (10.25)$$

and, for $|\,\mathbf{r} - \mathbf{r}_1\,|$ not small, Φ is still given by (10.16). For $|\,\mathbf{r} - \mathbf{r}_1\,|$ small, Φ will however remain finite, so that we can expand it in a Taylor series in $|\,\mathbf{r} - \mathbf{r}_1\,|$ near $\mathbf{r} = \mathbf{r}_1$,

$$\Phi(\mathbf{r} - \mathbf{r}_1) = A + B\,|\,\mathbf{r} - \mathbf{r}_1\,| + C\,|\,\mathbf{r} - \mathbf{r}_1\,|^2 + \dots, \ \mathbf{r} \simeq \mathbf{r}_1. \quad (10.26)$$

Now both $\nabla\Phi$ and Φ must be continuous at $\mathbf{r} = \mathbf{r}_1$. Hence $B = 0$. The constants $A, C, \dots$ depend on the exact form of $\zeta(\mathbf{r} - \mathbf{r}_1)$. The use of extended sources will be important in section 10.3.

It is clear that (10.18) does not include any exchange operators and it therefore describes the interaction through a neutral meson field. To obtain charged mesons the sources must contain the i-spin operators. Thus since $\tau_+\gamma = 0$ and $\tau_-\gamma = \delta$ [see (2.89)], where γ and δ are the i-spin wave functions of the proton and neutron, the operator τ_- converts a proton into a neutron state. If the source is given by

$$\tau_-\eta(\mathbf{r}) \tag{10.27}$$

then it turns the proton into a neutron in the process of generating the field. To conserve charge the field must therefore have positive charge and thus consists of a positive meson. The converse is true of τ_+, and a third possible meson field is generated by $\tau_3\eta(\mathbf{r})$. Since $\tau_3\gamma = \gamma$, $\tau_3\delta = -\delta$, this field is neutral, but is not identical with the neutral field introduced earlier, because of the minus sign in the last equation. We therefore have four possible meson fields,

$$\nabla^2\Phi_n - \mu^2\Phi_n = -4\pi\tau_n\eta(\mathbf{r}) \tag{10.28}$$

where $n = +, -, 3$ or 4, and we define $\tau_4 = 1$. The potential due to a source of mesons of type n, source strength g_n, at $\mathbf{r}_1$ is

$$\Phi_n = -g_n\tau_n\frac{e^{-\mu|\mathbf{r}-\mathbf{r}_1|}}{|\mathbf{r}-\mathbf{r}_1|}. \tag{10.29}$$

We now assume that the nucleon-nucleon interaction is due to all the four possible meson fields. The interaction energy (10.18) must then be generalized to

$$V = -\sum_n g_n^2\tau_n^{(1)}\tau_n^{(2)}\frac{e^{-\mu|\mathbf{r}_1-\mathbf{r}_2|}}{|\mathbf{r}_1-\mathbf{r}_2|} \tag{10.30}$$

where the i-spin operators $\tau_n^{(1)}$ and $\tau_n^{(2)}$ act on the wave functions of the nucleons at $\mathbf{r}_1$ and $\mathbf{r}_2$ respectively.

The three most commonly discussed theories are

(i) Neutral : $g_1 = g_2 = g_3 = 0, \quad g_4 = g,$ $\qquad(10.31)$

(ii) Charged : $g_1 = g_2 = 2^{-\frac{1}{2}}g, \quad g_3 = g_4 = 0,$ $\qquad(10.32)$

(iii) Symmetric : $g_1 = g_2 = g_3 = g, \quad g_4 = 0.$ $\qquad(10.33)$

The neutral theory has already been discussed. It leads to direct forces transmitted by neutral mesons. The charged theory yields a potential energy (10.30) which contains the operator

$$\tfrac{1}{2}(\tau_+^{(1)}\tau_+^{(2)} + \tau_-^{(1)}\tau_-^{(2)}) = \tfrac{1}{2}(\tau_1^{(1)}\tau_1^{(2)} + \tau_2^{(1)}\tau_2^{(2)}) \tag{10.34}$$

$$= \tfrac{1}{2}(\boldsymbol{\tau}^{(1)} \cdot \boldsymbol{\tau}^{(2)} - \tau_3^{(1)}\tau_3^{(2)}). \tag{10.35}$$

This gives exchange forces between unlike nucleons only, transmitted by charged mesons, as is also clear by comparing (10.35) with Table 4.1.

The potential of the symmetric theory contains the operator $\tau^{(1)} . \tau^{(2)}$. It gives charge-independent exchange forces, as can be seen from Table 4.1. As has already been noticed, the neutral mesons of this theory are not identical with the mesons of the neutral theory. This can also be seen from the corresponding exchange operators which are respectively $- (W_{12} + 2H_{12})$ and W_{12}. [See (4.56) and 4.59).]†

The theory discussed so far is only one of several possible ones. Which is correct only experiment can decide, and we now turn our attention to the properties of mesons as found in nature.

10.2 Properties of the Pion

A year after Yukawa had put forward his hypothesis, Anderson (1937) found the track of a meson in a cloud-chamber photograph of cosmic rays. During the next ten years these mesons were investigated, and the more became known about them, the less likely it became that they were the particles required by Yukawa. In particular, their interaction with nucleons was exceedingly weak, which made it impossible to account for the strength of nuclear forces. The mystery was solved by Lattes, Powell and Occhialini (1947) who discovered that there were two types of mesons of not very different mass, and that the shorter lived one, now known as the pion, which had never before been observed, interacted strongly with nuclei. If it was not captured by a nucleus, it decayed into the longer lived one, the muon, which was the particle that had been observed by Anderson. Since then more and heavier mesons have been discovered, and it is possible that they too are quanta of nuclear force fields. As they are several times heavier than the pion, they correspond to nuclear forces of very short range and they may be responsible for the repulsive core. At low energies, when the nucleons do not come sufficiently close together for these very short range forces to be important, it is to be expected that the nuclear force will be due to the pion field only. We shall therefore confine ourselves to a discussion of the properties of the pion, which, as it turns out, has all the properties required by a Yukawa-type particle.

In general, when a nucleus is broken up, pions are produced. This in itself is evidence in favour of their forming the " nuclear glue." They were first detected in photographic plates exposed at high altitudes to the primary cosmic rays, which consist of very fast light nuclei. If such a nucleus hits a nucleus in the emulsion, it disrupts it and the charged particles coming off ionize the emulsion

† Note the confusing nomenclature. The charged theory gives charge-symmetric forces, while the symmetric theory gives charge-independent forces.

and thus form microscopic tracks, which show up when the emulsion is developed. Neutral particles cannot be detected in this way, and the evidence for their existence must therefore be less direct.

Charged pions decay according to the scheme

$$\pi^+ \to \mu^+ + \nu_\mu, \quad \pi^- \to \mu^- + \bar{\nu}_\mu$$

and have a lifetime $2 \cdot 55 \times 10^{-8}$ sec. Recently an alternative mode of decay has been observed (Fuzzini, 1958),

$$\pi^+ \to e^+ + \nu, \quad \pi^- \to e^- + \bar{\nu}$$

but probably not more than one in every 10,000 pions decays in this way. This decay was originally postulated by Yukawa to explain β-decay by means of meson theory. A neutron would then decay according to the scheme

$$n \to p + \pi^- \to p + e^- + \bar{\nu}$$

where the first transition is a virtual one. However, this scheme has now lost its attraction. Since Yukawa published his theory the muon has been discovered and there is no way of incorporating this into our scheme. So the direct decay of the pion into an electron no longer offers the possibilities of unification and simplification originally hoped for.

The neutral pion cannot of course be observed directly. It decays with a lifetime of the order of 10^{-15} sec into two photons, each photon in turn producing a negaton-positon pair by pair creation. The existence of a neutral pion is therefore inferred from the simultaneous appearance of two negaton-positon pairs.

The masses of the pions are now very well known. There appears to be a small difference between the masses of the two charged mesons (Barkas, 1956), (Crowe and Phillips, 1954).

$$m(\pi^+) = 273 \cdot 3 \pm 0 \cdot 2 \, m_e, \quad m(\pi^-) = 272 \cdot 8 \pm 0 \cdot 3 m_e \quad (10.36)$$

but it is doubtful whether this difference is real. The mass of the neutral pion is obtained from the energy of the γ-rays resulting from the reaction

$$\pi^- + p \to n + \pi^\circ, \quad \pi^\circ \to 2\gamma. \quad (10.37)$$

(See example 10.4.4.) It is found (Chinowsky, 1954) that

$$m(\pi^\circ) = 264 \cdot 3 \pm 0 \cdot 3 m_e. \quad (10.38)$$

The difference between the masses of the charged and neutral pions is almost certainly an electromagnetic effect.

The spin of the positive pion follows from detailed balance arguments applied to the inverse reactions

$$p + p \overset{\leftarrow}{\to} d + \pi^+$$

provided these are performed with the same relative energies. If p_p and p_π are the relative momenta in the two reactions, then it follows from (6.24) that

$$\tfrac{1}{2}(2I_p + 1)(2I_p + 1)p_p^2\, \sigma_{\text{prod}} = (2I_d + 1)(2I_\pi + 1)p_\pi^2\, \sigma_{\text{abs}},\dagger$$

where prod. and abs. refer to the production and the absorption of the pion. Hence

$$2I_\pi + 1 = \frac{2}{3}\left(\frac{p_p}{p_\pi}\right)^2 \frac{\sigma_{\text{prod}}}{\sigma_{\text{abs}}}. \qquad (10.39)$$

It is apparent that even comparatively inaccurate experiments will be able to distinguish between values of I_π differing by half integers, and in fact there is no doubt about it that $I_\pi = 0$.

There is no direct evidence for the spin of the negative pion, but as it is to be expected that the negative pion will differ from the positive one merely in the sign of the charge, we shall assume that it too has zero spin. A separate proof is desirable for the neutral pion. It follows from its mode of decay into two photons.

A wave function of two photons must consist of products of the two polarization vectors of the photons, $\mathbf{e}_1$ and $\mathbf{e}_2$, and their relative momentum vector $\kappa_1 - \kappa_2$. If the neutral pion has spin 0, then this combination must be a scalar, and if it is 1 a vector. (We ignore the possibility of higher spins, since in fact a lower one will suffice.) The wave function is restricted in two further ways ; (a) since photons are Bose-Einstein particles, an interchange of 1 and 2 in the wave function must leave it unchanged, and (b) since the polarization vector of a photon is perpendicular to the momentum vector, we must have

$$\mathbf{e}_1 \cdot \kappa_1 = 0, \quad \mathbf{e}_2 \cdot \kappa_2 = 0$$

If we now choose a frame of reference in which the pion is at rest when decaying—and this is always possible—then we must have $\kappa_1 = -\kappa_2$ to conserve momentum. Hence restriction (b) can be written

$$\mathbf{e}_1 \cdot (\kappa_1 - \kappa_2) = 0, \quad \mathbf{e}_2 \cdot (\kappa_1 - \kappa_2) = 0.$$

We now form all possible products of $\mathbf{e}_1$, $\mathbf{e}_2$ and $\kappa_1 - \kappa_2$ that give scalars or vectors. They are

Scalar :	$\mathbf{e}_1 \cdot \mathbf{e}_2$	(10.40)
Pseudoscalar :	$(\mathbf{e}_1 \times \mathbf{e}_2) \cdot (\kappa_1 - \kappa_2)$	(10.41)
Vector :	$(\mathbf{e}_1 \times \mathbf{e}_2) \times (\kappa_1 - \kappa_2)$	(10.42)
	$(\mathbf{e}_1 \cdot \mathbf{e}_2)(\kappa_1 - \kappa_2)$	(10.43)
Pseudovector :	$\mathbf{e}_1 \times \mathbf{e}_2.$	(10.44)

$\dagger$ The reason for the factor $\tfrac{1}{2}$ on the left-hand side is that in the backward reaction the cross-section for both protons is measured, since we cannot distinguish between identical particles. Hence for each pion absorbed two protons are detected.

Of these (10.43) and (10.44) are forbidden by (*a*) and (10.42) by (*b*), while both (10.40) and (10.41) are permitted. The neutral pion has therefore either a scalar or a pseudo-scalar wave function, but in any case it has spin 0. It might be possible to distinguish between these possibilities experimentally, since in the former the photon polarizations are parallel and in the latter perpendicular.

Strictly speaking, the above proof only excludes spin 1, but not higher spins. The tensor product

$$(\mathbf{e}_1 \times \mathbf{e}_2)(\kappa_1 - \kappa_2) \tag{10.45}$$

[for definition of tensor product see (9.96)] is clearly permissible and corresponds to spin 2. It is just that scalar wave functions are simpler than tensor ones and that we are satisfied with the simpler theory until experiment forces us to abandon it.

The difference between a scalar and pseudoscalar wave function is one of parity, since the latter changes sign under an inversion of space co-ordinates and the former does not. We are thus led to consider the intrinsic parity of the wave function of an elementary particle. This only becomes important when particles are created or destroyed singly, since as long as particles are conserved or created and destroyed in pairs, their combined parity is conserved. For that reason we have not had to consider the parity of elementary particles before.

To discover the parity of the pion, we first use reaction (10.37) to show that negative and neutral pions have the same parity. Actually, when negative pions are absorbed in liquid hydrogen, there result two competing processes,

$$\pi^- + p \to n + \pi^\circ, \quad \pi^\circ \to 2\gamma \tag{10.46}$$

$$\pi^- + p \to n + \gamma. \tag{10.47}$$

It is easy to distinguish between the two processes, since in the second the energy of the resulting photon is equal to roughly the rest mass of the neutral pion, while in the first it is about half that. When the energy spectrum of the photons resulting from the reaction was measured (Panofsky, 1951), it was found that the two processes were about equally likely.

If negative pions are absorbed in liquid hydrogen, they displace the negatons in the atoms and form hydrogen-like pion-proton atoms with the pion in the lowest Bohr orbit. This is of course much nearer to the proton than the lowest negaton orbit, because of the larger mass of the pion. The initial capture of the pion is therefore due to its electrostatic interaction with the proton, and only when the pion is in the lowest Bohr orbit does the nuclear interaction come into play and reactions (10.46) and (10.47) take place. It follows that in these reactions the pion carries no orbital angular momentum. Since its spin is zero, the total angular momentum of $\pi^- + p$ initially is $I = \frac{1}{2}$. Now a photon, being a vector, has unit intrinsic angular momentum, and so the only way to conserve angular momentum in (10.47) is with $I(n) = \frac{1}{2}$, $I(\gamma) = 1$ and no orbital angular momentum in the final state. The transition is therefore allowed and, since the competing reaction (10.46) is found to occur with equal probability, it too must be allowed. This means that the final system $n + \pi^0$ in (10.46) has no orbital angular momentum so that the spatial parities of the initial and final wave functions are both even. As p and n have equal intrinsic parities, we are led to the conclusion that π^- and π^0 have the same intrinsic parity.

It will be noticed that the proof turns on the fact that (10.46) is an allowed transition. It would be equally possible to conserve angular momentum with unit orbital angular momentum in the final state, and this would lead to opposite intrinsic parities for π^- and π^0. However, a change in orbital angular momentum by one unit would imply a first forbidden transition.

If negative pions are absorbed in deuterium, the following processes can occur,

$$\pi^- + d \to n + n \tag{10.48}$$

$$\pi^- + d \to n + n + \gamma \tag{10.49}$$

$$\pi^- + d \to n + n + \pi^\circ, \quad \pi^\circ \to 2\gamma. \tag{10.50}$$

Process (10.48) is difficult to observe directly, but when the probabilities of the other two have been measured, that of the first can of course be calculated. The relative probabilities were found to be (Panofsky, 1951) in the ratio $2 \cdot 4 : 1 : 0$. Process (10.48) is therefore allowed.

The total angular momentum of $\pi^- + d$ initially is $I = 1$. In the final state the two neutrons, because of the exclusion principle, can only be in a ^1S, ^3P, ^1D, ... state, and of these only the ^3P-state can have $I = 1$. As its parity is odd, the parity of the pion is odd. This proves that the negative and the neutral pions are pseudoscalar, and we shall assume this to be true also for the positive pion.

Lastly we turn to the i-spin of the pion. Just as we consider the proton and the neutron as two substates of a nucleon i-spin doublet, $T = \frac{1}{2}$, so the three charge states of the pion can be considered to be substates of an i-spin triplet, $T = 1$, the negative, neutral and positive pion corresponding to $T_3 = +1$, 0, -1 respectively. Charge independence of nuclear forces then requires that the interaction between pions and nucleons depends only on the total i-spin of the two particles, if electromagnetic effects are neglected. This requirement is much stronger than that of charge conservation, for if the pion-nucleon interaction conserves i-spin, then it is invariant under all rotations in i-spin space, while charge conservation only requires invariance under rotation about the T_3-axis (see also section 4.3).

The pion-nucleon interaction can take place in states with total $T = \frac{3}{2}$ or $\frac{1}{2}$ as follows:

$$T = \tfrac{3}{2} : \pi^- + \text{n}, \quad T = \tfrac{3}{2} \text{ or } \tfrac{1}{2} : \pi^+ + \text{n}, \quad \pi^\circ + \text{n},$$
$$\pi^+ + \text{p}, \qquad\qquad\qquad \pi^- + \text{p}, \quad \pi^\circ + \text{p}.$$

A good example of the kind of prediction which the hypothesis of the conservation of i-spin allows us to make comes from the pion production by nucleon-nucleon collision. Let us consider the two processes

$$\text{n} + \text{p} \to \text{d} + \pi^\circ$$
$$\text{p} + \text{p} \to \text{d} + \pi^+.$$

Since the deuteron has $T = 0$ (see example 3.10.9), the final state has $T = 1$. The initial system $\text{n} + \text{p}$ is an equal mixture of $T = 0$ and $T = 1$ states, while the $\text{p} + \text{p}$ system has $T = 1$. [See (2.90).] Since the reaction can only occur for $T = 1$, the $\text{p} + \text{p}$ reaction should have a cross-section twice as large as the $\text{n} + \text{p}$ reaction at the same energy, and the angular distributions should be the same. This prediction neglects of course the electromagnetic effects. The experimental results are as follows (Durbin, 1951, Schluter, 1954 and Hildebrand, 1953).

$\text{p} + \text{p} \to \text{d} + \pi^+ : \; \sigma = 0.97 \pm 0.10 \times 10^{-27} \text{ cm}^2$ ⎫
$$\frac{\text{d}\sigma}{\text{d}\Omega} \propto 0.18 \pm 0.15 + \cos^2 \theta.$$ ⎬ 413 MeV (lab. system)
⎭

$\text{n} + \text{p} \to \text{d} + \pi^\circ : \; \sigma = 0.6 \pm 0.2 \times 10^{-27} \text{ cm}^2$ — 390-430 MeV (lab. system)
$$\frac{\text{d}\sigma}{\text{d}\Omega} \propto 0.21 \pm 0.06 + \cos^2 \theta.$$ 413 MeV (lab. system)

It is clear that within the limits of the rather wide experimental error these results verify the predictions. A similar result has recently been obtained by Homer *et al.* (1964), who bombarded protons and deuterons with 740 MeV protons. On the assumption that the deuteron bombardment is equivalent to both the above processes, the cross-section for single pion production should be 1.5 times as great for deuteron as for proton bombardment. The experimental result is 1.50 ± 0.15.

The fact that apparently i-spin is conserved in the above reactions enables us to give a more convincing proof for the value of the i-spin of the pion. The existence of three charge states merely yields the result $T_\pi \geqslant 1$, since there might be other charge states which have not yet been discovered. However conservation of i-spin in the reaction $n + p = d + \pi$ immediately yields $T_\pi = 0$ or 1, which together with the above result fixes $T_\pi = 1$ unambiguously.

The conservation of i-spin in nuclear reactions, which has by now been very firmly established by many experiments, is also the strongest argument for the charge-independence of nuclear forces. For if the total i-spin of a system, $T = \frac{1}{2} \mid \Sigma \tau^{(1)} \mid$, commutes with the Hamiltonian of the system, then the latter must be a scalar in i-spin space. For a two-particle system the Hamiltonian can then be only of the form

$$H = a + b\tau^{(1)} \cdot \tau^{(2)} \tag{10.51}$$

and we know from Table 4.1 that such a Hamiltonian gives charge-independent forces.

10.3 Pseudoscalar Meson Theory

Having established that the pion is a pseudoscalar particle that interacts strongly with nuclei we now assume that it is the quantum of the nuclear force field. It should be noticed that the property of integral spin is as essential as that of strong nuclear interaction for the pion to be a Yukawa-type particle, since a meson with half-integral spin could not satisfy angular momentum conservation in the reactions (10.23).

The difference between a scalar and pseudoscalar field only becomes apparent when the field interacts with particles, so that equation (10.14) with $\eta(\mathbf{r}) = 0$ is the free field equation of the pion field. Now if we apply space inversion to the field equation with a static source,

$$\nabla^2 \Phi(\mathbf{r}) - \mu^2 \Phi(\mathbf{r}) = - 4\pi\eta(\mathbf{r}) \tag{10.52}$$

we obtain

$$- \nabla^2 \Phi(\mathbf{r}) + \mu^2 \Phi(\mathbf{r}) = - 4\pi\eta(- \mathbf{r})$$

since $\Phi(- \mathbf{r}) = - \Phi(\mathbf{r})$ for a pseudoscalar field. Hence

$$\eta(- \mathbf{r}) = - \eta(\mathbf{r}) \tag{10.53}$$

so that the sources of a pseudoscalar field are pseudoscalar.

The next problem is to construct a pseudoscalar source. A scalar can be constructed simply from a strength parameter g and a localizing function $\zeta(\mathbf{r} - \mathbf{r}_l)$. To obtain a pseudoscalar source, we must multiply a scalar one by a pseudoscalar function or operator. Now we remember that a pseudoscalar can be formed as the scalar product of a polar and an axial vector, and we look for such vectors as could be associated with our source, which is a nucleon at rest. An obvious one is the spin of the nucleon $\boldsymbol{\sigma}$, which is an axial vector. The search for a polar vector is more difficult. Since the nucleon is at rest, it has no linear momentum, and we cannot use its position vector either, since this would lead to the absurd consequence that the source strength of a nucleon depends on the position of the nucleon in an arbitrary co-ordinate system. There is in fact no suitable polar vector associated with a nucleon at rest. The way out of this difficulty is to replace the scalar source function $\zeta(\mathbf{r} - \mathbf{r}_i)$ by a vector one, and this is easily achieved by taking the gradient of the scalar. Lastly we add an i-spin operator T_i, since nuclear forces may depend on i-spin. The resulting source is then of the form

$$\eta_i = -\frac{f}{\mu} T_i (\boldsymbol{\sigma}_i \cdot \nabla_i) \zeta(\mathbf{r} - \mathbf{r}_i), \tag{10.54}$$

where for charge independent sources $T_i = \boldsymbol{\tau}^{(1)}$. The coupling constant has been put as f/μ, so that the f here has the same dimensions as the g in the scalar theory. Note that ∇_i operates on $\mathbf{r}_i$, not on $\mathbf{r}$.

The source (10.54) is clearly not a relativistic invariant and thus can only be an approximation. In fact it can be shown that the source in the relativistic invariant equation (10.12) is correctly given in quantum mechanical form by [compare with (9.85)]

$$\eta = -iG\psi^\dagger \beta \gamma \psi, \tag{10.55}$$

where ψ is the nucleon wave function and G is a coupling constant still to be determined. We approximate ψ by the wave function for a free particle, so that, following (9.7) and (9.9), we can write it as the solution of the equations

$$\left. \begin{array}{l} -i\hbar c \boldsymbol{\sigma} \cdot \nabla \phi + Mc^2 \chi = E\chi \\ -i\hbar c \boldsymbol{\sigma} \cdot \nabla \chi - Mc^2 \phi = E\phi, \end{array} \right\} \tag{10.56}$$

where we have put ψ into partitioned form

$$\psi = \begin{pmatrix} \chi \\ \text{------} \\ \phi \end{pmatrix}. \tag{10.57}$$

Now, non-relativistically, $E \simeq Mc^2$, so that

$$\phi \simeq -\frac{i\hbar}{2Mc} \boldsymbol{\sigma} \cdot \nabla \chi. \tag{10.58}$$

Finally, it follows from (9.87) that, in the representation (9.7),

$$\gamma = \begin{pmatrix} 0 & 1 \\ \hline 1 & 0 \end{pmatrix} \tag{10.59}$$

Hence

$$\eta = -iG(\chi^\dagger \mid \phi^\dagger)\tau \begin{pmatrix} 0 & 1 \\ \hline 1 & 0 \end{pmatrix} \begin{pmatrix} \chi \\ \hline \phi \end{pmatrix}$$

$$= -iG(\chi^\dagger \tau \phi - \phi^\dagger \tau \chi)$$

$$\simeq -\frac{\hbar G}{2Mc} \nabla \cdot \chi^\dagger \boldsymbol{\sigma} \tau \chi \tag{10.60}$$

This is equivalent to the non-relativistic classical form (10.54) with

$$G = \frac{2M}{m} f \tag{10.61}$$

[The transition from classical to quantum mechanics introduces the nuclear wave function χ in the same way as in (8.42).] Here M and m are the masses of the nucleon and meson respectively.

The true coupling constant G is thus very much larger than the apparent one f, so that the perturbation series does not converge. In fact, if first-order perturbation theory were valid, we would have

$$\frac{f^2}{\hbar c} \simeq 0.08, \quad \frac{G^2}{\hbar c} \simeq 14. \tag{10.62}$$

It may be remarked that pseudoscalar sources are in no way peculiar to meson theory. The magnetostatic potential due to a distribution of magnetic material of dipole moment $\mathbf{M}(\mathbf{r})$ per unit volume is given by the equation

$$\nabla^2 \psi = 4\pi \nabla \cdot \mathbf{M}$$

and since $\mathbf{M}$ is an axial vector, $\nabla \cdot \mathbf{M}$ is a pseudoscalar.

The solution of (10.52) with a source (10.54) is obtained from (10.15),

$$\Phi_i(\mathbf{r}) = \frac{f}{\mu} T_i \int \frac{e^{-\mu|\mathbf{r}-\mathbf{r}'|}}{|\mathbf{r}-\mathbf{r}'|} (\boldsymbol{\sigma}_i \cdot \nabla_i) \zeta(\mathbf{r}' - \mathbf{r}_i) d\tau'$$

$$= \frac{f}{\mu} T_i(\boldsymbol{\sigma}_i \cdot \nabla_i) \int \frac{e^{-\mu|\mathbf{r}-\mathbf{r}'|}}{|\mathbf{r}-\mathbf{r}'|} \zeta(\mathbf{r}' - \mathbf{r}_i) d\tau' \tag{10.63}$$

since we can take the operator $(\boldsymbol{\sigma}_i \cdot \nabla_i)$ outside the integral. If $\zeta(\mathbf{r} - \mathbf{r}_i)$ represents a point source at $\mathbf{r} = \mathbf{r}_i$, then, in the manner of (10.11),

$$\Phi_i(\mathbf{r}) = \frac{f}{\mu} T_i(\boldsymbol{\sigma}_i \cdot \nabla_i) \frac{e^{-\mu|\mathbf{r}-\mathbf{r}_i|}}{|\mathbf{r}-\mathbf{r}_i|}. \tag{10.64}$$

The interaction of two nucleons at $\mathbf{r}_1$ and $\mathbf{r}_2$ is given by the integral over all space of the product of the source distribution (10.54) of the one and the potential (10.63) due to the other,

$$V = -\frac{f^2}{\mu^2} T_1 T_2 (\boldsymbol{\sigma}_1 \cdot \nabla_1)(\boldsymbol{\sigma}_2 \cdot \nabla_2) \int\int \zeta(\mathbf{r} - \mathbf{r}_1) \frac{e^{-\mu|\mathbf{r}-\mathbf{r}'|}}{|\mathbf{r} - \mathbf{r}'|} \zeta(\mathbf{r}' - \mathbf{r}_2) d\tau d\tau'. \tag{10.65}$$

If $|\mathbf{r}_1 - \mathbf{r}_2|$ is not small, then the double integral can be performed, and we obtain

$$V(\mathbf{r}_{12}) = \frac{f^2}{\mu^2} T_1 T_2 (\boldsymbol{\sigma}_1 \cdot \nabla)(\boldsymbol{\sigma}_2 \cdot \nabla) \frac{e^{-\mu r_{12}}}{r_{12}}, \quad r_{12} \text{ not small.} \tag{10.66}$$

We have put here $|\mathbf{r}_1 - \mathbf{r}_2| = r_{12}$, and used the fact that

$$\nabla_1 = -\nabla_2 = \nabla$$

say. If r_{12} is small, then the integrations cannot be performed explicitly. In that case the integral, which we shall denote by $\psi(r_{12})$, is the potential energy of an extended scalar source of strength $g = 1$ at $\mathbf{r}_1$ in the field of another extended scalar source of strength $g = 1$ at $\mathbf{r}_2$ [see (10.15) and (10.25)]. Just like Φ in (10.26), this potential energy must be finite with a finite gradient for small r, and so

$$\left(\frac{d^2}{dr^2} - \frac{1}{r}\frac{d}{dr}\right)\psi(r) = O(r). \tag{10.67}$$

Further it can be shown by the use of Green's theorem that

$$\nabla^2 \psi(r) = \mu^2 \psi(r) - 4\pi \int \zeta(\mathbf{r}')\zeta(\mathbf{r} - \mathbf{r}')d\tau' \tag{10.68}$$

for all r. The integral depends on the functional form of $\zeta(\mathbf{r})$, but as $\zeta(\mathbf{r} - \mathbf{r}')$ is very small except when $r \simeq r'$, it is clear that it must be a function of $\mathbf{r}$ which is large and positive for small r and vanishes everywhere else. As its integral over all $\mathbf{r}$ is unity, it must be a function very similar to $\zeta(\mathbf{r})$, and we shall denote it by $\zeta'(\mathbf{r})$. In the limiting case of point sources, when $\zeta(\mathbf{r} - \mathbf{r}') = 0$ except when $\mathbf{r} = \mathbf{r}'$, we actually have (see example 10.4.5)

$$\int \zeta(\mathbf{r}')\zeta(\mathbf{r} - \mathbf{r}')d\tau' = \zeta(\mathbf{r}). \tag{10.69}$$

That the result (10.68) is physically reasonable can be seen from the fact that $\psi(r)$ is essentially the potential due to a scalar source of strength $g = 1$ and hence must satisfy (10.25). It is of course not quite this, since the potential is defined as the potential energy of a point and not an extended source of unit strength placed in the field. For small r, $\zeta'(r)$ is very large, and it is then permissible to neglect $\mu^2 \psi(r)$ as well as terms $O(r)$ in the above equations.

Our task is now to split up the operator $(\sigma_1 \cdot \nabla)(\sigma_2 \cdot \nabla)$ into a linear combination of the operators ∇^2 and $d^2/dr^2 - (1/r)d/dr$. As the functions operated on are functions of r only, ∇ can be replaced by $\hat{r}d/dr$, where $\hat{r} = r/r$. Hence

$$(\sigma_1 \cdot \nabla)(\sigma_2 \cdot \nabla) = (\sigma_1 \cdot \nabla)(\sigma_2 \cdot \hat{r})\frac{d}{dr}$$

$$= (\sigma_1 \cdot \hat{r})(\sigma_2 \cdot \hat{r})\frac{d^2}{dr^2} + [(\sigma_1 \cdot \nabla)(\sigma_2 \cdot \hat{r})]\frac{d}{dr}.$$

Note that in the last term ∇ operates only on $\sigma_2 \cdot \hat{r}$ and not on anything beyond it.

Now

$$(\sigma_1 \cdot \nabla)(\sigma_2 \cdot \hat{r}) = (\sigma_1 \cdot \nabla)\left(\sigma_2 \cdot \frac{r}{r}\right)$$

$$= \frac{1}{r}(\sigma_1 \cdot \nabla)(\sigma_2 \cdot r) + (\sigma_2 \cdot r)(\sigma_1 \cdot \nabla)\frac{1}{r}$$

$$= \frac{1}{r}(\sigma_1 \cdot \sigma_2) - \frac{1}{r^2}(\sigma_1 \cdot r)(\sigma_2 \cdot r)$$

so that

$$(\sigma_1 \cdot \nabla)(\sigma_2 \cdot \nabla) = (\sigma_1 \cdot \hat{r})(\sigma_2 \cdot \hat{r})\left(\frac{d^2}{dr^2} - \frac{1}{r}\frac{d}{dr}\right) + \sigma_1 \cdot \sigma_2\frac{1}{r}\frac{d}{dr}$$

$$= \frac{1}{3}S_{12}\left(\frac{d^2}{dr^2} - \frac{1}{r}\frac{d}{dr}\right) + \frac{1}{3}\sigma_1 \cdot \sigma_2\left(\frac{d^2}{dr^2} + \frac{2}{r}\frac{d}{dr}\right)$$

$$= \frac{1}{3}S_{12}\left(\frac{d^2}{dr^2} - \frac{1}{r}\frac{d}{dr}\right) + \frac{1}{3}\sigma_1 \cdot \sigma_2\nabla^2 \qquad (10.70)$$

where S_{12} was defined by (4.4).

This can now be applied to the interaction (10.65). For small r, $\zeta'(r)$ is very large, and it is then permissible to neglect $\mu^2\psi(r)$ as well as terms $O(r)$ in (10.67) and (10.68). The differentiations of the Yukawa potential are easily carried out, and we finally obtain for the interaction potential,

$$V = -\frac{4\pi}{3}\frac{f^2}{\mu^2}T_1T_2(\sigma_1 \cdot \sigma_2)\zeta'(r_{12}), \qquad r_{12} \text{ small} \qquad (10.71)$$

$$V = \frac{1}{3}f^2T_1T_2\left\{(\sigma_1 \cdot \sigma_2) + \left(1 + \frac{3}{\mu r_{12}} + \frac{3}{\mu^2 r_{12}^2}\right)S_{12}\right\}\frac{e^{-\mu r_{12}}}{r_{12}},$$
$$r_{12} \text{ not small.} \qquad (10.72)$$

It is really rather remarkable that this theory should quite naturally have yielded the tensor operator S_{12}. If we now specialize to charge independent forces, i.e. $T_1 T_2 = \tau^{(1)} \cdot \tau^{(2)}$, then, for large r_{12} we have for the n-p system in triplet-even and singlet-even states respectively,

$$V(\text{trip-even}) = -f^2 \left\{ 1 + \left(1 + \frac{3}{\mu r_{12}} + \frac{3}{\mu^2 r_{12}^2} \right) S_{12} \right\} \frac{e^{-\mu r_{12}}}{r_{12}}, \qquad (10.73)$$

$$V(\text{sing-even}) = -f^2 \frac{e^{-\mu r_{12}}}{r_{12}}. \qquad (10.74)$$

As S_{12} is positive in the triplet-even state (see example 4.7.3) the forces are attractive in both states, but more so in the triplet state. This is in agreement with our phenomenological theory of nuclear forces.

The potentials (10.73) and (10.74) are due to the exchange of a single pion. For sufficiently large values of r_{12} they should therefore represent the nucleon-nucleon interaction completely, while for smaller values of r_{12} many-particle exchanges become important, so that it is no longer possible then to compare (10.73) and (10.74) with a phenomenological potential. We see therefore that, in spite of the large value of the coupling constant $G^2/\hbar c$, simple perturbation theory can be expected to give valid results in the region of large r_{12}. It is in fact found that experimentally determined phenomenological potentials have a tail ($r_{12} > 2 \cdot 5$ fm) corresponding to the one-pion-exchange potential (Moravscik, 1963).

In the inner region, our simple formulae tell of course only part of the story. It is nevertheless interesting to look at distances of the order of the nucleon Compton wavelength, $\hbar/Mc \simeq 0 \cdot 2$ fm, where we have to use (10.71). This is important only for S-states at very high energies, since in higher angular momentum states nucleons cannot approach each other so closely, i.e. wave functions for $l > 0$ states vanish at the origin. Now in an S-state, $(\tau^{(1)} \cdot \tau^{(2)}) (\sigma_1 \cdot \sigma_2)$ is negative, so that the potential becomes strongly repulsive. As was mentioned in section 4.6, such a repulsive core had been postulated on phenomenological grounds to account for some of the surprising results in high energy n-p and p-p scattering. Unfortunately there it was required only for ^{1}S-states, while here it appears in both ^{1}S and ^{3}S-states.

The pseudoscalar theory can also give a qualitative explanation of the anomalous magnetic moments of the nucleons. We consider neutrons and protons as dynamic equilibria,

$$\text{n} \rightleftarrows \text{p} + \pi^-, \quad \text{p} \rightleftarrows \text{n} + \pi^+ \qquad (10.75)$$

respectively, where the nucleons spend a fraction $(1 - \alpha)$ of their time without an accompanying pion and a fraction α with the pion. Since the pion magnetic moment is of order M_p/m_π of a nuclear magnetic moment, it is clear that the magnetic moment of, for instance, $n + \pi^+$ can be very different from that of p. The pions cannot have an intrinsic magnetic moment, as they have spin zero, but they can have a magnetic moment due to their orbital motion.

In a scalar theory the wave function of the pion [see (10.16)] is spherically symmetric and the pion is therefore in an S-state which does not produce a magnetic moment. The wave function in the pseudoscalar theory is given by (10.64). The space dependent part of this function is a vector, giving angular momentum one, i.e. a P-state. To conserve angular momentum it is then necessary for the neutron and proton in (10.75) to have opposite spin.

The magnetic moments can now be written down. In units of the nuclear magneton they are,

$$\mu_n = 0 + \alpha\left(-1 - \frac{M_p}{m_\pi}\right) \qquad (10.76)$$

$$\mu_p = (1 - \alpha) + \alpha\frac{M_p}{m_\pi}. \qquad (10.77)$$

Hence

$$\mu_n + \mu_p = 1 - 2\alpha < 1 \qquad (10.78)$$

which is correct, and if we use the experimental value $M_p/m_\pi \simeq 7$, then a best fit is obtained with $\alpha \simeq 0\cdot25$. It gives

$$\mu_n = -2\cdot0, \quad \mu_p = +2\cdot5.$$

This is far too good agreement with experiment, considering the crudeness of the approximations made. More exact calculations, which take into account the motion of the nucleons as well as the next term in the perturbation expansion, in fact give worse agreement.

It cannot be said that the meson theory of nuclear forces is in a satisfactory state. Owing to the large value of the coupling constant it is impossible to use perturbation theory to obtain numerical results, except in the outer region of the tail of the potential. Further, the recent discovery of many heavy mesons has shown that the inner region must be one of extreme complexity and it is doubtful whether simple ideas of potential can be applicable there. Our knowledge of nuclear phenomena has increased immeasurably in the last decade; the same cannot be said of our understanding of them in terms of fundamental concepts.

10.4. EXAMPLES

10.4.1. Show that the Lorentz gauge condition (10.1′) can be written
$$\square \cdot \mathbf{A}\mu = 0. \qquad (10.79)$$

10.4.2. Prove that the spherically symmetric solution of

$$\nabla^2\phi - \mu^2\phi = 0$$

which vanishes at infinity is

$$\phi = \frac{e^{-\mu r}}{r}.$$

By analogy with the Coulomb field show that this is the potential due to a unit mesic point source at the origin, and hence that (10.15) is that solution of (10.14) that vanishes at infinity.

10.4.3. If the mesic charge density on a nucleon is assumed to be spread uniformly over a sphere of radius a, show that the potential due to a scalar meson of strength g is

$$\phi(r) = \begin{cases} -\dfrac{3g}{\mu^2 a^3}\left[1 - (1+\mu a)\,e^{-\mu a}\dfrac{\sinh \mu r}{\mu r}\right], & r < a \\[2ex] -\dfrac{3g}{\mu^2 a^3}\,(\mu a \cosh \mu a - \sinh \mu a)\,\dfrac{e^{-\mu r}}{\mu r}, & r > a. \end{cases} \tag{10.80}$$

Find the limit of this when $\mu a \ll 1$.

10.4.4. Show that if the maximum and minimum circular frequencies of γ-rays emitted in the reaction (10.37) are ω_{max} and ω_{min}, then the mass of the neutral pion is given by either of the following expressions

$$m_{\pi^o} = \frac{2\hbar}{c^2}\,(\omega_{max}\omega_{min})^{\frac{1}{2}}, \tag{10.81}$$

or

$$m_{\pi^o}^2 = \left(m_{\pi^-} - M_n + M_p\right)^2$$
$$- 2\left(m_{\pi^-} + M_p\right)\left\{\left[M_n^2 + \frac{\hbar^2}{c^4}\left(\omega_{max} - \omega_{min}\right)^2\right]^{\frac{1}{2}} - M_n\right\}. \tag{10.82}$$

Why is the second expression more useful?

[Hint : Use relativistic expressions for energy and momentum.]

10.4.5. Show that

$$\zeta(\mathbf{r}) = \pi^{-3/2}a^{-3}\,e^{-r^2/a^2} \tag{10.83}$$

satisfies (10.24) for small a, and that it satisfies (10.69) in the limit $a \to 0$.

10.4.6. Evaluate the nucleon-nucleon potential for the pseudoscalar meson theory with the same assumption about the distribution of mesic charge as in example 10.4.3, taking $\mu a \ll 1$, and show that, if a is the nucleon Compton wavelength, the strength of the repulsive core is about 40,000 MeV in an S-state.

APPENDIX

Cross-sections for Nuclear Reactions

A.1 Cross-section Formulae

In a nuclear reaction, the target nucleus changes its quantum mechanical state, so that we are dealing with a transition between states. For that reason our starting point must be the time-dependent Schrödinger equation, of which we met a special case in (7.35). Its general form is

$$i\hbar \frac{\partial \Psi}{\partial t} = H(t)\, \Psi. \tag{A.1}$$

In general it is not possible to solve this equation exactly, and we shall employ a perturbation method. We therefore assume that the Hamiltonian $H(t)$ can be split up into two parts,

$$H(t) = H_0 + \epsilon H_1(t) \tag{A.2}$$

where H_0 does not depend on the time, and the effect of $\epsilon H_1(t)$, which may or may not depend on time, is always small compared with H_0.[†] We further assume that we know the eigenvalues E_n and the correctly normalized eigenfunctions u_n of the unperturbed Hamiltonian H_0, and we shall treat $\epsilon H_1(t)$ as a perturbation. The u_n represent the stationary states of the unperturbed system, i.e.

$$H_0 u_n = E_n u_n \tag{A.3}$$

and the corresponding solutions of (A.1) for $\epsilon = 0$ are clearly

$$\psi_n = u_n e^{-\frac{i}{\hbar} E_n t}. \tag{A.4}$$

Now the eigenfunctions of an equation like (A.1) with given boundary conditions form what is known as a complete set of functions. Such a set has the property that any function with the same boundary conditions as the functions of the set can be expanded in terms of them, so that we can develop Ψ as

$$\Psi = \sum_n a_n(t) u_n e^{-\frac{i}{\hbar} E_n t}. \tag{A.5}$$

[†] From the point of view of perturbation theory it is convenient to use ϵH_1 rather than H_1 for the second part of the Hamiltonian, where ϵ is a small constant parameter and $H_1(t)$ is not necessarily small.

The coefficients $a_n(t)$ depend on time, even if H_1 does not depend on time explicitly.†

If (A.5) is substituted into (A.1), we obtain

$$\sum_n i\hbar\dot{a}_n(t)u_n e^{-\frac{i}{\hbar}E_n t} + \sum_n a_n(t)E_n u_n e^{-\frac{i}{\hbar}E_n t}$$
$$= \sum_n a_n(t)[H_0 + \epsilon H_1(t)]u_n e^{-\frac{i}{\hbar}E_n t}. \quad (A.6)$$

We now multiply (A.6) by u_m^* and integrate over all configuration space, i.e. over the multi-dimensional space of all the co-ordinates that specify the system. If use is made of (A.3) as well as of the orthonormal property of the u_n, according to which

$$\int u_m^* u_n \mathrm{d}\tau = \delta_{mn} \quad (A.7)$$

where the integration is over all configuration space, then (A.6) simplifies to

$$i\hbar\dot{a}_m e^{-\frac{i}{\hbar}E_m t} = \sum_n a_n(t) e^{-\frac{i}{\hbar}E_n t} \langle m \mid \epsilon H_1(t) \mid n \rangle \quad (A.8)$$

where

$$\langle m \mid \epsilon H_1(t) \mid n \rangle = \int u_m^* \epsilon H_1(t) u_n \mathrm{d}\tau \quad (A.9)$$

is called the matrix element of the perturbation between states n and m.

So far the treatment is exact. To apply perturbation theory we expand the a_n in a power series in ϵ,

$$a_n(t) = a_n^{(0)}(t) + \epsilon a_n^{(1)}(t) + \epsilon^2 a_n^{(2)}(t) + \ldots , \quad (A.10)$$

substitute in (A.8) and compare like powers of ϵ. We obtain

$$\dot{a}_m^{(0)}(t) = 0 \quad (A.11)$$

$$\dot{a}_m^{(r+1)}(t) = -\frac{i}{\hbar} \sum_n a_n^{(r)}(t) e^{\frac{i}{\hbar}(E_m - E_n)t} \langle m \mid H_1(t) \mid n \rangle, \ r = 0, 1, 2, \ldots$$
$$(A.12)$$

From (A.11) it follows at once that

$$a_m^{(0)}(t) = \text{constant} = a_m^{(0)} \quad (A.13)$$

where the $a_m^{(0)}$ denote the components of the initial state of the system, before the perturbation is applied. We shall consider the

† The summation in (A.5) consists strictly speaking of a sum over the discrete part of the energy spectrum of the unperturbed states plus an integral over the continuous part. This point is discussed in detail by most books on quantum mechanics, but need not worry us here.

special case in which the system is in a definite state before the perturbation is applied, so that all the $a_m^{(0)}$ vanish except one, say $a_i^{(0)}$, and $a_i^{(0)} = 1$. If the system is to be in a definite state initially, it must have been in that state for a time long enough for energy uncertainties to be negligible. We therefore take it that the system was in that state at time $t = -\infty$. Integration of (A.12) then yields for the coefficients of the final states, which we now denote by subscript f,

$$a_f^{(1)}(t) = -\frac{i}{\hbar} \int_{-\infty}^{t} e^{\frac{i}{\hbar}(E_f - E_i)t'} \langle f \mid H_1(t') \mid i \rangle dt' \qquad (A.14)$$

$$a_f^{(2)}(t) = -\frac{1}{\hbar^2} \sum_n \int_{-}^{t} e^{\frac{i}{\hbar}(E_f - E_n)t'} \langle f \mid H_1(t') \mid n \rangle dt'$$

$$\times \int_{-\infty}^{t'} e^{\frac{i}{\hbar}(E_n - E_i)t''} \langle n \mid H_1(t'') \mid i \rangle dt'' \qquad (A.15)$$

and so on.

These expressions are particularly simple in two special cases. The first is that of a perturbation which is constant in time, except that it is switched on at time $t = 0$ and switched off at time t. Then

$$\langle m \mid H_1(t') \mid n \rangle = \begin{cases} 0 & -\infty < t' < 0 \\ \langle m \mid H_1 \mid n \rangle & 0 < t' < t \quad (A.16) \\ 0 & t < t' \end{cases}$$

so that

$$a_f^{(1)}(t) = -\frac{\langle f \mid H_1 \mid i \rangle}{E_f - E_i} \left\{ e^{\frac{i}{\hbar}(E_f - E_i)t} - 1 \right\} \qquad (A.17)$$

$$a_f^{(2)}(t) = \sum_n \frac{\langle f \mid H_1 \mid n \rangle \langle n \mid H_1 \mid i \rangle}{E_n - E_i} \left\{ \frac{e^{\frac{i}{\hbar}(E_f - E_i)t} - 1}{E_f - E_i} - \frac{e^{\frac{i}{\hbar}(E_f - E_n)t} - 1}{E_f - E_n} \right\}$$

$$(A.18)$$

Thus to first-order in the perturbation the probability that the system, which initially was in state i, is at time t in state f is given by

$$\mid \epsilon a_f^{(1)}(t) \mid^2 = \frac{4 \mid \langle f \mid \epsilon H_1 \mid i \rangle \mid^2}{(E_f - E_i)^2} \sin^2 \frac{E_f - E_i}{2\hbar} t. \qquad (A.19)$$

To interpret (A.19) physically, we plot the function

$$F(t, E_f) = \left[\frac{2\hbar}{(E_f - E_i)t} \right]^2 \sin^2 \frac{E_f - E_i}{2\hbar} t \qquad (A.20)$$

against $E_f/\hbar$. This is done in Fig. A.1. Clearly, for sufficiently large t, $\mid t^{-1} a_f^{(1)}(t) \mid^2$ differs from zero appreciably only for

$$\mid E_f - E_i \mid < \frac{4\pi\hbar}{t}, \tag{A.21}$$

so that, within the limits imposed by the uncertainty principle, energy is conserved in the transition. This does not mean of course that no transitions are possible, but merely that the states of the system must form a continuous or nearly continuous set of states in the neighbourhood of the initial state i. By nearly continuous we mean that although the states are discrete, they are so closely spaced that the separation energy between states is less than the energy uncertainty that is a consequence of the uncertainty principle.

In the limit as $t \to \infty$, the function $F(t, E_f)$ vanishes for all E_f except for $E_f = E_i$, when it is infinite. Also, if $x = (E_f - E_i)\, t/2\hbar$, we have

$$\int_{-\infty}^{\infty} F(t, E_f)\mathrm{d}E_f = \frac{2\hbar}{t}\int_{-\infty}^{\infty} \frac{\sin^2 x}{x^2}\, \mathrm{d}x. \tag{A.22}$$

It is easily shown by contour integration that

$$\int_{-\infty}^{\infty} \frac{\sin^2 x}{x^2}\, \mathrm{d}x = \int_{-\infty}^{\infty} \frac{1 - \cos y}{y^2}\, \mathrm{d}y = \pi, \tag{A.23}$$

so that

$$\int_{-\infty}^{\infty} F(t, E_f)\, \mathrm{d}E_f = \frac{2\pi\hbar}{t}. \tag{A.24}$$

Hence the function has all the properties of the Dirac δ-function, i.e.

$$\lim_{t \to \infty} \frac{t}{2\pi\hbar}\, F(t, E_f) = \delta(E_f - E_i) \tag{A.25}$$

and

$$\mid \epsilon a_f^{(1)}(t) \mid^2 = \frac{2\pi t}{\hbar}\mid \langle f \mid \epsilon H_1 \mid i \rangle \mid^2 \delta(E_f - E_i). \tag{A.26}$$

Now the probability that in time t the perturbation should have thrown the system into a state in the energy interval E_f to $E_f + \mathrm{d}E_f$ is proportional to $\mid \epsilon a_f^{(1)}(t) \mid^2$, to the density of states† $\rho(E_f)$ of energy E_f and to the interval $\mathrm{d}E_f$. Hence the transition probability per unit time is given by

$$w = \frac{2\pi}{\hbar}\epsilon^2 \mid \langle f \mid H_1 \mid i \rangle \mid^2 \rho(E_f)\delta(E_f - E_i)\mathrm{d}E_f. \tag{A.27}$$

† We calculate such a density of states for a special case in (5.6).

We must now look more closely at the next term in the perturbation expansion, given by (A.18). Because of energy conservation, $E_f \simeq E_i$, so that in general the second term in the bracket of (A.18) is negligible compared with the first. The exception occurs of course when $E_n \simeq E_f \simeq E_i$. The second term actually arises from

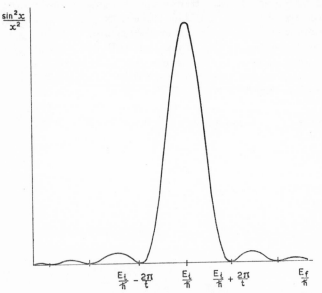

Fig. A.1. Plot of $\sin^2 x / x^2$ against $E_f/\hbar$, where $x = (E_f - E_i)t/2\hbar$

the switching on of the perturbation and is similar in effect to the transients that arise in the switching on of an electric current. We shall therefore ignore this term except when the state n is identical with the state i. In that case the term is not small, and we must in fact keep it, since then for $n = i$ the whole of the bracket vanishes and thus just cancels the infinity arising from the term $(E_n - E_i)$ in the denominator outside the bracket. The finite limit can be obtained in the standard manner, and the final result is

$$a_f^{(2)}(t) = \sum_n{}' \frac{\langle f \mid H_1 \mid n \rangle \langle n \mid H_1 \mid i \rangle}{E_n - E_i} \cdot \frac{e^{\frac{i}{\hbar}(E_f - E_i)t} - 1}{E_f - E_i}$$

$$+ \langle f \mid H_1 \mid i \rangle \langle i \mid H_1 \mid i \rangle \left\{ \frac{it}{\hbar} \frac{e^{\frac{i}{\hbar}(E_f - E_i)t}}{E_f - E_i} - \frac{e^{\frac{i}{\hbar}(E_f - E_i)t} - 1}{(E_f - E_i)^2} \right\} \quad (A.28)$$

where the prime on the summation sign denotes the fact that the term $n = i$ is to be omitted from the summation. The second coefficient in the perturbation expansion is thus finite—which was not immediately obvious from (A.18)—and we are therefore justified in neglecting the term $\epsilon^2 a_n^{(2)}(t)$ in (A.10) in comparison with $\epsilon a_n^{(1)}(t)$, if ϵ is sufficiently small.

When $\langle f \mid H_1 \mid i \rangle \neq 0$, the corresponding transition is called " allowed." When $\langle f \mid H_1 \mid i \rangle = 0$, we speak of a first forbidden transition, meaning that in first-order perturbation theory the transition cannot take place. This does not mean of course that it cannot take place at all, but merely that its probability is proportional to $\mid \epsilon^2 a_f^{(2)}(t) \mid^2$, and so an order of magnitude smaller. It follows from (A.28) that it is given by

$$w = \frac{2\pi\epsilon^4}{\hbar} \left| \sum_n{}' \frac{\langle f \mid H_1 \mid n \rangle \langle n \mid H_1 \mid i \rangle}{E_n - E_i} \right|^2 \rho(E_f)\delta(E_f - E_i)\mathrm{d}E_f \quad (A.29)$$

Similarly for higher-order forbidden transitions.

The physical interpretation of these transitions of various degrees of forbiddenness is as follows. In an allowed transition the system passes from the initial to the final state directly, while in forbidden transitions this is not possible and the transition takes place through one or more intermediate states, the summations being taken over all the possible ways in which a transition can take place through intermediate states. Energy need not be conserved in transitions to or from intermediate states. Thus in (A.29) we need not have $E_n \simeq E_f$, $E_n \simeq E_i$, although it is of course necessary that $E_f \simeq E_i$. The reason for this is that the lifetime of such an intermediate state is so short that, according to the uncertainty principle, the energy change may be large.

A second case in which (A.14) can be evaluated simply is that of a harmonic perturbation of frequency ω for which

$$\langle m \mid H_1(t') \mid n \rangle = \left\{ \begin{array}{cc} 0 & -\infty < t' < 0 \\ \langle m \mid H_1 \mid n \rangle \mathrm{e}^{\pm \mathrm{i}\omega t'} & 0 < t' < t \\ 0 & t < t'. \end{array} \right\} \quad (A.30)$$

It then follows that

$$a_f^{(1)}(t) = - \langle f \mid H_1 \mid i \rangle \frac{\mathrm{e}^{\frac{\mathrm{i}}{\hbar}(E_f - E_i \pm \hbar\omega)t} - 1}{E_f - E_i \pm \hbar\omega}. \quad (A.31)$$

Thus the probability of finding the system in a state f is large only if

$$E_f \simeq E_i \pm \hbar\omega. \quad (A.32)$$

In those cases the transition probability w will be given by

$$w = \frac{2\pi}{\hbar} \epsilon^2 \mid \langle f \mid H_1 \mid i \rangle \mid^2 \rho(E_f)\delta(E_f - E_i \mp \hbar\omega)\mathrm{d}E_f \quad \text{(A.33)}$$

This case is of particular interest to us. The electromagnetic field acts as a harmonic perturbation on the nucleus, and the interpretation of (A.32) is that the nucleus can either absorb a quantum $\hbar\omega$ of the electromagnetic field or emit one into the field.

It may seem surprising that in the case of the harmonic perturbation we have a definite energy jump, as given by (A.32), while previously we had required energy to be conserved. This arises from an implicit simplification of our treatment of the interaction of a nucleus with the electromagnetic field. We assume that the field is unchanged by the interaction, that it is in fact an infinitely large source or sink of quanta. Energy conservation then clearly does not apply. In a complete quantum mechanical treatment the state of the electromagnetic field must be included in the description of the initial and final states of the system. We, however, assume it to be something outside our quantum mechanical system that remains unchanged by the interaction, so that i and f refer solely to the states of the nucleus.

We can now calculate the cross-section for a nuclear reaction

$$x(X, \, Y)y$$

in first-order perturbation theory. We shall find it convenient to normalize all our wave functions to unit volume, rather than to volume L^3, as we did in section 5.2. The density of final states of particle y in the momentum range $\hbar k_y$ to $\hbar(k_y + \mathrm{d}k_y)$ with the momentum vector $\hbar k_y$ in the direction of the solid angle $\mathrm{d}\Omega$ is then given by

$$\rho(E_y)\mathrm{d}E_y = (2\pi)^{-3} \, k_y{}^2 \mathrm{d}k_y \, \mathrm{d}\Omega. \quad \text{(A.34)}$$

This formula is equivalent to (5.6).† Also

$$E_y = \frac{\hbar^2 k_y{}^2}{2\mu_y}, \; \mathrm{d}E_y = \hbar^2 \frac{k_y}{\mu_y} \mathrm{d}k_y, \quad \text{(A.35)}$$

where μ_y is the reduced mass in the exit channel. Note that we are using a c.m. frame of reference for the whole system, so that $\hbar k_y$ is the relative momentum of y and Y.

If we now substitute in (A.27) for w, we have

$$w = \frac{2\pi}{\hbar} (2\pi)^{-3}\hbar^{-2}|\langle f \mid \epsilon H_1 \mid i \rangle| \, ^2 \mu_y k_y \mathrm{d}E_y \delta(E_y - E_x + E_Y - E_X)\mathrm{d}\,\Omega. \quad \text{(A.36)}$$

† Note that in (5.6) we integrated over $\mathrm{d}\Omega$ and also allowed two spin states in each momentum state.

We next integrate over all final energies E_y in order to remove the δ-function—

$$w = \frac{\mu_y k_y}{4\pi^2\hbar^3} \mid \langle f \mid \epsilon H_1 \mid i \rangle \mid^2 d\Omega \qquad (A.37)$$

where now, because of the δ-function,

$$\hbar^2 k_y{}^2 = \hbar^2 k_x{}^2 - 2\mu_y(E_Y - E_X). \qquad (A.38)$$

The cross-section for the reaction is given by the transition probability per unit incident flux. As the incident wave function is normalized to unit volume, its incident flux is given by its velocity v_x in the centre-of-mass system. Hence, $v_x = \hbar k_x/\mu_x$ and we have

$$\frac{d\sigma}{d\Omega} = \frac{\mu_x \mu_y}{4\pi^2\hbar^4} \frac{k_y}{k_x} \mid \langle f \mid \epsilon H_1 \mid i \rangle \mid^2. \qquad (A.39)$$

A special case arises when the incident particle is a photon. We then have to integrate (A.33) over all E_f and obtain for the probability of absorption of a photon by a nuclear system—

$$w_{abs} = \frac{2\pi}{\hbar} \epsilon^2 \mid \langle f \mid H_1 \mid i \rangle \mid^2 \rho(E_f) \qquad (A.40)$$

where E_f is now given by (A.32) and $\rho(E_f)$ is the density of final states of the nuclear system. The flux of incident energy is given by the Poynting vector $\mathbf{S}$ [see (8.18)], and the differential cross-section is therefore obtained on dividing w_{abs} by $S/\hbar\omega$, i.e. by the number of photons in the incident beam,

$$\left(\frac{d\sigma}{d\Omega}\right)_{abs} = \frac{2\pi\omega}{S} \epsilon^2 \mid \langle f \mid H_1 \mid i \rangle \mid^2 \rho(E_f). \qquad (A.41)$$

If both the initial and final nuclear states are discrete states, then it follows from (A.33) that the capture probability is

$$w_{abs} = \frac{2\pi}{\hbar} \epsilon^2 \mid \langle f \mid H_1 \mid i \rangle \mid^2 \delta(E_f - E_i - \hbar\omega). \qquad (A.42)$$

The infinity in (A.42) is removed through taking into account the finite spread in frequency of the incident radiation. This is shown in section 8.1.

A.2 Born Approximation

For elastic scattering at very high energies, we may take the kinetic energy operator as our unperturbed Hamiltonian and the scattering potential $V(\mathbf{r})$ as our perturbation. The initial and final wave functions are then plane waves,

$$u_i = e^{i\mathbf{k}_1 \cdot \mathbf{r}}, \quad u_f = e^{i\mathbf{k}_f \cdot \mathbf{r}}, \quad k_i = k_f, \qquad (A.43)$$

so that the scattering cross-section reduces to

$$\frac{\mathrm{d}\sigma}{\mathrm{d}\Omega} = \left(\frac{\mu}{2\pi\hbar^2}\right)^2 \left| \int e^{\mathrm{i}(\mathbf{k}_i - \mathbf{k}_f) \cdot \mathbf{r}} \, V(\mathbf{r}) \mathrm{d}^3 r \right|^2. \qquad (A.44)$$

This is called the *Born approximation*. For spherically symmetric scattering potentials, the integral can be simplified. Putting the momentum transfer

$$\mathbf{q} = \mathbf{k}_i - \mathbf{k}_f, \qquad (A.45)$$

we have

$$\int e^{\mathrm{i}\mathbf{q} \cdot \mathbf{r}} \, V(r) \mathrm{d}^3 r = \int_0^\infty \int_0^{2\pi} \int_0^\pi e^{\mathrm{i}qr\cos\theta} \, V(r) r^2 \sin\theta \, \mathrm{d}\theta \mathrm{d}\phi \mathrm{d}r$$

$$= \frac{4\pi}{q} \int_0^\infty r V(r) \sin qr \mathrm{d}r. \qquad (A.46)$$

For inelastic scattering of a particle with co-ordinate $\mathbf{r}_0$ by a nucleus with co-ordinates $\mathbf{r}_1, \mathbf{r}_2, \ldots, \mathbf{r}_A$, we write the Hamiltonian

$$H = H_A(\mathbf{r}_1, \ldots \mathbf{r}_A) + T_0 + \sum_{n=1}^A V(\mathbf{r}_0 - \mathbf{r}_n) \qquad (A.47)$$

where the successive terms are the internal Hamiltonian of the nucleus, the kinetic energy of the incident particle, and the interaction between this particle and the nucleus. The wave equation is

$$H\Psi = E\Psi \qquad (A.48)$$

where we expand Ψ in terms of the complete set of target eigenfunctions ψ_j,

$$\Psi(\mathbf{r}_0, \mathbf{r}_1, \mathbf{r}_2, \ldots, \mathbf{r}_A) = \sum_j \psi_j(\mathbf{r}_1, \ldots \mathbf{r}_A) u_j(\mathbf{r}_0). \qquad (A.49)$$

Here the ψ_j are eigenfunctions of H_A and the u_j of T_0. The latter are therefore plane waves. If the interaction is a small perturbation, Ψ is almost an eigenfunction of $H_A + T_0$ and we can then put approximately

$$\Psi_i \simeq \psi_i u_i, \quad \Psi_f \simeq \psi_f u_f,$$

where ψ_i and ψ_f are the initial and final target wave functions and u_i and u_f are given by (A.43), except that now $k_i \neq k_f$. Hence the matrix element for inelastic scattering reduces to

$$\int e^{\mathrm{i}(\mathbf{k}_i - \mathbf{k}_f) \cdot \mathbf{r}_0} \, V_{if}(\mathbf{r}_0) \mathrm{d}^3 \mathbf{r}_0 \qquad (A.50)$$

where

$$V_{fi}(\mathbf{r}_0) = \int \psi_f^*(\mathbf{r}_1, \ldots \mathbf{r}_A) \sum_{n=1}^A V(\mathbf{r}_0 - \mathbf{r}_n) \psi_i(\mathbf{r}_1, \ldots \mathbf{r}_A) \mathrm{d}^3 r_1 \ldots \mathrm{d}^3 r_A \qquad (A.51)$$

is the so-called *coupling potential* for the initial and final states of the nucleus. This approximation is called the *plane-wave Born approximation*. It may be noted that only one term of the sum (A.51) need be carried, since in a correct formulation the total wave function would be anti-symmetrized and correctly normalized.

So far we have assumed that the incident and scattered particles are represented by plane waves. This is clearly incorrect, since these waves are bound to be distorted by the target nucleus. To allow for this we write down the wave equation (A.48), using (A.49) and (A.47),

$$\left[H_A + T + \sum_{n=1}^{A} V(\mathbf{r}_0 - \mathbf{r}_n) \right] \sum_j \psi_j u_j = E \sum_j \psi_j u_j. \qquad (A.52)$$

We now pre-multiply this equation by $\psi_i{}^*$ and integrate over all target co-ordinates $\mathbf{r}_1, \ldots \mathbf{r}_A$. Using the fact that the ψ_j are eigenfunctions of H_A, i.e.

$$H_A \psi_j = \epsilon_j \psi_j, \qquad (A.53)$$

and that the ψ_j are an orthonormal set, we have

$$(\epsilon_i + T + \sum_j V_{ij}) u_i = E u_i. \qquad (A.54)$$

Now, because of the greater overlap of the wave functions, the V_{ij} with $i = j$ are dominant and we shall neglect the others. Hence we finally obtain u_i as the solution of the wave equation

$$(T + V_{ii}) u_i = (E - \epsilon_i) u_i. \qquad (A.55)$$

This clearly describes the elastic scattering of the incident particle by the potential V_{ii}, so that V_{ii} can be thought of as the real part of an optical potential for elastic scattering by the ground state of the nucleus. Similarly for u_f. The imaginary part of the potential cannot be obtained in this way, and in practice an optical potential is obtained from elastic scattering, and is then used to derive the distorted waves u_i and u_f. These are then used in place of the plane waves (A.43). The resulting approximation is called the *distorted-wave Born approximation*. It is in general a good deal more accurate, and with the availability of electronic computers is rapidly replacing the plane-wave approximation except in exploratory work.

Table of Nuclear Constants

THE table of the first edition has been brought up to date with the help of the references below. Sincere thanks are due to Professor Mattauch and to Dr. Lindgren for sending me their tables in preprint form and for allowing me to make generous use of them.

Data in brackets are either uncertain or have been obtained from theoretical considerations.

References

(a) J. H. E. Mattauch, W. Thiele and A. H. Wapstra, *Nuclear Physics*, to be published.

(b) I. Lindgren and W. A. Nierenberg in *Proceedings of the Conference on Perturbed Angular Correlations* (Amsterdam, North-Holland, 1964); and in K. Siegbahn (editor), *Alpha-, Beta- and Gamma-ray Spectroscopy* (Amsterdam, North-Holland, 1964).

(c) *Concise Encyclopaedia of Nuclear Energy* (London, Newnes, 1962).

(d) F. Baumgärtner, *Die Naturwissenschaften*, **51**, 1 (1964).

Explanation of columns

1. Mass number A

2. Proton number Z

3. Neutron number $N = A - Z$

4. Chemical symbol

5. Percentage abundance of isotope, if nuclide stable; mode of decay, if nuclide unstable. Emission of α-particles (α), protons (p), neutrons (n), positons (e^+), negatons (e^-); fission (f); negaton capture (e_k); existence of excited isomeric state (I)

6. Half-life in years (y), days (d), hours (h), minutes (m), seconds (s)

7. Mass excess $M - A$ in mu

8. Angular momentum in units of $\hbar$

9. Magnetic moment in nuclear magnetons

10. Electric quadrupole moment in barns

If with a figure in either column 9 or 10 no sign is given, then only the magnitude is known.

1	2	3	4	5	6	7	8	9	10
1	0	1	n	e^-	12·8 m	8·665	½	− 1·9131	
	1	0	H	99·985	stable	7·825	½	+ 2·7927	
2	1	1	H	0·015	stable	14·102	1	+ 0·8574	+ 0·00282
3	1	2	H		12·3y	16·050	½	+ 2·9788	
	2	1	He	1·3 × 10⁻⁴	stable	16·030	½	− 2·1275	
4	2	2	He	100	stable	2·603	0		
5	2	3	He	n		12·30			
	3	2	Li	p		12·54			
6	2	4	He	e^-	0·80s	18·893	(0)		
	3	3	Li	7·42	stable	15·125	1	+ 0·8220	− 0·0011
7	3	4	Li	92·58	stable	16·004	3/2	+ 3·2563	− 0·0405
	4	3	Be	e_k	53d	16·929			
8	3	5	Li	e^-	0·9s	22·487	(2, 3)	+ 1·6533	
	4	4	Be	α	$\sim 10^{-15}$s	5·308	(0)		
	5	3	B	e^+	0·78s	24·609	(2, 3)		
9	3	6	Li	e^-	0·17s	24·80			
	4	5	Be	100	stable	12·185	3/2	− 1·1774	+ 0·029
	5	4	B	p		13·332			
10	4	6	Be	e^-	2·5 × 10⁶y	13·534	(0)		
	5	5	B	19·58	stable	12·939	3	+ 1·8006	+ 0·074
	6	4	C	e^+	19s	16·81	(0)		
11	5	6	B	80·42	stable	9·305	3/2	+ 2·6885	+ 0·036
	6	5	C	e^+	20·4 m	11·432	5/2		
12	5	7	B	e^-	0·018s	14·354	(1)		
	6	6	C	98·89	stable	0	0		
	7	5	N	e^+	0·013s	18·641	(1)		
13	5	8	B	e^-	0·035s	17·780	3/2		
	6	7	C	1·11	stable	3·354	½	+ 0·7024	
	7	6	N	e^+	10·1 m	5·738	½	0·3221	
14	6	8	C	e^-	5568y	3·242	0		
	7	7	N	99·64	stable	3·074	1	+ 0·4036	+ 0·01
	8	6	O	e^+	72s	8·597	(0)		
15	6	9	C	e^-	2·3s	10·599	5/2		
	7	8	N	0·36	stable	0·108	½	− 0·2831	
	8	7	O	e^+	124s	3·070	½	0·7189	
16	7	9	N	e^-	7·4s	6·103	2		
	8	8	O	99·76	stable	− 5·085	0		
17	7	10	N	e^-	4·2s	8·45	(½)		
	8	9	O	0·04	stable	− 0·867	5/2	− 1·8937	− 0·027
	9	8	F	e^+	66s	2·095	(5/2)		
18	8	10	O	0·20	stable	− 0·840	0		< 0·004
	9	9	F	e^+	1·87h	0·937	(1)	(+ 0·8)	
	10	8	Ne	e^+	1·6s	5·711	(0)		
19	8	11	O	e^-	29·4s	3·578	(5/2)		
	9	10	F	100	stable	− 1·595	½	+ 2·6287	
	10	9	Ne	e^+	18·5s	1·881	½	1·81	
20	9	11	F	e^-	12s	− 0·013	(2, 3)	+ 2·092	
	10	10	Ne	90·92	stable	− 7·559	(0)	∼ 0	
	11	9	Na	α, e^+	0·385s	8·9			
21	9	12	F		5s	− 0·049			
	10	11	Ne	0·26	stable	− 6·151	3/2	− 0·6618	+ 0·093
	11	10	Na	e^+	23s	− 2·345	(3/2)		
22	10	12	Ne	8·82	stable	− 8·615	0		
	11	11	Na	e^+, e_k	2·6y	− 5·563	3	+ 1·75	
23	10	13	Ne	e^-	38s	− 5·527	(5/2)		
	11	12	Na	100	stable	− 10·229	3/2	+ 2·2175	+ 0·10
	12	11	Mg	e^+	11s	− 5·875	(3/2)		

1	2	3	4	5	6	7	8	9	10
24	10	14	Ne	e^-	3·38m	− 6·387	(0)		
	11	13	Na	e^-, I	15·0h	− 9·038	4	+ 1·69	
	12	12	Mg	78·60	stable	−14·958	0		
	13	11	Al	e^+	2·1s	0·1	(4)		
25	11	14	Na	e^-	62s	−10·045	$(\frac{3}{2})$		
	12	13	Mg	10·11	stable	−14·161	$\frac{5}{2}$	− 0·8551	
	13	12	Al	e^+	7·6s	− 9·588	$(\frac{5}{2})$		
26	12	14	Mg	1·29	stable	−17·407	0		
	13	13	Al	e^+, I	8×10^5y	− 13·109			
27	12	15	Mg	e^-	9·5m	− 15·655	$(\frac{1}{2})$		
	13	14	Al	100	stable	− 18·461	$\frac{5}{2}$	+ 3·6414	+ 0·15
	14	13	Si	e^+	4·3s	− 13·297	$(\frac{5}{2})$		
28	12	16	Mg	e^-	21·4h	− 16·125	(0)		
	13	15	Al	e^-	2·30m	− 18·095	(3)		
	14	14	Si	92·27	stable	− 23·071	0		
	15	13	P	e^+	0·28s	− 8·2	(2, 3)		
29	13	16	Al	e^-	6·6m	− 19·558	$(\frac{5}{2})$		
	14	15	Si	4·68	stable	− 23·504	$\frac{1}{2}$	− 0·5552	$< 10^{-4}$
	15	14	P	e^+	4·5s	− 18·192	$(\frac{1}{2})$		
30	14	16	Si	3·05	stable	− 26·237	0		
	15	15	P	e^+	2·52m	− 21·683	(1)	(0·6)	
31	14	17	Si	e^-	2·65h	− 24·651	$(\frac{1}{2})$		
	15	16	P	100	stable	− 26·235	$\frac{1}{2}$	+ 1·1317	
	16	15	S	e^+	2·5s	− 20·39	$(\frac{1}{2})$		
32	14	18	Si	e^-	∼ 700y	− 25·98	0		
	15	17	P	e^-	14·3d	− 26·090	(1)	− 0·2523	
	16	16	S	95·02	stable	− 27·926	0		
	17	15	Cl	e^+	0·35s	− 13·8	(1)		
33	15	18	P	e^-	25d	− 28·272	$(\frac{1}{2})$		
	16	17	S	0·75	stable	− 28·538	$\frac{3}{2}$	+ 0·6434	− 0·064
	17	16	Cl	e^+	2·8s	− 22·56	$(\frac{3}{2})$		
34	15	19	P	e^-	12·4s	− 26·6	(1)		$< 2 \times 10^-$
	16	18	S	4·21	stable	− 32·135	0		
	17	17	Cl	e^+, I	1·6s	− 26·250	3	+ 1	
35	16	19	S	e^-	87·1d	− 30·969	$\frac{3}{2}$	1·0	+ 0·054
	17	18	Cl	75·53	stable	− 31·149	$\frac{3}{2}$	+ 0·8218	− 0·078
	18	17	A	e^+	1·83s	− 24·75	$(\frac{3}{2})$		
36	16	20	S	0·02	stable	− 32·910	0		< 0·01
	17	19	Cl	e_k, e^-	$3·1 \times 10^5$y	− 31·691	2	+ 1·2854	− 0·017
	18	18	A	0·34	stable	− 32·455	(0)		
37	16	21	S	e^-	5·0m	− 29·00	$(\frac{7}{2})$		
	17	20	Cl	24·47	stable	− 34·101	$\frac{3}{2}$	+ 0·6841	− 0·063
	18	19	A	e_k	34·1d	− 33·228	$\frac{3}{2}$	+ 0·97	
	19	18	K	e^+	1·2s	− 26·63	$(\frac{3}{2})$		
38	17	21	Cl	e^-	37·29m	− 31·995	2		
	18	20	A	0·05	stable	− 37·272	(0)		
	19	19	K	e^+	7·7m	− 30·903	3	+ 1·4	
39	17	22	Cl	e^-	56m	− 31·99	$(\frac{3}{2})$		
	18	21	A	e^-	265y	− 35·683	$\frac{7}{2}$		
	19	20	K	93·08	stable	− 36·290	$\frac{3}{2}$	+ 0·3915	+ 0·09
	20	19	Ca	e^+	0·95s	− 29·31	$(\frac{3}{2})$		
40	17	23	Cl	e^-	1·4m	− 29·6	(2)		
	18	22	A	99·60	stable	− 37·615	0		
	19	21	K	0·01, e^-, e_k	$1·3 \times 10^9$y	− 36·000	4	− 1·298	− 0·093
	20	20	Ca	96·97	stable	− 37·411	0		
	21	19	Sc	e^+	0·22s	− 22·4	(4)		
41	18	23	A	e^-	1·78h	− 35·500	$(\frac{7}{2})$		
	19	22	K	6·91	stable	− 38·168	$\frac{3}{2}$	+ 0·2148	+ 0·11
	20	21	Ca	e_k	$1·2 \times 10^5$y	− 37·725	$(\frac{7}{2})$	− 1·5946	
	21	20	Sc	e^+	0·87s	− 30·753	$(\frac{7}{2})$		

1	2	3	4	5	6	7	8	9	10
42	18	24	A	e^-	3·5y	− 36·95	0		
	19	23	K	e^-	12·5h	− 37·594	2	− 1·141	
	20	22	Ca	0·64	stable	− 41·374	0		
	21	21	Sc	e^+	0·65s	− 34·51	0		
43	19	24	K	e^-	22h	− 39·27	$\frac{3}{2}$	0·163	
	20	23	Ca	0·15	stable	− 41·220	$\frac{7}{2}$	− 1·3172	
	21	22	Sc	e^+	3·9h	− 38·835	$\frac{7}{2}$		
44	19	25	K	e^-	22m	− 38·0			
	20	24	Ca	2·06	stable	− 44·509	0		
	21	23	Sc	e^+, e_k, I	4·0h	− 40·594	(2, 3)	2·56	0·14
	22	22	Ti	e_k	∼ 10³y	− 40·43	0		
45	19	26	K		34m	− 39·3	$(\frac{3}{2})$		
	20	25	Ca	e^-, e_k	164d	− 43·810	$(\frac{5}{2})$		
	21	24	Sc	100	stable	− 44·081	$\frac{7}{2}$	+ 4·7563	− 0·22
	22	23	Ti	e^+	3·07h	− 41·871	$\frac{7}{2}$		
46	20	26	Ca	0·003	stable	− 46·311	0		
	21	25	Sc	e^-, I	85d	− 44·827	4	+ 3·04	+ 0·119
	22	24	Ti	7·99	stable	− 47·368	0		
	23	23	V	e^+	0·40s	− 39·786	(0)		
47	20	27	Ca	e^-	4·7d	− 45·462	$(\frac{7}{2})$		
	21	26	Sc	e^-	3·44d	− 47·587	$(\frac{7}{2})$		
	22	25	Ti	7·32	stable	− 48·231	$\frac{5}{2}$	− 0·7881	
	23	24	V	e^+	33m	− 45·101	$(\frac{7}{2})$		
48	20	28	Ca	0·18	(stable)	− 47·469	0		
	21	27	Sc	e^-	1·83d	− 47·779	(6, 7)		
	22	26	Ti	73·99	stable	− 52·050	0		
	23	25	V	e^+, e_k	16·1d	− 47·741	(4)		
	24	24	Cr	e_k	24h	− 46·2	0		
49	20	29	Ca	e^-	8·8m	− 44·32	$(\frac{3}{2})$		
	21	28	Sc	e^-	57·2m	− 49·974	$(\frac{7}{2})$		
	22	27	Ti	5·46	stable	− 52·130	$\frac{7}{2}$	− 1·1036	
	23	26	V	e_k	330d	− 51·477	$\frac{7}{2}$	4·46	
	24	25	Cr	e^+	41·9m	− 48·73	$\frac{5}{2}$		
50	21	29	Sc	e^-	1·7m	− 48·2	(5, 4)		
	22	28	Ti	5·25	stable	− 55·214	0		
	23	27	V	$0·24, e_k$	4×10^{14}y	− 52·836	6	+ 3·347	
	24	26	Cr	4·31	stable	− 53·945	0		
	25	25	Mn	e^+	0·28s	− 45·78	(0)		
51	22	29	Ti	e^-	5·8m	− 53·397	$(\frac{3}{2})$		
	23	28	V	99·76	stable	− 56·039	$\frac{7}{2}$	+ 5·147	+ 0·20
	24	27	Cr	e_k	27d	− 55·232	$\frac{7}{2}$		
	25	26	Mn	e^+	45m	− 51·81	$(\frac{5}{2}, \frac{7}{2})$		
52	23	29	V	e^-	3·77m	− 55·220	(2)		
	24	28	Cr	83·76	stable	− 59·487	0		
	25	27	Mn	e^+, e_k, I	5·7d	− 54·432	(6)	3·0	
	26	26	Fe	e^+	7·8h	− 51·88	0		
53	23	30	V	e^-	1·7m	− 56	$(\frac{5}{2})$		
	24	29	Cr	9·55	stable	− 59·347	$\frac{3}{2}$	− 0·4744	− 0·03
	25	28	Mn	e_k	2×10^6y	− 58·705	$\frac{7}{2}$	5·05	
	26	27	Fe	e^+	8·9m	− 54·43	$(\frac{7}{2})$		
54	23	31	V	e^-	55s	− 53			
	24	30	Cr	2·38	stable	− 61·118	0		
	25	29	Mn	e_k, e^-, I	291d	− 59·638	3	3·29	
	26	28	Fe	5·84	stable	− 60·383	0		
	27	27	Co	e^+	0·18s	− 51·525	(0)		
55	24	31	Cr	e^-	3·6m	− 59·167	$(\frac{3}{2})$		
	25	30	Mn	100	stable	− 61·950	$\frac{5}{2}$	+ 3·4677	+ 0·35
	26	29	Fe	e_k	2·9y	− 61·701	$(\frac{3}{2})$		
	27	28	Co	e^+	18·2h	− 57·987	$(\frac{7}{2})$	4·3	

1	2	3	4	5	6	7	8	9	10
56	25	31	Mn	e^-	2·58h	— 61·090	3	+ 3·2403	
	26	30	Fe	91·68	stable	— 65·064	0		
	27	29	Co	e^+	77d	— 60·153	4	3·803	
	28	28	Ni	e_k	6·4d	— 57·88	0		
57	25	32	Mn	e^-	1·7m	— 61·7	$(\frac{5}{2}, \frac{7}{2})$		
	26	31	Fe	2·17	stable	— 64·602	$\frac{1}{2}$	+ 0·0905	
	27	30	Co	e_k	270d	— 63·704	$\frac{7}{2}$	4·58	
	28	29	Ni	e^+	36h	— 60·23	$(\frac{3}{2})$		
58	26	32	Fe	0·31	stable	— 66·718	0		
	27	31	Co	e^+, e_k, I	72d	— 64·239	2	3·996	
	28	30	Ni	68	stable	— 64·658	0		
	29	29	Cu	e^+	7·9m	— 55·459			
59	26	33	Fe	e^-	45·1d	— 65·122	$\frac{3}{2}$		
	27	32	Co	100	stable	— 66·811	$\frac{7}{2}$	+ 4·583	+ 0·404
	28	31	Ni	e_k	1×10^5y	— 65·658	$(\frac{3}{2})$		
	29	30	Cu	e^+	82s	— 60·50	$(\frac{3}{2})$		
60	27	33	Co	e^-, I	5·3y	— 66·187	5	+ 3·754	
	28	32	Ni	26·3	stable	— 69·213	0		
	29	31	Cu	e^+	24m	— 62·638	2		
61	26	35	Fe	e^-	5·5m	— 63	$(\frac{5}{2}, \frac{3}{2})$		
	27	34	Co	e^-	1·66h	— 67·56	$\frac{7}{2}$		
	28	33	Ni	1·13	stable	— 68·944	$\frac{3}{2}$	0·70	
	29	32	Cu	e^+	3·3h	— 66·453	$\frac{3}{2}$	+ 2·16	
	30	31	Zu	e^+	1·5m	— 60·7	$(\frac{3}{2})$		
62	27	35	Co	e^-	14m	— 66·05			
	28	34	Ni	3·66	stable	— 71·658	0		
	29	33	Cu	e^+	9·7m	— 67·434	1		
	30	32	Zn	e^+	9·3h	— 65·62	0		
63	28	35	Ni	e^-	125y	— 70·336	$(\frac{5}{2})$		
	29	34	Cu	69·1	stable	— 70·408	$\frac{3}{2}$	+ 2·226	0·16
	30	33	Zn	e^+	38·3m	— 66·794	$(\frac{3}{2}, \frac{5}{2})$		
64	28	36	Ni	1·01	stable	— 72·042	0		
	29	35	Cu	e^+, e^-	12·8h	— 70·241	1	+ 0·216	
	30	34	Zn	48·89	stable	— 70·855	0		
	31	33	Ga	e^+	2·6m	— 63·26	(1)		
65	28	37	Ni	e^-	2·56h	— 69·928	$(\frac{5}{2})$		
	29	36	Cu	30·9	stable	— 72·214	$\frac{3}{2}$	+ 2·385	0·15
	30	35	Zn	e^+	245d	— 70·766	$\frac{5}{2}$	+ 0·7693	— 0·027
	31	34	Ga	e^+	15m	— 67·27	$(\frac{3}{2})$		
66	28	38	Ni	e^-	55h	— 70·91	0		
	29	37	Cu	e^-	5·1m	— 71·129	(1)		
	30	36	Zn	27·81	stable	— 73·948	0		
	31	35	Ga	e^+	9·8h	— 68·393	(0)		
	32	34	Ge	(e^+)	~150m	— 65·2	0		
67	29	38	Cu	e^-	61h	— 72·24	$(\frac{3}{2})$		
	30	37	Zn	4·11	stable	— 72·85	$\frac{5}{2}$	+ 0·8755	+ 0·18
	31	36	Ga	e_k	78h	— 71·78	$\frac{3}{2}$	+ 1·85	+ 0·22
	32	35	Ge	e^+	19m	— 67·0	$(\frac{3}{2}, \frac{5}{2})$		
68	29	39	Cu	e^-	32s	— 70·23	(1)		
	30	38	Zn	18·56	stable	— 75·143	0		
	31	37	Ga	e^+	68m	— 72·008	1	0·0118	0·0318
	32	36	Ge	e_k	275d	— 71	0		
69	30	39	Zn	e^-, I	52m	— 73·459	$(\frac{1}{2})$		
	31	38	Ga	60·2	stable	— 74·426	$\frac{3}{2}$	+ 2·016	+ 0·137
	32	37	Ge	e^+	39·6h	— 72·037	$(\frac{3}{2}, \frac{5}{2})$		

1	2	3	4	5	6	7	8	9	10
70	30	40	Zn	0·62	stable	— 74·666	0		
	31	39	Ga	e^-	21·1m	— 73·965	1		
	32	38	Ge	20·55	stable	— 75·748	0		< 0·007
	33	37	As	e^+	52m		(4, 5)		
	34	36	Se	e^+	44m		0		
71	30	41	Zn	e^-	2·2m	— 72·49	$(\frac{1}{2})$		
	31	40	Ga	39·5, I	stable	— 75·294	$\frac{3}{2}$	+ 2·562	+ 0·180
	32	39	Ge	e_k	12d	— 75·044	$(\frac{1}{2})$	+ 0·65	
	33	38	As	e^+	62h	— 72·887	$(\frac{5}{2})$		
72	30	42	Zn	e^-	49h	— 73·157	0		
	31	41	Ga	e^-	14·1h	— 73·628	3	0·12	
	32	40	Ge	27·37	stable	— 77·918	0		< 0·007
	33	39	As	e^+	26h	— 73·237	2		
	34	38	Se	e_k	8·4d	— 72	0		
73	31	42	Ga	e^-	5·0h	— 74·87	$(\frac{3}{2})$		
	32	41	Ge	7·67, I	stable	— 76·537	$\frac{9}{2}$	— 0·8788	+ 0·2
	33	40	As	e_k	90d	— 76·13	$(\frac{3}{2})$		
	34	39	Se	e^+	7·1h	— 73·18	$(\frac{9}{2})$		
74	32	42	Ge	36·74	stable	— 78·819	0		< 0·007
	33	41	As	e^+, e^-	17·5d	— 76·067	2		
	34	40	Se	0·87	stable	— 77·524	0		< 0·002
75	32	43	Ge	e^-, I	82m	— 77·12	$(\frac{1}{2})$		
	33	42	As	100	stable	— 78·404	$\frac{3}{2}$	+ 1·4390	+ 0·3
	34	41	Se	e_k	127d	— 77·475	$\frac{5}{2}$		+ 1·1
	35	40	Br	e^+	1·6h	— 74·55	$(\frac{3}{2}, \frac{5}{2})$		
76	32	44	Ge	7·67	stable	— 78·595	0		
	33	43	As	e^-	26·5h	— 77·60	2	— 0·906	
	34	42	Se	9·02	stable	— 80·793	0		
	35	41	Br	e^+	17·2h	— 75·82	1	0·5430	0·26
77	32	45	Ge	e^-, I	12h	— 76·40	$(\frac{7}{2})$		
	33	44	As	e^-	39h	— 79·354	$(\frac{3}{2})$		
	34	43	Se	7·58, I	stable	— 80·089	$\frac{1}{2}$	+ 0·5344	< 0·002
	35	42	Br	e^+	57·2h	— 78·624	$(\frac{3}{2})$		
	36	41	Kr	e^+	1·2h	— 75·52	$(\frac{1}{2})$		
78	32	46	Ge	e^-	86m		0		
	33	45	As	e^-	90m	— 78·1	(2)		
	34	44	Se	23·52	stable	— 82·686	0		
	35	43	Br	e^+	6·4m	— 78·850	(1)		
	36	42	Kr	0·35	stable	— 79·597	0		
79	33	46	As	e^-	9m	— 79·11	$(\frac{3}{2})$		
	34	45	Se	e^-, I	$6·5 \times 10^4$y	— 81·506	$\frac{7}{2}$	— 1·02	+ 0·9
	35	44	Br	50·56, I	stable	— 81·67	$\frac{3}{2}$	+ 2·1056	+ 0·33
	36	43	Kr	e^+, I	34·5h	— 79·932	$(\frac{1}{2})$		
80	34	46	Se	49·82	stable	— 83·473	0		
	35	45	Br	e^-, e^+, I	18m	— 81·464	1	0·5138	0·19
	36	44	Kr	2·27	stable	— 83·620	(0)		
81	34	47	Se	e^-, I	17m	— 82·016	$(\frac{1}{2})$		
	35	46	Br	49·44, I	stable	— 83·708	$\frac{3}{2}$	+ 2·2696	+ 0·28
	36	45	Kr	e_k	$2·1 \times 10^5$y	— 83·4	$(\frac{7}{2})$		
	37	44	Rb	e^+, I	4·7h	— 81·0	$\frac{3}{2}$	+ 2·05	
	38	43	Sr	e^+	29m				
82	34	48	Se	9·19, I	stable	— 83·293	0		
	35	47	Br	e^-	35·5h	— 83·198	5	1·626	0·73
	36	46	Kr	11·56	stable	— 86·518	0		
	37	45	Rb	e^+	1·25m	— 82·04			
	38	44	Sr	e_k	26d	— 82	(0)		

1	2	3	4	5	6	7	8	9	10
83	34	49	Se	e^-	25m		($\frac{3}{2}$)		
	35	48	Br	e^-	2·4h	− 84·83			
	36	47	Kr	11·55	stable	− 85·869	$\frac{9}{2}$	− 0·9702	+ 0·25
	37	46	Rb	e_k	90d	− 85	$\frac{5}{2}$	+ 1·42	
	38	45	Sr	e^+	38h	− 83			
84	34	50	Se	e^-	2m		(0)		
	35	49	Br	e^-	33m	− 83·45	(2, 1)		
	36	48	Kr	56·90	stable	− 88·497	0		
	37	47	Rb	e^+, e^-, I	33d	− 85·619	2	− 1·32	
	38	46	Sr	0·56	stable	− 86·570	(0)		
	39	45	Y	e^+	3·7h	− 79·8			
85	35	50	Br	e^-	3·0m	− 84·5	($\frac{3}{2}$)		
	36	49	Kr	e^-, I	10·6y	− 87·477	$\frac{9}{2}$	− 1·004	+ 0·45
	37	48	Rb	72·15	stable	− 88·200	$\frac{5}{2}$	+ 1·3527	+ 0·286
	38	47	Sr	e_k, I	65d	− 87·01	($\frac{9}{2}$)		
86	36	50	Kr	17·37	stable	− 89·384	0		
	37	49	Rb	e^-, I	18·6d	− 88·807	2	− 1·6912	
	38	48	Sr	9·86	stable	− 90·715	0		
	39	47	Y	e^+	15h	− 85·05			
	40	46	Zr	e_k	17h	− 84	(0)		
87	35	52	Br	e^-	55·6s	− 78·0	($\frac{3}{2}, \frac{5}{2}$)		
	36	51	Kr	e^-	78m	− 86·635	($\frac{1}{2}$)		
	37	50	Rb	27·85, e^-	$\sim 5 \times 10^{10}$y	− 90·813	$\frac{3}{2}$	+ 2·7505	+ 0·140
	38	49	Sr	7·02, I	stable	− 91·108	$\frac{9}{2}$	− 1·0930	+ 0·36
	39	48	Y	e^+, I	80h	− 89·3	($\frac{1}{2}$)		
	40	47	Zr	e^+	1·6h	− 85·5	($\frac{7}{2}, \frac{9}{2}$)		
88	35	53	Br	e^-	15·5s				
	36	52	Kr	e^-	2·77h	− 85·7	(0)		
	37	51	Rb	e^-	17·7m	− 88·7	2		
	38	50	Sr	82·56	stable	− 94·359	0		
	39	49	Y	e^+	105d	− 90·472	(4)		
	40	48	Zr	e_k	85d	− 89·9	(0)		
89	35	54	Br	e^-	4·51s				
	36	53	Kr	e^-	3·18m	− 83·4	($\frac{5}{2}, \frac{7}{2}$)		
	37	52	Rb	e^-	15m	− 88·35	($\frac{5}{2}$)		
	38	51	Sr	e^-, I	51d	− 92·558	($\frac{5}{2}$)		
	39	50	Y	100, I	stable	− 94·128	$\frac{1}{2}$	− 0·13732	
	40	49	Zr	e^+, I	73·3h	− 91·086	($\frac{9}{2}$)		
	41	48	Nb	e^+, I	1·9h	− 86·9	($\frac{9}{2}$)		
90	36	54	Kr	e^-	33s	− 80·3	(0)		
	37	53	Rb	e^-	2·74m	− 85·2			
	38	52	Sr	e^-	27·7y	− 92·253	(0)		
	39	51	Y	e^-	65h	− 92·837	2	− 1·629	− 0·155
	40	50	Zr	51·46	stable	− 95·300	(0)		
	41	49	Nb	e^+, I	15h	− 88·74			
	42	48	Mo	e^+	5·7h	− 86·0	(0)		
91	36	55	Kr	e^-	10s		($\frac{5}{2}, \frac{7}{2}$)		
	37	54	Rb	e^-	(100s)	− 84	($\frac{3}{2}, \frac{5}{2}$)		
	38	53	Sr	e^-	9·7h	− 89·84	($\frac{5}{2}$)		
	39	52	Y	e^-, I	57·5d	− 92·71	$\frac{1}{2}$	0·1640	
	40	51	Zr	11·23	stable	− 94·358	$\frac{5}{2}$	− 1·3029	
	41	50	Nb	e_k, I	long	− 93·14	$\frac{9}{2}$		
	42	49	Mo	e^+, I	15·7m	− 88·35	($\frac{9}{2}$)		
92	36	56	Kr	e^-	3·0s				
	37	55	Rb	e^-	80s	− 81			
	38	54	Sr	e^-	2·7h	− 89·02	(0)		
	39	53	Y	e^-	3·5h	− 91·07	(2)		
	40	52	Zr	17·11	stable	− 94·969	(0)		
	41	51	Nb	e_k, I	10d	− 92·789	(2, 3)		
	42	50	Mo	15·86	stable	− 93·190	0		
	43	49	Tc	e^+	4·3m	− 84·5			

1	2	3	4	5	6	7	8	9	10
93	36	57	Kr	e^-	2·0s				
	37	56	Rb	e^-	short				
	38	55	Sr	e^-	7m	− 85·3			
	39	54	Y	e^-	10·0h	− 90·45	$(\frac{1}{2})$		
	40	53	Zr	e^-	$9·5 \times 10^5$y	− 93·550	$(\frac{5}{2})$		
	41	52	Nb	100, I	stable	− 93·618	$\frac{9}{2}$	+ 6·167	− 0·2
	42	51	Mo	e_k, I	> 2y	− 93·17	$(\frac{5}{2})$		
	43	50	Tc	e^+, I	2·7h	− 89·75	$(\frac{9}{2})$		
94	36	58	Kr	e^-	1·4s				
	37	57	Rb	e^-	short				
	38	56	Sr	e^-	$\sim$2m	− 84·6			
	39	55	Y	e^-	16·5m	− 88·3	(2)		
	40	54	Zr	17·40	stable	− 93·687			
	41	53	Nb	e^-, I	2×10^4y	− 92·70	(6)		
	42	52	Mo	9·12	stable	− 94·910	0		
	43	51	Tc	e^+, e_k	53m	− 90·337			
95	36	59	Kr	e^-	short				
	37	58	Rb	e^-	short				
	39	56	Y	e^-	10·5m	− 87			
	40	55	Zr	e^-	65d	− 91·965	$(\frac{5}{2})$		
	41	54	Nb	e^-, I	35d	− 93·168	$(\frac{9}{2})$		
	42	53	Mo	15·7	stable	− 94·161	$\frac{5}{2}$	− 0·9133	
	43	52	Tc	e_k, I	20h	− 92·38	$\frac{9}{2}$		
	44	51	Ru	e^+	1·6h	− 90·20	$(\frac{5}{2}, \frac{7}{2})$		
96	37	59	Rb	e^-	short				
	40	56	Zr	2·8	stable	− 91·714			
	41	55	Nb	e^-	23h	− 91·94	(6, 7)		
	42	54	Mo	16·5	stable	− 95·326	0		
	43	53	Tc	e_k, I	4·35d	− 92·17	(6, 7)		
	44	52	Ru	5·50	stable	− 92·402			
97	36	61	Kr	e^-	$\sim$1s				
	37	60	Rb	e^-	short				
	38	59	Sr	e^-	short				
	39	58	Y	e^-	short				
	40	57	Zr	e^-	17h	− 89·03			
	41	56	Nb	e^-, I	74m	− 91·904	$(\frac{9}{2})$		
	42	55	Mo	9·45	stable	− 93·978	$\frac{5}{2}$	− 0·9325	
	43	54	Tc	e_k, I	$2·6 \times 10^6$y	− 94·6	$(\frac{9}{2})$		
	44	53	Ru	e_k	2·44d	− 92	$(\frac{5}{2})$		
98	42	56	Mo	23·75	stable	− 94·591	0		
	43	55	Tc	e^-	$1·5 \times 10^6$y	− 92·9	(6)		
	44	54	Ru	1·91	stable	− 94·711	(0)		
	45	53	Rh	e^+	8·7m	− 90·2	(2, 3)		
99	41	58	Nb	e^-	3·8m	− 89			
	42	57	Mo	e^-	68h	− 92·280	$(\frac{1}{2})$		
	43	56	Tc	e^-, I	$2·1 \times 10^5$y	− 93·751	$\frac{9}{2}$	+ 5·680	+ 0·34
	44	55	Ru	12·70	stable	− 94·064	$\frac{5}{2}$	− 0·63	
	45	54	Rh	e^+	4·7h	− 91·81	$(\frac{7}{2}, \frac{9}{2})$		
100	42	58	Mo	9·62	stable	− 92·525	0		
	43	57	Tc	e^-	15·8s	− 92·16			
	44	56	Ru	12·69	stable	− 95·782	(0)		
	45	55	Rh	e^+	20·8h	− 91·87	(2)		
	46	54	Pd	e_k	4·0d	− 91	(0)		
101	42	59	Mo	e^-	14·6m	− 89·65	$(\frac{5}{2})$		
	43	58	Tc	e^-	14m	− 92·67	$(\frac{9}{2})$		
	44	57	Ru	17·01	stable	− 94·423	$\frac{5}{2}$	− 0·69	
	45	56	Rh	e_k	4·5d	− 93·82	$(\frac{9}{2})$		
	46	55	Pd	e^+	8·5h	− 91·93	$(\frac{7}{2})$		

1	2	3	4	5	6	7	8	9	10
102	42	60	Mo	e^-	11m	− 90	(0)		
	43	59	Tc	e^-	4·5m	− 91	(1)		
	44	58	Ru	31·52	stable	− 95·652			
	45	57	Rh	e^+, e^-	215d	− 93·158	(2)		
	46	56	Pd	0·96	stable	− 94·391			
103	44	59	Ru	e^-	39·5d	− 93·69			
	45	58	Rh	100, I	stable	− 94·489	$\frac{1}{2}$	− 0·0883	
	46	57	Pd	e_k	17d	− 93·89	$(\frac{5}{2}, \frac{7}{2})$		
	47	56	Ag	e^+	59m	− 91·1	$(\frac{9}{2})$		
104	44	60	Ru	18·67	stable	− 94·570			
	45	59	Rh	e^-, I	44s	− 93·341	(1)		
	46	58	Pd	10·97	stable	− 95·989	(0)		
	47	57	Ag	e^+	1·1h	− 91·40	5	+ 4·1	
	48	56	Cd	e_k	59m	− 90			
105	42	63	Mo	e^-	$\sim$2m				
	43	62	Tc	e^-	10m	− 88·7			
	44	61	Ru	e^-	4·5h	− 92·32			
	45	60	Rh	e^-, I	36·5h	− 94·33	$(\frac{7}{2})$		
	46	59	Pd	22·23	stable	− 94·94	$\frac{5}{2}$	− 0·57	
	47	58	Ag	e_k	45d	− 94	$\frac{1}{2}$	0·101	
	48	57	Cd	e^+	54·7m	− 91			
106	44	62	Ru	e^-	1·0y	− 92·68	(0)		
	45	61	Rh	e^-	30s	− 92·72	(1)		
	46	60	Pd	27·33	stable	− 96·521	(0)		
	47	59	Ag	e^-, e^+, e	24m	− 93·339	1		
	48	58	Cd	1·22	stable	− 95·537			
107	44	63	Ru	e^-	4m	− 89·9			
	45	62	Rh	e^-	25m	− 93·25			
	46	61	Pd	e^-, I	7×10^6y	− 94·868	$(\frac{5}{2})$		
	47	60	Ag	51·35, I	stable	− 94·906	$\frac{1}{2}$	− 0·1136	
	48	59	Cd	e^+	6·7h	− 93·385	$\frac{5}{2}$	− 0·616	+ 0·79
	49	58	In	e^+	33m	− 89·6	$(\frac{9}{2})$		
108	46	62	Pd	26·7	stable	− 96·109			
	47	61	Ag	e^-, e^+, e_k	2·3m	− 94·051	(1)		
	48	60	Cd	0·88	stable	− 95·813	(0)		
	49	59	In	e^+, I	40m	− 90·29			
	50	58	Sn	e_k	9m				
109	45	64	Rh	e^-	< 1h	− 91			
	46	63	Pd	e^-, I	13·6h	− 94·046	$(\frac{5}{2})$		
	47	62	Ag	48·65, I	stable	− 95·244	$\frac{1}{2}$	− 0·1305	
	48	61	Cd	e_k	470d	− 95·072	$\frac{5}{2}$	− 0·8286	+ 0·78
	49	60	In	e^+, I	4·2h	− 92·90	$\frac{9}{2}$	+ 5·54	+ 1·20
	50	59	Sn	e^+	18m	− 91·9	$(\frac{5}{2})$		
110	46	64	Pd	11·81	stable	− 94·84			
	47	63	Ag	e^-, I	24·5s	− 93·905	(1)		
	48	62	Cd	12·39	stable	− 96·988	0		
	49	61	In	e^+, I	66m	− 92·77	(2, 3)		
111	46	65	Pd	e^-, I	22m	− 92·33	$\frac{1}{2}$		
	47	64	Ag	e^-, I	7·5d	− 94·68	$\frac{1}{2}$	− 0·146	
	48	63	Cd	12·75, I	stable	− 95·812	$\frac{1}{2}$	− 0·5950	+ 1·18
	49	62	In	e_k	2·84d	− 94·6	$\frac{9}{2}$	+ 5·53	
	50	61	Sn	e^+	33m	− 91·9	$\frac{7}{2}$		
112	46	66	Pd	e^-	21h	− 92·61	(0)		
	47	65	Ag	e^-	3·2h	− 92·94			
	48	64	Cd	24·07	stable	− 97·237	0		
	49	63	In	e^+, e^-, I	14·5m	− 94·456	(1)		
	50	62	Sn	0·95	stable	− 95·165			

1	2	3	4	5	6	7	8	9	10
113	46	67	Pd		1·5m				
	47	66	Ag	e^-, I	5·3h	− 93·44	½	0·159	
	48	65	Cd	12·26, I	stable	− 95·591	½	− 0·6224	
	49	64	In	4·23, I	stable	− 95·911	9/2	+ 5·523	+ 1·14
	50	63	Sn	k	118d	− 94·81	$(\tfrac{1}{2}, \tfrac{3}{2})$		
114	47	67	Ag	e^-	2m	− 91·7			
	48	66	Cd	28·86	stable	− 96·640	0		
	49	65	In	e^+, e^-, I	72s	− 95·095	1		
	50	64	Sn	0·65	stable	− 97·227	(0)		
115	47	68	Ag	e^-, I	21m	− 91·0	(½)		
	48	67	Cd	e^-, I	2·33d	− 94·569	(½)		
	49	66	In	95·77, e^-, I	10^{15}y	− 96·129	9/2	+ 5·535	+ 1·16
	50	65	Sn	0·34	stable	− 96·654	½	− 0·9178	
116	48	68	Cd	7·58	stable	− 95·238	0		
	49	67	In	e^-, I	13s	− 94·68	(1)		
	50	66	Sn	14·24	stable	− 98·255	0		
	51	65	Sb	e^+	15·5m	− 93·37	(3)		
117	48	69	Cd	e^-, I	50m	− 92·76			
	49	68	In	e^-, I	1·1h	− 95·466	(9/2)		
	50	67	Sn	7·57, I	stable	− 97·042	½	− 0·9998	
	51	66	Sb	e_k	2·8h	− 95·09	(5/2)		
	52	65	Te	e^+	61m		½		
118	48	70	Cd	e^-	50m	− 93			
	49	69	In	e^-	4·5m	− 93·9			
	50	68	Sn	24·01	stable	− 98·394	0		
	51	67	Sb	e_k, I	5·1h	− 94·426			
	52	66	Te	e_k	6·0d	− 94			
119	49	70	In	e^-	17·5m	− 94·0	(½)		
	50	69	Sn	8·58, I	stable	− 96·687	½	− 1·0462	
	51	68	Sb	e_k	39h	− 96·06	(5/2)		
	52	67	Te	e_k	4·5d	− 93·60	11/2		
120	50	70	Sn	32·97	stable	− 97·802	0		
	51	69	Sb	e^+, I	16·4m	− 94·919	(1)		
	52	68	Te	0·09	stable	− 95·98			
121	50	71	Sn	e^-, I	27·5h	− 95·773	(3/2)		
	51	70	Sb	57·25	stable	− 96·184	5/2	+ 3·3589	− 0·5
	52	69	Te	e_k	17d	− 94·80	(½)		
	53	68	I	e^+	1·6h	− 92·27	(5/2)		
	54	67	Xe	e^+	~ 40m				
122	50	72	Sn	4·71	stable	− 96·559	(0)		
	51	71	Sb	e^+, e^-, I	2·75d	− 94·817	(2)	− 1·904	+ 0·47
	52	70	Te	2·46	stable	− 96·934	(0)		
	53	69	I	e^+	3·5m	− 92·49	(1)		
	54	68	Xe	e_k	19h		(0)		
123	50	73	Sn	e^-	(40m)	− 94·26	(3/2)		
	51	72	Sb	42·75	stable	− 95·787	7/2	+ 2·5465	− 0·7
	52	71	Te	0·87, I	stable	− 95·723	½	− 0·7358	
	53	70	I	e_k	13h	− 94	5/2		
	54	69	Xe	e^+	1·8h	− 91	$(\tfrac{3}{2}, \tfrac{1}{2})$		
	55	68	Cs	e^+	6m				
124	50	74	Sn	5·98	stable	− 94·728			
	51	73	Sb	e^-, I	60d	− 94·027	3		
	52	72	Te	4·61	stable	− 97·158	(0)		
	53	71	I	e^+	4d	− 93·75	2		
	54	70	Xe	0·10	stable	− 93·9			
125	50	75	Sn	e^-	9·7d	− 92·25			
	51	74	Sb	e^-	2y	− 94·768	(7/2)		
	52	73	Te	6·99, I	stable	− 95·582	½	− 0·8871	
	53	72	I	e_k	60d	− 95·422	2	3·0	− 0·66
	54	71	Xe	e_k, I	18h	− 93			
	55	70	Cs	e^+	45m	− 90	(5/2)		

1	2	3	4	5	6	7	8	9	10
126	50	76	Sn	e^-	$\sim$ 50m	$-$ 92			
	51	75	Sb	e^-	(9h)	$-$ 92·7			
	52	74	Te	18·71	stable	$-$ 96·678	0		
	53	73	I	e^+, e^-	13·3d	$-$ 94·369	2		
	54	72	Xe	0·09	stable	$-$ 95·712	(0)		
	55	71	Cs	e^+	1·6m	$-$ 90·6	(1)		
127	50	77	Sn	e^-	2·1h	$-$ 90			
	51	76	Sb	e^-	93h	$-$ 93·07	$(\frac{7}{2})$		
	52	75	Te	e^-, I	9·4h	$-$ 94·791	$(\frac{3}{2})$		
	53	74	I	100	stable	$-$ 95·530	$\frac{5}{2}$	+ 2·809	$-$ 0·69
	54	73	Xe	e_k, I	25d	$-$ 94·8	$(\frac{3}{2})$		
	55	72	Cs	e^+	6·2h	$-$ 92·5	$\frac{1}{2}$	+ 1·43	
	56	71	Ba	e^+	12m	$-$ 89			
128	52	76	Te	31·79	stable	$-$ 95·524	0		
	53	75	I	e^+, e^-	25m	$-$ 94·162	1		
	54	74	Xe	1·92	stable	$-$ 96·460	(0)		
	55	73	Cs	e^+	3·8m	$-$ 92·24	(1)		
	56	72	Ba	e_k	2·4d	$-$ 91	(0)		
129	51	78	Sb	e^-	4·6h	$-$ 91	$(\frac{7}{2})$		
	52	77	Te	e^-, I	74m	$-$ 93·425	$(\frac{3}{2})$		
	53	76	I	e^-	$1·72 \times 10^7$y	$-$ 95·013	$\frac{7}{2}$	+ 2·6173	$-$ 0·55
	54	75	Xe	26·44, I	stable	$-$ 95·216	$\frac{1}{2}$	$-$ 0·7768	
	55	74	Cs	e_k	31h	$-$ 94	$\frac{1}{2}$	+ 1·48	
	56	73	Ba	e^+	2·45h	$-$ 91			
130	52	78	Te	34·49	stable	$-$ 93·762	0		
	53	77	I	e^-	12·5h	$-$ 93·32	5		
	54	76	Xe	4·08	stable	$-$ 96·491	(0)		
	55	75	Cs	e^+, e^-	30m	$-$ 93·28	1	1·4	
	56	74	Ba	0·10	stable	$-$ 93·75			
131	51	80	Sb	e^-	23·1m				
	52	79	Te	e^-, I	25m	$-$ 91·42	$(\frac{3}{2})$		
	53	78	I	e^-	8d	$-$ 93·873	$\frac{7}{2}$	+ 2·738	$-$ 0·40
	54	77	Xe	21·18, I	stable	$-$ 94·915	$\frac{3}{2}$	+ 0·6906	$-$ 0·12
	55	76	Cs	e_k	9·7d	$-$ 94·534	$\frac{5}{2}$	+ 3·53	
	56	75	Ba	e_k	11·5d	$-$ 93·28	$(\frac{1}{2})$		
	57	74	La	e^+	58m	$-$ 90·11			
132	51	81	Sb	e^-	2·1m				
	52	80	Te	e^-	77·7h	$-$ 91·48	(0)		
	53	79	I	e^-	2·4h	$-$ 92·019	4	3·084	0·09
	54	78	Xe	26·89	stable	$-$ 95·839	0		
	55	77	Cs	e_k	6·2d	$-$ 93·61	2	+ 2·22	
	56	76	Ba	0·10	stable	$-$ 94·9	(0)		
	57	75	La	e^+	4·5h	$-$ 89·7			
133	51	82	Sb	e^-	4·4m				
	52	81	Te	e^-, I	2m		$(\frac{3}{2})$		
	53	80	I	e^-	20·8h	$-$ 92·25	$\frac{7}{2}$	2·837	0·26
	54	79	Xe	e^-, I	5·27d	$-$ 94·18	$(\frac{3}{2})$		
	55	78	Cs	100	stable	$-$ 94·64	$\frac{7}{2}$	+ 2·579	$-$ 0·003
	56	77	Ba	e_k, I	7·2y	$-$ 94·12	$(\frac{1}{2})$		
	57	76	La	e^+	4·0h	$-$ 91·8			
	58	75	Ce	e^+	6·3h	$-$ 89			
134	52	82	Te	e^-	44m				
	53	81	I	e^-	53m	$-$ 90·15	(2, 3)		
	54	80	Xe	10·44	stable	$-$ 94·603	0		
	55	79	Cs	e^-, I	2·3y	$-$ 93·18	4	+ 2·990	
	56	78	Ba	2·42	stable	$-$ 95·39	0		
	57	77	La	e^+	6·5m	$-$ 91·34	(1)		
	58	76	Ce	e_k	72·0h	$-$ 91·19			

1	2	3	4	5	6	7	8	9	10
135	52	83	Te	e^-	$\sim$1m				
	53	82	I	e^-	6·68h	− 90	$(\frac{5}{2}, \frac{7}{2})$		
	54	81	Xe	e^-, I	9·2h	− 93·0	$(\frac{3}{2})$		
	55	80	Cs	e^-	2·0 × 10⁶y	− 94·2	$\frac{7}{2}$	+ 2·7290	+ 0·049
	56	79	Ba	6·59, I	stable	− 94·4	$\frac{3}{2}$	+ 0·8371	+ 0·128
	57	78	La	e_k	19·5h	− 93·0	$(\frac{5}{2})$		
	58	**77**	Ce	e^+	22h	− 91	$(\frac{3}{2})$		
	59	76	Pr	e^+	22m		$(\frac{5}{2})$		
136	53	83	I	e^-	86s	− 85·3	(0, 1)		
	54	82	Xe	8·87	stable	− 92·779	0		
	55	81	Cs	e^-	12·9d	− 92·66	(4, 5)		
	56	80	Ba	7·81	stable	− 95·70	0		
	57	79	La	e^+	9·5m	− 92·6	(1)		
	58	78	Ce	0·19	stable	− 92·9	(0)		
	59	77	Pr	e^+	70m		(1)		
137	53	84	I	e^-	22·0s				
	54	83	Xe	e^-	3·9m	− 88·9	$(\frac{7}{2}, \frac{9}{2})$		
	55	82	Cs	e^-	30y	− 93·23	$\frac{7}{2}$	+ 2·8382	+ 0·050
	56	81	Ba	11·32, I	stable	− 94·50	$\frac{3}{2}$	+ 0·9365	+ 0·20
	57	80	La	e_k	6 × 10⁴y	− 94	$(\frac{7}{2})$		
	58	79	Ce	e_k, I	8·7h	− 93	$(\frac{3}{2})$		
	59	78	Pr	e^+	1·5h	− 90	$(\frac{5}{2})$		
138	53	85	I	e^-	5·9s				
	54	84	Xe	e^-	17m	− 86	(0)		
	55	83	Cs	e^-	32m	− 89	(3)		
	56	82	Ba	71·66	stable	− 95·00	0		
	57	81	La	0·09, e_k, e^-	$\sim$10¹¹y	− 93·09	5	+ 3·7071	1·0
	58	80	Ce	0·25	stable	− 94·17	(0)		
	59	79	Pr	e^+	2·0h	− 89·5	(3, 5)		
139	53	86	I	e^-	2·7s				
	54	85	Xe	e^-	41s	− 82·2			
	55	84	Cs	e^-	10m	− 87·1	$(\frac{7}{2}, \frac{5}{2})$		
	56	83	Ba	e^-	85m	− 91·40	$(\frac{7}{2})$		
	57	82	La	99·91	stable	− 93·86	$\frac{7}{2}$	+ 2·7781	+ 0·23
	58	81	Ce	e_k, I	140d	− 93·57	$(\frac{3}{2})$	0·90	
	59	80	Pr	e^+	4·5h	− 91·4	$(\frac{5}{2})$		
	60	79	Nd	e^+	5·5h	− 88	$(\frac{3}{2})$		
140	54	86	Xe	e^-	16·0s				
	55	85	Cs	e^-	66s	− 83			
	56	84	Ba	e^-	12·8d	− 89·43	(0)		
	57	83	La	e^-	40·2h	− 90·56	3		
	58	82	Ce	88·48	stable	− 94·61	(0)		
	59	81	Pr	e^+	3·5m	− 90·99	(1)		
	60	80	Nd	e_k	3·3d	− 91	(0)		
141	54	87	Xe	e^-	1·7s				
	55	86	Cs	e^-	short				
	56	85	Ba	e^-	18m	− 85·9	$(\frac{7}{2}, \frac{9}{2})$		
	57	84	La	e^-	3·7h	− 89·17	$(\frac{7}{2}, \frac{5}{2})$		
	58	83	Ce	e^-	33d	− 91·78	$\frac{7}{2}$	0·97	
	59	82	Pr	100	stable	− 92·40	$\frac{5}{2}$	+ 4·2	− 0·059
	60	81	Nd	e^+	2·42h	− 90·47	$\frac{3}{2}$		
	61	80	Pm	e^+	20m	− 86·6	$(\frac{5}{2})$		
142	55	87	Cs	e^-	$\sim$1m				
	56	86	Ba	e^-	6m	− 83·6			
	57	85	La	e^-	81m	− 86·02			
	58	84	Ce	11·07, α	5 × 10¹⁵y	− 90·86	(0)		
	59	83	Pr	e^-	19·2h	− 90·02	(2)	0·25	0·030
	60	82	Nd	27·09	stable	− 92·33	(0)		

1	2	3	4	5	6	7	8	9	10
143	54	89	Xe	e^-	1·0s				
	55	88	Cs	e^-	short				
	56	87	Ba	e^-	< 0·5m				
	57	86	La	e^-	$\sim$19m	− 84·13			
	58	85	Ce	e^-	33·4h	− 87·67	$(\frac{7}{2})$	1·0	
	59	84	Pr	e^-	14d	− 89·22	$\frac{7}{2}$		
	60	83	Nd	12·14	stable	− 90·22	$\frac{7}{2}$	− 1·07	< 0·5
	61	82	Pm	e_k	320d	− 89·0	$(\frac{5}{2}, \frac{7}{2})$	3·8	
	62	81	Sm	e^+	9m	− 85·45	$(\frac{3}{2})$		
144	54	90	Xe	e^-	$\sim$1s				
	55	89	Cs	e^-	short				
	56	88	Ba	e^-	short				
	57	87	La	e^-	short	− 80			
	58	86	Ce	e^-	290d	− 86·40	(0)		
	59	85	Pr	e^-	17·5m	− 86·79	(0)		
	60	84	Nd	23·83	stable	− 89·96	(0)		
	61	83	Pm	e_k	300d	− 87	(5, 6)	1·7	
	62	82	Sm	3·16	stable	− 88·01			
145	58	87	Ce	e^-	3·0m	− 83	$(\frac{7}{2}, \frac{9}{2})$		
	59	86	Pr	e^-	6·0h	− 85·52	$(\frac{5}{2}, \frac{7}{2})$		
	60	85	Nd	8·29	stable	− 87·46	$\frac{7}{2}$	− 0·63	< 0·25
	61	84	Pm	e_k	18y	− 87·31	$(\frac{5}{2}, \frac{7}{2})$		
	62	83	Sm	e_k	340d	− 86·61	$(\frac{7}{2}, \frac{9}{2})$		
	63	82	Eu	e_k	5d	− 83·61			
146	58	88	Ce	e^-	13·9m	− 81·3	(0)		
	59	87	Pr	e^-	24·4m	− 82·4	(3)		
	60	86	Nd	17·26	stable	− 86·91	(0)		
	61	85	Pm	e^-	$\sim$1y	− 85·37			
	62	84	Sm	α	5×10^7y	− 87·00	(0)		
147	60	87	Nd	e^-	11d	− 83·93	$\frac{5}{2}$	0·577	
	61	86	Pm	e^-	2·6y	− 84·89	$\frac{7}{2}$	+ 2·7	0·95
	62	85	Sm	15·07, α	$1·3 \times 10^{11}$y	− 85·13	$\frac{7}{2}$	− 0·80	< 0·21
	63	84	Eu	α, e_k	24d	− 83·2	$(\frac{5}{2}, \frac{7}{2})$		
148	60	88	Nd	5·74	stable	− 83·13	(0)		
	61	87	Pm	e^-	5·4d	− 82·58	(1)	1·82	
	62	86	Sm	11·27	stable	− 85·20	(0)		
	63	85	Eu	e_k	54d	− 81·89			
	64	84	Gd	$\alpha, (e_k)$	130y	− 81·90			
149	60	89	Nd	e^-	1·8h	− 79·88	$\frac{5}{2}$		
	61	88	Pm	e^-	50h	− 81·67	$\frac{7}{2}$	3·3	
	62	87	Sm	13·84	stable	− 82·82	$\frac{7}{2}$	− 0·64	+ 0·06
	63	86	Eu	e_k	120d	− 82	$(\frac{5}{2}, \frac{7}{2})$		
	64	85	Gd	$\alpha, (e_k)$	9d	− 80·7			
	65	84	Tb	$\alpha, (e_k)$	4·1h	− 76·65			
150	60	90	Nd	5·63	stable	− 79·08	2	+ 0·46	
	61	89	Pm	e^-	2·7h	− 79·04	(5, 6)		
	62	88	Sm	7·47	stable	− 82·72	(0)		
	63	87	Eu	e^-	13·7h	− 80·31	(0, 1)		
	64	86	Gd	α	long	− 81·39	(0)		
151	60	91	Nd	e^-	12m	− 76·2	$(\frac{9}{2})$		
	61	90	Pm	e^-	28h	− 78·80	$\frac{5}{2}$	1·8	1·9
	62	89	Sm	e^-	93y	− 80·08	$(\frac{9}{2})$		
	63	88	Eu	47·77	stable	− 80·16	$\frac{5}{2}$	+ 3·44	+ 0·95
	64	87	Gd	e_k	$\sim$150d	− 80	$(\frac{7}{2}, \frac{9}{2})$		
	65	86	Tb	$\alpha, (e_k)$	19h	− 76·9			
152	62	90	Sm	26·63	stable	− 80·24	(0)		
	63	89	Eu	e_k, e^-	13y	− 78·25	(3)	+ 1·91	
	64	88	Gd	0·20	stable	− 80·21	(0)		

1	2	3	4	5	6	7	8	9	10
153	62	91	Sm	e^-	47h	− 77·90	$\frac{3}{2}$		
	63	90	Eu	52·23	stable	− 78·76	$\frac{5}{2}$	+ 1·52	+ 2·42
	64	89	Gd	e_k	236d	− 78·50	$(\frac{7}{2})$		
	65	88	Tb	e_k	5·1d	− 77	$(\frac{3}{2})$		
154	62	92	Sm	22·53	stable	− 77·72	(0)		
	63	91	Eu	e_k, e^-	16y	− 76·95	3	+ 1·971	+ 3·29
	64	90	Gd	2·15	stable	− 79·07	(0)		
	65	89	Tb	e^+	17·2h	− 75			
155	62	93	Sm	e^-	23·5m	− 75·30	$(\frac{9}{2})$		
	63	92	Eu	e^-	1·7y	− 77·07	$(\frac{5}{2})$		
	64	91	Gd	14·73	stable	− 77·34	$\frac{3}{2}$	0·242	+ 1·4
	65	90	Tb	e_k	5·6d	− 76	$(\frac{3}{2})$		
	66	89	Dy	e_k	10h	− 74	$(\frac{3}{2})$	0·21	
156	62	94	Sm	e^-	10h	− 74·43	(0)		
	63	93	Eu	e^-	15·4d	− 75·20	3	2·1	
	64	92	Gd	20·47	stable	− 77·82	0		
	65	91	Tb	e^+, e^-, I	5d	− 75	(3)	1·41	+ 1·40
	66	90	Dy	0·05	stable	− 76·0	(0)		
157	63	94	Eu	e^-	15·4h	− 74·61	$(\frac{5}{2}, \frac{7}{2})$		
	64	93	Gd	15·68	stable	− 75·97	$\frac{3}{2}$	− 0·323	+ 1·0
	66	91	Dy	e_k	8·2h	− 75	$(\frac{3}{2})$	0·32	
158	64	94	Gd	24·87	stable	− 75·82			
	65	93	Tb	I	11s	− 74·54			
	66	92	Dy	0·09	stable	− 75·55			
159	64	95	Gd	e^-	18h	− 73·63	$\frac{3}{2}$		
	65	94	Tb	100	stable	− 74·65	$\frac{3}{2}$	1·90	+ 1·32
	66	93	Dy	e_k	134d	− 74·24			
160	64	96	Gd	21·90	stable	− 72·88	(0)		
	65	95	Tb	e^-	73d	− 72·85		1·56	+ 1·87
	66	94	Dy	2·35	stable	− 74·80	(0)		
	67	93	Ho	e^+, I	28m	− 71·26			
	68	92	Er		29h				
161	64	97	Gd	e^-	3·7m	− 70·28	$(\frac{7}{2}, \frac{9}{2})$		
	65	96	Tb	e^-	7·15d	− 72·43	$\frac{3}{2}$		
	66	95	Dy	18·88	stable	− 73·05	$\frac{5}{2}$	− 0·455	+ 1·35
	67	94	Ho	e_k	2·5h	− 72	$\frac{3}{2}$		
	68	93	Er	e^+	3·1h	− 70	$(\frac{7}{2}, \frac{9}{2})$		
162	66	96	Dy	25·53	stable	− 73·20	(0)		
	67	95	Ho	e_k	67m	− 70·88			
	68	94	Er	0·14	stable	− 71·26	(0)		
163	66	97	Dy	24·97, I	stable	− 71·24	$\frac{5}{2}$	+ 0·635	+ 1·62
	67	96	Ho	e_k	5·20d	− 71·23			
	68	95	Er	e_k	75m	− 69·93			
164	66	98	Dy	28·18	stable	− 70·80	(0)		
	67	97	Ho	e, e^-	36·7m	− 69·61			
	68	96	Er	1·56	stable	− 70·71	(0)		
165	66	99	Dy	e^-, I	140m	− 68·18	$\frac{7}{2}$		
	67	98	Ho	100	stable	− 69·58	$\frac{7}{2}$	4·03	2·82
	68	97	Er	e_k	10h	− 69·18	$\frac{5}{2}$		
	69	96	Tm	e_k	24·5h	− 67	$(\frac{1}{2})$		
166	66	100	Dy	e^-	82h	− 67·2	(0)		
	67	99	Ho	e^-	27·3h	− 67·71	(0)		
	68	98	Er	33·41	stable	− 69·69	(0)		
	69	97	Tm	e^+	7·7h	− 66·49	2	0·047	4·36
	70	96	Yb	e_k	60h	− 66·1			
167	67	100	Ho	e^-	3h	− 66·9	$(\frac{7}{2})$		
	68	99	Er	22·94, I	stable	− 67·94	$\frac{7}{2}$	− 0·564	2·82
	69	98	Tm	e_k	9·6d	− 67	$\frac{1}{2}$		
	70	97	Yb	e^+	(74m)	− 65			

1	2	3	4	5	6	7	8	9	10
168	68	100	Er	27·07	stable	− 67·62	(0)		
	69	99	Tm	e_k, e^-	85d	− 65·77			
	70	98	Yb	0·14	stable	− 65·8	(0)		
169	68	101	Er	e^-	9d	− 65·39	$\frac{1}{2}$	+ 0·513	
	69	100	Tm	100	stable	− 65·75	$\frac{1}{2}$	− 0·23	
	70	99	Yb	e_k	30·6d	− 64			
170	68	102	Er	14·88	stable	− 64·44	(0)		
	69	101	Tm	e_k, e^-	127d	− 63·94	1	0·247	0·574
	70	100	Yb	3·03	stable	− 64·98	(0)		
	71	99	Lu	e_k	1·7d	− 61·17	(0)		
	72	98	Hf	e^+	1·87h		(0)		
171	68	103	Er	e^-	7·8h	− 61·87	$\frac{5}{2}$	0·697	2·37
	69	102	Tm	e^-	680d	− 63·47	$\frac{1}{2}$	0·230	
	70	101	Yb	14·31, I	stable	− 63·57	$\frac{1}{2}$	+ 0·493	
	71	100	Lu	e_k	8·5d	− 62	$(\frac{7}{2})$		
	72	99	Hf	e_k	16·0h				
172	70	102	Yb	21·82	stable	− 63·64	(0)		
	71	101	Lu	e_k	6·7d	− 61			
	72	100	Hf	e_k	∼ 5y		(0)		
173	70	103	Yb	16·13	stable	− 61·94	$\frac{5}{2}$	− 0·678	+ 2·4
	71	102	Lu	e_k	500d	− 61·20	$(\frac{7}{2})$		
	72	101	Hf	e_k	23·6h		$\frac{1}{2}$		
174	70	104	Yb	31·84	stable	− 61·26	(0)		
	71	103	Lu	e_k, e^-	165d	− 59·65			
	72	102	Hf	0·20	stable	− 59·64			
175	70	105	Yb	e^-	4·2d	− 58·86	$(\frac{7}{2})$	0·15	
	71	104	Lu	97·40	stable	− 59·36	$\frac{7}{2}$	+ 2·23	+ 5·68
	72	103	Hf	e_k	70d	− 58	$(\frac{5}{2})$		
176	70	106	Yb	12·73	stable	− 57·32	(0)		
	71	105	Lu	2·60, e^-, I	3 × 10¹⁰y	− 57·34	7	+ 3·14	+ 8
	72	104	Hf	5·23	stable	− 58·43	(0)		
	73	103	Ta	e_k	8h				
	74	102	W	e^+, e_k	80m		(0)		
177	70	107	Yb	e^-	1·8h	− 54·59	$(\frac{5}{2})$		
	71	106	Lu	e^-	6·8d	− 56·07	$\frac{7}{2}$	+ 2·236	+ 5·51
	72	105	Hf	18·55	stable	− 56·60	$\frac{7}{2}$	+ 0·61	
	73	104	Ta	e_k	2·2d	− 55·35	$(\frac{5}{2})$		
	74	103	W	e_k	2·2h				
178	72	106	Hf	27·23, I	stable	− 56·12	0		
	73	105	Ta	e^+	(9·35m)	− 54·1			
	74	104	W	e^+	22d		(0)		
179	72	107	Hf	13·73, I	stable	− 53·97	$\frac{9}{2}$	− 0·47	
	73	106	Ta	e_k	∼600d	− 53·84	$(\frac{5}{2})$		
	74	105	W	e_k	40m		$(\frac{7}{2})$		
180	72	108	Hf	35·07, I	stable	− 53·18	0		
	73	107	Ta	0·01, e_k, e^-, I	10¹²y	− 52·45			
	74	106	W	0·14, I	stable	− 53·00	(0)		
181	72	109	Hf	e^-	45d	− 50·89	$(\frac{3}{2})$		
	73	108	Ta	99·99	stable	− 51·99	$\frac{7}{2}$	+ 2·35	+ 3·9
	74	107	W	e_k	140d	− 51·79	$(\frac{7}{2})$		
182	73	109	Ta	e^-, I	111d	− 49·83			
	74	108	W	26·4	stable	− 51·70	0		
	75	107	Re	e_k	13h	− 48·63			
	76	106	Os	e_k	24h		(0)		
183	72	111	Hf	e^-	64m	− 46·2	$(\frac{1}{2})$		
	73	110	Ta	e^-	5d	− 48·53	$\frac{7}{2}$		
	74	109	W	14·4, I	stable	− 49·68	$\frac{1}{2}$	+ 0·1172	
	75	108	Re	e_k	68d	− 49			
	76	107	Os	e_k, I	12h				

1	2	3	4	5	6	7	8	9	10
184	73	111	Ta	e^-	8·7h	− 46·02			
	74	110	W	30·6	stable	− 48·97	0		
	75	109	Re	e_k	50d	− 47			
	76	108	Os	0·02	stable	− 47·25			
185	73	112	Ta	e^-	49m	− 44·44	$(\frac{7}{2})$		
	74	111	W	e^-, I	73d	− 46·48	$\frac{3}{2}$		
	75	110	Re	37·07	stable	− 46·94	$\frac{5}{2}$	+ 3·172	+ 2·8
	76	109	Os	e_k	97d	− 45·89	$(\frac{1}{2})$		
186	74	112	W	28·4	stable	− 45·56	0		
	75	111	Re	e_k, e^-	3·7d	− 44·98	1		
	76	110	Os	1·59	stable	− 46·13	(0)		
187	74	113	W	e^-	24h	− 42·76	$\frac{3}{2}$		
	75	112	Re	62·93, e^-	$< 10^{11}$y	− 44·17	$\frac{5}{2}$	+ 3·204	+ 2·6
	76	111	Os	1·64, I	stable	− 44·17	$\frac{1}{2}$	+ 0·065	
	77	110	Ir	e_k	14h	− 42	$(\frac{3}{2})$		
188	74	114	W	e^-	65d	− 41·16			
	75	113	Re	e^-, I	17h	− 41·85	1		
	76	112	Os	13·3	stable	− 43·92	(0)		
	77	111	Ir	e^+	41h	− 40·88			
	78	110	Pt	e_k	10d	− 40·33	(0)		
189	76	113	Os	16·1, I	stable	− 41·70	$\frac{3}{2}$	+ 0·6559	+ 0·8
	77	112	Ir	e_k	11d	− 41	$(\frac{3}{2})$		
	78	111	Pt	e_k	10·5h	− 39	$(\frac{1}{2})$		
190	76	114	Os	26·4, I	stable	− 41·37			
	77	113	Ir	e^+	11d	− 39·2			
	78	112	Pt	0·01, α	$5·9 \times 10^{11}$y	− 40·05			
	79	111	Au	e_k	39m	− 35	1	0·063	
191	76	115	Os	e^-, I	16·0d	− 39·03	$(\frac{7}{2})$		
	77	114	Ir	38·5, I	stable	− 39·36	$\frac{3}{2}$	+ 0·16	+ 1·5
	78	113	Pt	e_k	3d	− 39	$(\frac{1}{2})$		
	79	112	Au	e_k	3h	− 36	$\frac{3}{2}$	0·137	
192	76	116	Os	41·0	stable	− 38·55	(0)		
	77	115	Ir	e_k, e^-, I	74d	− 37·30	4		
	78	114	Pt	0·78, α	10^{15}y	− 38·85	(0)		
	79	113	Au	e^+, e_k	4·1h	− 35·38	1	0·008	
193	76	117	Os	e^-	31·5h	− 35·77	$(\frac{1}{2})$		
	77	116	Ir	61·5, I	stable	− 36·99	$\frac{3}{2}$	+ 0·17	+ 1·5
	78	115	Pt	e_k, I		− 36·94	$(\frac{1}{2})$		
	79	114	Au	e_k, I	17·5h	− 36	$\frac{3}{5}$	0·140	
	80	113	Hg	e_k, I	6h	− 33	$(\frac{1}{2})$		
194	76	118	Os	e^-	$\sim$ 700d	− 34·77			
	77	117	Ir	e^-	19h	− 34·87	1		
	78	116	Pt	32·8	stable	− 37·27	0		
	79	115	Au	e^+	40h	− 34·58	1	0·074	
195	77	118	Ir	e^-	2·3h	− 34·1	$(\frac{3}{2})$		
	78	117	Pt	33·7, I	stable	− 35·19	$\frac{1}{2}$	+ 0·6060	
	79	116	Au	e_k, I	185d	− 34·95	$\frac{3}{2}$	0·148	
	80	115	Hg	e_k, I	9·5h	− 33	$\frac{1}{2}$	+ 0·5389	
	81	144	Tl	e_k, I	1·2h	− 30	$\frac{1}{2}$		
196	78	118	Pt	25·4	stable	− 35·03	0		
	79	117	Au	e_k, e^-	5·6d	− 33·44	2	0·6	
	80	116	Hg	0·15	stable	− 34·18	0		
197	78	119	Pt	e^-, I	18h	− 32·65	$(\frac{1}{2})$		
	79	118	Au	100, I	stable	− 33·46	$\frac{3}{2}$	+ 0·145	+ 0·60
	80	117	Hg	e_k, I	65h	− 32·64	$\frac{1}{2}$	+ 0·5241	
	81	116	Tl	e_k, I	2·8h	− 30·2	$\frac{1}{2}$		
198	77	121	Ir	e^-	50s	− 27·4			
	78	120	Pt	7·23	stable	− 32·10	(0)		
	79	119	Au	e_k, e^-	2·7d	− 31·77	2	0·56	
	80	118	Hg	10·02	stable	− 33·24	0		
	81	117	Tl	e_k, I	5·3h	− 29·53	2	0·002	
	82	116	Pb	e_k	2·3h	− 28	(0)		
	83	115	Bi	α, e_k	7m	− 20			

1	2	3	4	5	6	7	8	9	10
199	78	121	Pt	e^-	30m	$-29 \cdot 42$	$(\frac{5}{2})$		
	79	120	Au	e^-	3·2d	$-31 \cdot 23$	$\frac{3}{2}$	0·27	
	80	119	Hg	16·84, I	stable	$-31 \cdot 72$	$\frac{1}{2}$	$+0 \cdot 5027$	
	81	118	Tl	e_k	7·4h	$-30 \cdot 5$	$\frac{1}{2}$	1·58	
	82	117	Pb	e_k, I	90m	-27	$(\frac{5}{2})$		
	83	116	Bi	α, e_k	25m	-22	$\frac{9}{2}$		
200	79	121	Au	e^-	48m	$-29 \cdot 3$	(0, 1)		
	80	120	Hg	23·13	stable	$-31 \cdot 67$	0		
	81	119	Tl	e_k	20h	$-29 \cdot 03$	2		
	82	118	Pb	e_k	18h	-28	(0)		
	83	117	Bi	e_k	35m	-21	7		
	84	116	Po	α, e_k	8m	-17	(0)		
201	79	122	Au	e^-	26m	$-28 \cdot 08$	$\frac{3}{2}$		
	80	121	Hg	13·22	stable	$-29 \cdot 69$	$\frac{3}{2}$	$-0 \cdot 5567$	$+0 \cdot 50$
	81	120	Tl	e_k	3d	$-29 \cdot 25$	$\frac{1}{2}$	1·59	
	82	119	Pb	e_k, I	9·4h	-27	$(\frac{1}{2})$		
	83	118	Bi	e_k	1·85h	-23	$\frac{3}{2}$		
	84	117	Po	α, e_k	18m	-17	$\frac{9}{2}$		
202	80	122	Hg	29·80	stable	$-29 \cdot 36$	0		
	81	121	Tl	e_k, I	12d	$-28 \cdot 05$	2		
	82	120	Pb	e_k, I	3×10^5y	$-28 \cdot 00$	(0)		
	83	119	Bi	e_k	90m	-22	5		
	84	118	Po	α, e_k	43m	-19			
203	79	124	Au	e^-	55s	-25	$(\frac{3}{2})$		
	80	123	Hg	e^-	47d	$-27 \cdot 12$	$(\frac{5}{2})$		
	81	122	Tl	29·50	stable	$-27 \cdot 65$	$\frac{1}{2}$	$+1 \cdot 6117$	
	82	121	Pb	e_k, I	52h	$-26 \cdot 77$	$(\frac{3}{2}, \frac{5}{2})$		
	83	120	Bi	α, e_k	12h	$-23 \cdot 35$	$\frac{9}{2}$	$+4 \cdot 59$	$-0 \cdot 64$
	84	119	Po	e_k	42m	-19	$\frac{5}{2}$		
204	80	124	Hg	6·85	stable	$-26 \cdot 50$	0		
	81	123	Tl	e_k, e^-, I	4·3y	$-26 \cdot 13$	2	0·089	
	82	122	Pb	1·40, I	stable	$-26 \cdot 96$	0		
	83	121	Bi	e_k	11·6h	-22	6	$+4 \cdot 25$	$-0 \cdot 41$
	84	120	Po	α, e_k	3·5h	-20	(0)		
	85	119	At	e_k	$\sim$25m	-12			
205	80	125	Hg	e^-	5·66m	$-23 \cdot 8$	$(\frac{1}{2})$		
	81	124	Tl	70·50	stable	$-25 \cdot 56$	$\frac{1}{2}$	$+1 \cdot 6275$	
	82	123	Pb	e_k	5×10^7y	$-25 \cdot 52$	$(\frac{5}{2})$		
	83	122	Bi	e^+	14·5h	$-22 \cdot 62$	$\frac{9}{2}$		
	84	121	Po	α, e_k	1·5h	-19	$\frac{5}{2}$		$-0 \cdot 17$
	85	120	At	α, e_k	25m	-14			
206	81	125	Tl	e^-	4·2m	$-23 \cdot 90$	(0)		
	82	124	Pb	25·2	stable	$-25 \cdot 53$	0		
	83	123	Bi	e_k	6·4d	$-21 \cdot 61$	6	$+4 \cdot 56$	$-0 \cdot 19$
	84	122	Po	α, e_k	9d	$-19 \cdot 68$	(0)		
	85	121	At	e_k	2·6h	-13			
	86	120	Rn	α	6·5m	-9			
207	81	126	Tl	e^-	4·79m	$-22 \cdot 55$	$(\frac{1}{2})$		
	82	125	Pb	21·7, I	stable	$-24 \cdot 10$	$\frac{1}{2}$	$+0 \cdot 5895$	
	83	124	Bi	e_k	8y	$-21 \cdot 56$	$(\frac{9}{2})$		
	84	123	Po	α, e_k	5·7h	$-18 \cdot 44$	$\frac{5}{2}$		0·28
	85	122	At	α, e_k	2h	$-14 \cdot 44$			
	86	121	Rn	α, e_k	11m	-9			
208	81	127	Tl	e^-	3·1m	$-17 \cdot 99$	5		
	82	126	Pb	51·7	stable	$-23 \cdot 35$	0		
	83	125	Bi	e_k	long	$-20 \cdot 27$			
	84	124	Po	α, e_k	2·9y	$-18 \cdot 76$	(0)		
	85	123	At	e_k	6·3h	-13			
	86	122	Rn	α, e_k	23m	-10	(0)		

1	2	3	4	5	6	7	8	9	10
209	81	128	Tl	e^-	2·2m	− 14·70	$(\frac{1}{2})$		
	82	127	Pb	e^-	3·3h	− 18·92	$(\frac{9}{2})$		
	83	126	Bi	100	$> 2 \times 10^{18}$y	− 19·61	$\frac{9}{2}$	+ 4·080	− 0·4
	84	125	Po	α, e_k	103y	− 17·57	$\frac{1}{2}$		
	85	124	At	α, e_k	5·5h	− 13·83			
	86	123	Rn	α, e_k	30m	− 10			
210	81	129	Tl	e^-	1·3m	− 9·95			
	82	128	Pb	e^-	19·4y	− 15·81	(0)		
	83	127	Bi	α	10^6y	− 15·88	1	0·044	0·13
	84	126	Po	α	138·4d	− 17·12	(0)		
	85	125	At	α, e_k	8·3h	−· 12·96			
	86	124	Rn	α, e_k	2·7h	− 10·46	(0)		
211	82	129	Pb	e^-	36·1m	− 11·26	$(\frac{7}{2}, \frac{9}{2})$		
	83	128	Bi	α, e^-	2·16m	− 12·70	$(\frac{9}{2})$		
	84	127	Po	α, I	0·52s	− 13·34	$(\frac{9}{2})$		
	85	126	At	α, e_k	7·2h	− 12·53	$\frac{9}{2}$		
	86	125	Rn	α, e_k	16h	− 9·43	$(\frac{9}{2})$		
212	82	130	Pb	e^-	10·64h	− 8·09	(0)		
	83	129	Bi	α, e^-	60·5m	− 8·72	(1)		
	84	128	Po	α	3×10^{-7}s	− 11·13	(0)		
	85	127	At	α	0·22s	− 9·28			
	86	126	Rn	α	23m	− 9·29			
	87	125	Fr	α, e_k	19·3m	− 4			
213	82	131	Pb			− 4			
	83	130	Bi	α, e^-	47m	− 5·68	$(\frac{9}{2})$		
	84	129	Po	α	$4·2 \times 10^{-6}$s	− 7·17	$(\frac{7}{2}, \frac{9}{2})$		
	85	128	At	α		− 6·9			
	86	127	Rn			− 6·07			
	87	126	Fr			− 3·82			
	88	125	Ra	α	2·7m	0			
214	82	132	Pb	e^-	27m	− 0·23	(0)		
	83	131	Bi	α, e^-	20m	− 1·31	(1)		
	84	130	Po	α	$1·6 \times 10^{-4}$s	− 4·80	(0)		
	85	129	At	α	2×10^{-6}s	− 3·07			
	86	128	Rn			− 5			
215	83	132	Bi	e^-	8m	1·8			
	84	131	Po	α, e^-	$1·83 \times 10^{-3}$s	− 0·58			
	85	130	At	α	$\sim 10^{-4}$s	− 1·34			
	86	129	Rn	α	$\sim 10^{-6}$s	− 1·3			
216	84	132	Po	α	0·158s	1·92			
	85	131	At	α	$\sim 3 \times 10^{-4}$s	2·41			
	86	130	Rn	α	$\sim 10^{-4}$s	0·27			
217	85	132	At	α	0·018s	4·65			
	86	131	Rn	α	$\sim 10^{-3}$s	3·90			
	87	130	Fr	α		4·7			
218	84	134	Po	α, e^-	3·05m	8·93			
	85	133	At	α, e^-	~ 2s	8·61			
	86	132	Rn	α	0·019s	5·60			
	87	131	Fr	α	5×10^{-3}	7·54			
219	85	134	At	α, e^-	0·9m	11·29			
	86	133	Rn	α	3·92s	9·48			
	87	132	Fr	α	0·02s	9·26			
	88	131	Ra	α	$\sim 10^{-3}$	10			
220	86	134	Rn	α	54·5s	11·40			
	87	133	Fr	α	27·5s	12·34			
	88	132	Ra	α	0·03s	11·03			
221	86	135	Rn	α, e^-	25m	15			
	87	134	Fr	α	4·8m	14·18			
	88	133	Ra	α	30s	13·89			
	89	132	Ac	α		15·7			

1	2	3	4	5	6	7	8	9	10
222	86	136	Rn	α	3·825d	17·53			
	87	135	Fr	α, e^-	14·8m	18			
	88	134	Ra	α	38s	15·38			
	89	133	Ac	α	5·5s	17·76			
223	87	136	Fr	α, e^-	21m	19·74			
	88	135	Ra	α	11·1d	18·50			
	89	134	Ac	α, e_k	2·2m	19·14			
	90	133	Th	α	$\sim 0·1$s	20·9			
224	88	136	Ra	α	3·64d	20·22			
	89	135	Ac	α, e_k	2·9h	21·69			
	90	134	Th	α_k	~ 1s	21·48			
225	88	137	Ra	e^-	14·8d	23·52	$(\frac{9}{2})$		
	89	136	Ac	α	10·0h	23·15	$(\frac{7}{2})$		
	90	135	Th	α, e_k	8·0m	23·93			
226	88	138	Ra	α, f	1622y	25·36			
	89	137	Ac	e^-, e_k	29h	26·2	(1)		
	90	136	Th	α	30·9m	24·90	(0)		
	91	135	Pa	α	1·8m	27·8			
227	88	139	Ra	e^-	41·2m	29·16			
	89	138	Ac	α, e^-	22y	27·75	$\frac{3}{2}$	+ 1·1	+ 1·7
	90	137	Th	α	18·2d	27·71	$(\frac{1}{2})$		
	91	136	Pa	α, e_k	38·3m	28·81			
	92	135	U	α	1·3m	31			
228	88	140	Ra	e^-	6·7y	31·14	(0)		
	89	139	Ac	e^-	6·13h	31·08			
	90	138	Th	α	1·90y	28·75	(0)		
	91	137	Pa	α, e_k	22h	31·01			
	92	136	U	α, e_k	9·3m	31·39			
229	88	141	Ra	e^-	short				
	89	140	Ac	e^-	16·6m	33			
	90	139	Th	α	7340y	31·65	$\frac{5}{2}$	0·34	
	91	138	Pa	α, e_k	1·5d	32·02			
	92	137	U	α, e_k	58m	33·48			
230	88	142	Ra	^-e	1h				
	89	141	Ac	e^-	< 1m	36·0			
	90	140	Th	α, f	$8·0 \times 10^4$y	33·09	(0)		
	91	139	Pa	α, e^+, e^-	17·7d	34·43	(0, 1)		
	92	138	U	α	20·8d	33·94	(0)		
231	90	141	Th	e^-	26h	36·29	$(\frac{7}{2})$		
	91	140	Pa	α, f	$3·43 \times 10^4$y	35·88	$\frac{3}{2}$	+ 1·98	
	92	139	U	α, e_k	4·2d	36·27			
	93	138	Np	α	~ 50m	38·28			
232	90	142	Th	$100, \alpha, f$	$1·39 \times 10^{10}$y	38·12			
	91	141	Pa	e^-	1·31d	38·61			
	92	140	U	α, f	70y	37·17	(0)		
	93	139	Np	e_k	~ 13m	40			
	94	138	Pu	α, e_k	36m	41·18			
233	90	143	Th	e^-	23·6m	41·47			
	91	142	Pa	e^-	27·4d	40·13	$\frac{3}{2}$	+ 3·4	− 3·0
	92	141	U	α, f	$1·6 \times 10^5$y	39·52	$\frac{5}{2}$	0·54	2·7
	93	140	Np	α, e_k	35m	40·67			
234	90	144	Th	e^-	24d	43·58	(0)		
	91	143	Pa	e^-, I	6·66h	43·30			
	92	142	U	$0·006, \alpha, f$	$2·48 \times 10^5$y	40·90	(0)		
	93	141	Np	e_k	4·4d	42·9			
	94	140	Pu	α, e_k	9h	43·31	(0)		
235	90	145	Th	e^-	< 10m				
	91	144	Pa	e^-	23·7m	45·4			
	92	143	U	$0·72, \alpha, f, I$	$7·13 \times 10^8$y	43·91	$\frac{7}{2}$	0·35	3·8
	93	142	Np	α, e_k	410d	44·05	$\frac{5}{2}$		
	94	141	Pu	α, e_k	26m	45·27			

1	2	3	4	5	6	7	8	9	10
236	92	144	U	α, f	$2 \cdot 39 \times 10^7 \text{y}$	45·64	(0)		
	93	143	Np	e_k, e^-	22h	46·62	(0, 1)		
	94	142	Pu	α, f	2·7y	46·07	(0)		
237	92	145	U	e^-	6·75d	48·61	$(\frac{1}{2})$		
	93	144	Np	α, f	$2 \cdot 2 \times 10^6 \text{y}$	48·06	$\frac{5}{2}$	6	
	94	143	Pu	α, e_k, I	45·6d	48·30	$(\frac{5}{2})$		
	95	142	Am	α, e_k	$\sim 1 \cdot 3 \text{h}$	49·84			
238	92	146	U	$99 \cdot 28, \alpha, f$	$4 \cdot 51 \times 10^9 \text{y}$	50·77	(0)		
	93	145	Np	e^-	2·1d	50·90	2		
	94	144	Pu	α, f	86·4y	49·51	(0)		
	95	143	Am	e_k	2·1h	52			
	96	142	Cm	α, e_k	2·5h	53·04			
239	92	147	U	e^-	23·5m	54·30			
	93	146	Np	e^-, f	2·3d	52·92	$\frac{5}{2}$		
	94	145	Pu	α, f	$2 \cdot 44 \times 10^4 \text{y}$	52·15	$\frac{1}{2}$	$+ 0 \cdot 2$	
	95	144	Am	α, e_k	12h	53·02			
	96	143	Cm	e_k	$\sim 3 \text{h}$	55			
240	92	148	U	e^-	14·1h	56·59	(0)		
	93	147	Np	e^-	1h	56·08	(0, 1)		
	94	146	Pu	α, f	6500y	53·88	(0)		
	95	145	Am	e_k	51h	55			
	96	144	Cm	α, f	26·8d	55·54			
241	93	148	Np	e^-	60m	58·2			
	94	147	Pu	α, e^-	12·9y	56·74	$\frac{5}{2}$	$+ 2 \cdot 15$	
	95	146	Am	α, f	460y	56·71	$\frac{5}{2}$	$+ 1 \cdot 4$	$+ 4 \cdot 9$
	96	145	Cm	α, e_k	35d	57·54			
242	94	148	Pu	α, f	$3 \cdot 8 \times 10^5 \text{y}$	58·72	(0)		
	95	147	Am	α, e_k, e^-, I	16h	59·50	1	0·33	2·76
	96	146	Cm	α, f	162·5d	58·79	(0)		
243	94	149	Pu	e^-, f	4·98h	61·97			
	95	148	Am	α	$8 \cdot 8 \times 10^3 \text{y}$	61·37	$\frac{5}{2}$	$+ 1 \cdot 4$	$+ 4 \cdot 9$
	96	147	Cm	α	35y	61·37			
	97	146	Bk	α, e_k	4·5h	62·96			
244	95	149	Am	e_k, e^-	26m	64·35	(0)		
	96	148	Cm	α, f	19y	62·82	(0)		
	97	147	Bk	α, e_k	5h	65			
	98	146	Cf	α	25m	65·97			
245	95	150	Am	e^-	1·98h	66·34			
	96	149	Cm	α	14000y	65·37			
	97	148	Bk	α, e_k	4·98h	66·27			
	98	147	Cf	α, e_k	44m	67·91			
246	95	151	Am	e^-	25m	69·67			
	96	150	Cm	α, f	4000y	67·20			
	97	149	Bk	e_k	1·8d	69			
	98	148	Cf	α, f	1·5d	68·77			
	99	147	Es	α, e_k	7·3m	72			
247	96	151	Cm	α	$> 4 \times 10^7 \text{y}$	70			
	97	150	Bk	α	$\sim 10^4 \text{y}$	70·26			
	98	149	Cf	e_k	2·5h	71			
	99	148	Es			74			
248	96	152	Cm	α, f	$4 \cdot 7 \times 10^5 \text{y}$	72·2			
	97	151	Bk	e^-, e_k	16h	79·96			
	98	150	Cf	α	350d	72·26			
	99	149	Es	α, e_k	25m	75			
249	96	153	Cm	e^-	65m	75·8			
	97	152	Bk	e^-, α	290d	74·88			
	98	151	Cf	α	470y	74·75			
	99	150	Es	α, e_k	2h	76·26			
250	97	153	Bk	e^-	3·1h	78·27			
	98	152	Cf	α	10y	76·38			
	99	151	Es	e_k	8h	79			
	100	150	Fm	α	30m	79·49			

1	2	3	4	5	6	7	8	9	10
251	98	153	Cf	α	800y	79			
	99	152	Es	α, e_k	1·5d	79-93			
	100	151	Fm	e_k, α	7h	81			
252	98	154	Cf	α, f	2·2y	81·5			
	99	153	Es	α	140d	82·81			
	100	152	Fm	α, f	23h	82·56			
253	98	155	Cf	e^-	18d	85·02			
	99	154	Es	α	20d	84·73			
	100	153	Fm	α, e_k	4·5d	84·93			
254	99	155	Es	e^-, e_k	37h	87·90			
	100	154	Fm	α, f	3·2h	86·84			
	101	153	Md			89			
	102	152	No	α	$\sim$ 3s	91·1			
255	99	156	Es	e^-	24d				
	100	155	Fm	α	22h	90			
256	100	156	Fm	f	3·4h				
	101	155	Md	e_k	30m				
257	103	154	Lw	α	8s	99			

References

ANDERSON, C. D., and NEDDERMEYER, S. H., *Phys. Rev.*, **51**, 884 (1937).
AUFFRAY, J. P., *Phys. Rev. Let.*, **6**, 120 (1961).
AWSHALOM, M., *Phys. Rev.*, **101**, 1,041 (1956).
BARKAS, W. H., BIRNBAUM, W., and SMITH, F. M., *Phys. Rev.*, **101**, 778 (1956).
BARSCHALL, H. H., *Phys. Rev.*, **86**, 431 (1952).
BLAIR, J. S., *Phys. Rev.*, **115**, 928 (1959).
BLATT, J. M., and JACKSON, J. D., *Phys. Rev.*, **76**, 18 (1949).
BLIN-STOYLE, R. J., *Proc. Rutherford Jubilee Conf., Manchester*, p. 677 (1961).
BOHR, A., and MOTTLESON, B. R., *Dan. Mat. Fys. Medd.*, **27**, No. 16 (1953).
BOHR, N., *Nature*, **137**, 344 (1936).
BURGY, M. T., *et al.*, *Phys. Rev.*, **84**, 1,160 (1951).
BUTLER, S. T., *Proc. Roy. Soc. A*, **208**, 559 (1951).
BUTLER, S. T., AUSTERN, N., and PEARSON, C., *Phys. Rev.*, **112**, 1,227 (1958).
BUTTON, J., *et al.*, *Phys. Rev.*, **108**, 1,557 (1957).
CASE, K. M., and PAIS, A., *Phys. Rev.*, **80**, 203 (1950).
CHAMBERLAIN, O., *et al.*, *Phys. Rev.*, **100**, 947, (1955).
CHINOWSKY, W., and STEINBERGER, J., *Phys. Rev.*, **93**, 586 (1954).
COHEN, V. W., CORNGOLD, N. R., and RAMSEY, N. F., *Phys. Rev.*, **104**, 283 (1956).
COHEN, E. R., CROWE, K. M., and DUMOND, T. W. M., *The Fundamental Constants of Physics* (London, Interscience, 1957).
CORK, B., *et al.*, *Phys. Rev.*, **104**, 1,193 (1956).
COWAN, C. L., and REINES, F., *Science*, **124**, 103 (1956).
CROWE, K. M., and PHILLIPS, R. H., *Phys. Rev.*, **96**, 470 (1954).
DANBY, G., *et al.*, *Phys. Rev. Let.*, **9**, 36 (1962).
DRELL, S. D., and HUANG, K., *Phys. Rev.*, **91**, 1,527 (1953).
DUDZIAK, W., SAGANE, R., and VEDDER, J., *Phys. Rev.*, **114**, 336 (1959).
DURBIN, R., LOAR, H., and STEINBERGER, J., *Phys. Rev.*, **83**, 646 (1951).
EISBERG, R. M., and IGO, G., *Phys. Rev.*, **93**, 1,039 (1954).
ELTON, L. R. B., *Rev. Mod. Phys.*, **30**, 557 (1958).
ELTON, L. R. B., *Nuclear Sizes* (Oxford University Press, 1961).
ELTON, L. R. B., and GOMES, L. C., *Phys. Rev.*, **105**, 1,027 (1957).
FESHBACH, H., PEASLEE, D. C., and WEISSKOPF, V. F., *Phys. Rev.*, **71**, 145 (1947).
FESHBACH, H., PORTER, C. E., and WEISSKOPF, V. F., *Phys. Rev.*, **96**, 448 (1954).
FESHBACH, H., and WEISSKOPF, V. F., *Phys. Rev.*, **76**, 1,550 (1949).
FLOWERS, B. H., *Prog. Nucl. Phys.*, **2**, 235 (1952).
FUZZINI, T., *et al.*, *Phys. Rev. Let.*, **1**, 247 (1958).
GAMMEL, T. L., and THALER, R. M., *Phys. Rev.*, **107**, 291 (1957).
GHOSHAL, S. N., *Phys. Rev.*, **80**, 939 (1950).
GOTTFRIED, K., *Phys. Rev.*, **103**, 1,107 (1956).

322 REFERENCES

GREEN, A. E. S., *Phys. Rev.*, **95**, 1,006 (1954).
HAFNER, E. M., *et al.*, *Phys. Rev.*, **89**, 204 (1953).
HAMILTON, D. R., ALFORD, W. P., and GROSS, L., *Phys. Rev.*, **92**, 1,521 (1953).
HEISENBERG, W., *Z. Phys.*, **77**, 1 (1932).
HENSINKVELD, M., and FREIER, G., *Phys. Rev.*, **85**, 80 (1952).
HILDEBRAND, R. H., *Phys. Rev.*, **89**, 1,090 (1953).
HOMER, R. J., *et al.*, *Phys. Let.*, **9**, 72 (1964).
HUGHES, D. J., and HARVEY, J. A., *Neutron Cross-sections* (London, McGraw-Hill, 1955).
JACKSON, J. D., and BLATT, J. M., *Rev. Mod. Phys.*, **22**, 77 (1950).
JASTROW, R., *Phys. Rev.*, **81**, 165 (1951).
KELLOGG, J. M. B., RABI, I. I., and ZACHARIAS, J. R., *Phys. Rev.*, **55**, 318 (1939).
KNOWLES, J. W., *Canad. J. Phys.*, **40**, 257 (1962).
KOFOED-HANSEN, O., *Phys. Rev.*, **96**, 1,045 (1954).
KURATH, D., *Phys. Rev.*, **91**, 1,430 (1953).
LATTES, C. M. G., OCCHIALINI, G. P. S., and POWELL, C. F., *Nature*, **159**, 186 (1947).
LEE, T. D., and YANG, C. N., *Phys. Rev.*, **104**, 254 (1956).
McCARTHY, I. E., *Nuclear Phys.*, **11**, 574 (1959).
MAYER, M. G., and JENSEN, T. H. D., *Elementary Theory of Nuclear Shell Structure* (London, Wiley, 1955).
MELKONIAN, E., *Phys. Rev.*, **76**, 1,744 (1949).
MORAVCSIK, M. J., *The Two-nucleon Interaction* (especially section 4.3) (Oxford University Press, 1963).
NILSSON, S. G., *Dan. Mat. Fys. Medd.*, **29**, No. 16 (1955).
NOYES, H. P., *Phys. Rev.*, **130**, 2,025 (1963).
NOYES, H. P., *Phys. Rev. Let.*, **12**, 171 (1964).
PANOFSKY, W. K. H., AAMODT, R. L., and HADLEY, J., *Phys. Rev.*, **81**, 565 (1951).
PETRZHAK, J. S., and FLEROV, G. N., *J. Phys. U.S.S.R.*, **3**, 275 (1940).
RABI, I. I., KELLOGG, J. M. B., and ZACHARIAS, J. R., *Phys. Rev.*, **46**, 157 (1934).
RAINWATER, J., *Phys. Rev.*, **79**, 432 (1950).
RAMSEY, N. F., *Nuclear Moments* (London, Wiley, 1953).
ROST, E., and AUSTERN, N., *Phys. Rev.*, **120**, 1,375 (1960).
RUTHERFORD, E., *Phil. Mag.*, **21**, 669 (1911).
SCHLUTER, R. A., *Phys. Rev.*, **95**, 639 (1954).
SIGNELL, P. S., and MARSHAK, R. E., *Phys. Rev.*, **109**, 1,229 (1958).
SMITH, F. M., BIRNBAUM, W., and BARKAS, W. H., *Phys. Rev.*, **91**, 765 (1953).
SUTTON, R. B., *et al.*, *Phys. Rev.*, **72**, 1,147 (1947).
THOMSON, J. J., *Rays of Positive Electricity* (London, Longmans, 1913).
WHALING, W., *et al.*, *Phys. Rev.*, **83**, 512 (1951).
WIGNER, E. P., *Phys. Rev.*, **43**, 252 (1933).
WILKINSON, D. H., *Phys. Rev.*, **109**, 1,603 (1958).
WILSON, R., *The Nucleon–Nucleon Interaction* (London, Interscience, 1963).
WU, C. S., *et al.*, *Phys. Rev.*, **105**, 1,413 (1957).
YUKAWA, H., *Proc. Phys.-Math. Soc. Japan*, **17**, 48 (1935).

Further Reading

THE following books, some of which are referred to in the text, constitute a short list for background and further reading—

BETHE, H. A., and MORRISON, P., *Elementary Nuclear Theory* (London, Chapman and Hall, 1956).

BLATT, J. M., and WEISSKOPF, V. F., *Theoretical Nuclear Physics* (London, Chapman and Hall, 1952).

BURCHAM, W. E., *Nuclear Physics* (London, Longmans, 1963).

CORBEN, H. C., and STEHLE, P., *Classical Mechanics* (London, Chapman and Hall, 1950).

ENDT, P. M., and DEMEUR, M. (editors), *Nuclear Reactions*, Vol. 1 (Amsterdam, North-Holland, 1959).

FEENBERG, E., and PAKE, G. E., *Notes on the Quantum Theory of Angular Momentum* (Cambridge, Mass., Addison-Wesley, 1953).

MOTT, N. F., and MASSEY, H. S. W., *The Theory of Atomic Collisions*, 2nd edition (Oxford University Press, 1949).

PRESTON, M. A., *Physics of the Nucleus* (Cambridge, Mass., Addison-Wesley, 1962).

SCHIFF, L. I., *Quantum Mechanics*, 2nd edition (New York, McGraw-Hill, 1955).

Review articles which keep the reader up-to-date are published periodically in the following—

Annual Review of Nuclear Science (Palo Alto, California, Annual Reviews).

Progress in Nuclear Physics (London, Pergamon).

Reports on Progress in Physics (London, Physical Society).

Reviews of Modern Physics (New York, American Institute of Physics).

Index